Modeling with Mathematics: A Bridge to Algebra II

Modeling with Mathematics: A Bridge to Algebra II

Virginia's Algebra, Functions, and Data Analysis

PROJECT LEADERSHIP

Jo Ann Wheeler
REGION 4 ESC, HOUSTON, TX

Solomon Garfunkel
COMAP INC., LEXINGTON, MA

David Eschberger
REGION 4 ESC, HOUSTON, TX

LEAD AUTHORS

Gary Cosenza
REGION 4 ESC, HOUSTON, TX

Paul Gray
REGION 4 ESC, HOUSTON, TX

Julie Horn
REGION 4 ESC, HOUSTON, TX

AUTHORS

Sharon Benson
REGION 4 ESC, HOUSTON, TX

David Eschberger
REGION 4 ESC, HOUSTON, TX

Jo Ann Wheeler
REGION 4 ESC, HOUSTON, TX

W. H. Freeman and Company
New York
www.whfreeman.com

Published and distributed by
W. H. Freeman and Company
41 Madison Avenue, New York NY 10010

Library of Congress Control Number: 2006921261

ISBN 10 — 1-4292-2549-1
ISBN 13 — 978-1-4292-2549-6

Printed in the United States of America
First Printing 2009

SENIOR PUBLISHER: Craig Bleyer
EXECUTIVE MARKETING MANAGER: Cindi Weiss
CUSTOM PUBLISHER: Susan Brennan
VIRGINIA STATE REPRESENTATIVE: Chad Zamkoff
SUPPLEMENTS AND NEW MEDIA EDITOR: Roland Cheyney
PRINT PRODUCTION: COMAP, Inc.
COVER DESIGN: Diana Blume
COVER IMAGE: Skip Willits Fine Art Photography
MANUFACTURING: RR Donnelley

PROJECT LEADERS:

Jo Ann Wheeler, Region 4 ESC, Houston, TX

David Eschberger, Region 4 ESC, Houston, TX

Solomon Garfunkel, COMAP, Lexington, MA

LEAD AUTHORS:

Gary Cosenza, Region 4 ESC, Houston, TX

Paul Gray, Region 4 ESC, Houston, TX

Julie Horn, Region 4 ESC, Houston, TX

AUTHORS:

Sharon Benson, Region 4 ESC, Houston, TX

David Eschberger, Region 4 ESC, Houston, TX

Jo Ann Wheeler, Region 4 ESC, Houston, TX

REVIEWER:

Sandra Nite, Texas A&M University,
College Station, TX

Writers who contributed material used from
COMAP's *Mathematical Models with Applications*
and Region 4's *Mathematical Models with
Applications/Algebra II Alignment*:

Marsha Davis, Eastern Connecticut State
University, Williamantic, CT

Juliann Doris, Seguin High School, Seguin, TX

Anne Konz, Cypress-Fairbanks Independent
School District, Cypress, TX

Jerry Lege, COMAP, Inc., Lexington, MA

Jennifer May, Independent Consultant

Paul Mlakar, St. Mark's School, Dallas, TX

Sandra Nite, Texas A&M University,
College Station, TX

Richard Parr, Rice University, Houston, TX

Gary Simundza, Wentworth Institute of
Technology, Boston, MA

Ann Worley, Spring Branch Independent School
District, Houston, TX

Region 4 and COMAP would like to thank the
following teachers and school districts for
piloting *Modeling with Mathematics: A Bridge to
Algebra II* and providing essential feedback:

Kim Armstrong
Lindale High School
Lindale Independent School District
Lindale, Texas

Toni Ericson
Hallsville High School
Hallsville Independent School District
Hallsville, Texas

Jason Hendricks
Madison High School
North East Independent School District
San Antonio, Texas

Sara Kamphaus
Summit High School
Mansfield Independent School District
Mansfield, Texas

Mary Ann Knight
Mansfield High School
Mansfield Independent School District
Mansfield, Texas

Connie Koehn
Elsik High School
Alief Independent School District
Houston, Texas

Garnette Lamm
Madison High School
North East Independent School District
San Antonio, Texas

Caroline Martin
Timberview High School
Mansfield Independent School District
Mansfield, Texas

Michael McCabe
Grapevine High School
Grapevine-Colleyville Independent School
District
Grapevine, Texas

Robert McFarland
Aldine Senior High School
Aldine Independent School District
Houston, Texas

Jerry McHugh
MacArthur High School
North East Independent School District
San Antonio, Texas

Monica Merchant
Aldine Senior High School
Aldine Independent School District
Houston, Texas

Theresa Patton
Elsik High School
Alief Independent School District
Houston, Texas

Brenda Porter
Reagan High School
North East Independent School District
San Antonio, Texas

DeAnna Ramirez
Mansfield High School
Mansfield Independent School District
Mansfield, Texas

Clint Reynolds
Van High School
Van Independent School District
Van, Texas

Laura Salazar
Reagan High School
North East Independent School District
San Antonio, Texas

Michael Seibert
Grapevine High School
Grapevine-Colleyville Independent School
District
Grapevine, Texas

Glenn T. Smith
Aldine Senior High School
Aldine Independent School District
Houston, Texas

Sheryl Smith
Taylor High School
Alief Independent School District
Houston, Texas

Diane Tobin
Aldine Senior High School
Aldine Independent School District
Houston, Texas

Maria Tolentino
Hastings High School
Alief Independent School District
Houston, Texas

Ron Van Raemdonck
Aldine Senior High School
Aldine Independent School District
Houston, Texas

Michael Williams
Gilmer High School
Gilmer Independent School District
Gilmer, Texas

Yangki Wojcik
Reagan High School
North East Independent School District
San Antonio, Texas

Aubrey Wright
Colleyville Heritage High School
Grapevine-Colleyville Independent School
District
Colleyville, Texas

Randy Zelahy
Aldine Senior High School
Aldine Independent School District
Houston, Texas

Dear Student,

The state of Virginia recently created an important new course: Algebra, Functions and Data Analysis. Its main goal is to successfully build on material from your Algebra and Geometry courses and get you ready for success in your Algebra II class.

But when we set out to write this book specifically for Virginia students such as yourself, we asked a question: Could we go beyond just telling you that mathematics is useful and actually *show* you first-hand how to use math to solve *real* problems in the world? Why not create hands-on activities in science, business, design and other fields and have you learn and use the mathematics is these real-world settings? This text uses a tool called *mathematical modeling* to explore these and other fields of interest.

Mathematical modeling is used to clarify and solve a wide range of real-world problems. It is a tool used by engineers when they design a new style of MP3 player and by architects when they design a skyscraper. The best part about mathematical modeling is that it can simplify a tricky problem to help you focus on the things that really matter. The hard part about modeling is that it makes you read more, think more, and write more. We also think modeling makes learning math more interesting because it allows you to solve *real* problems rather than made-up problems just for practice.

In a few place in this text, you will see **A Look Ahead** section. These sections are a chance for you to see a little of the math you will do when you take Algebra II.

We understand you may not feel completely confident in your math skills. The goal of this book is to help you get back on track with mathematics. It's a chance for you to look back at some of the math you've seen before but may not have fully understood. It's also a chance for you to prepare for an even better experience in Algebra II. We also hope you'll see the importance and the relevance of mathematics—not just in school, but throughout your world. Our goal is to build your confidence and further your mathematics success!

Sincerely,

Sharon Benson
Region 4 ESC, Houston, TX

Solomon Garfunkel
COMAP, Lexington, MA

Table of Contents

CHAPTER 6 Growth & Decay: Exponential Functions 344–413

CHAPTER 7: What Are the Chances? Probability   414–510

CHAPTER 8: Data and Statistics   512–605

The Modeling Process

INTRODUCTION

The process of starting with a situation or problem and gaining understanding about that situation through the use of mathematics is known as **mathematical modeling**.

Mathematical modeling attempts to describe real-world relationships in mathematical terms. Mathematical descriptions are useful because mathematics provides ways to obtain solutions. There are several ways to represent real-world relationships.

Mathematical modelers use a number of representations in their work. Among them are:

- verbal descriptions

- graphs, such as the graph of a straight line

- formulas, such as the formula for the area of a square

- tables, such as a table of values of length and width that give a rectangle with an area of 24 square inches

- drawings, such as a scale drawing of a room in a house

- diagrams, such as an arrow diagram or flow chart.

Length (l)	Width (w)
2	12
4	6
6	4
8	3
12	2

The mathematical modeling process can be described in steps.

Step 1. Identify the problem.

Read and ask questions about the situation. Identify a problem that you want to solve.

Step 2. Simplify the situation.

Select the features of the situation that you think are most important. These are your assumptions that you will use to build a model. Note the features that you will ignore at first.

Step 3. Build the model and solve the problem.

Describe relationships among the parts of the problem in mathematical terms. Then find a mathematical solution to the problem. In this step you might do all or some of the following:

* define variables

* write equations

* draw shapes

* measure objects

* gather data and organize into tables

* make graphs.

Step 4. Evaluate and revise the model.

Go back to the original situation and see if the results of the mathematical model make sense. If so, use the model until new information becomes available or assumptions change. If not, reconsider the assumptions you made in step 2 and revise them.

You might go through a revision process several times before you have a good mathematical model. One helpful principle that guides all modelers is *keep it simple*. All models ignore something, and first models usually ignore several things.

A way of visualizing the mathematical modeling process is shown in **Figure 1**.

FIGURE 1.
The modeling process.

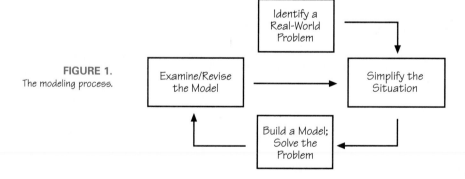

Mathematical modeling is often used to describe the relationship between two or more real-world variables. (A variable is a quantity that changes.) Discovering and describing a relationship among variables allows modelers to predict values of one of the variables from values of the others.

Some examples of real-world situations where the modeling process might be used include:

* predicting the growth of a population based on variables such as the quantity of food available, disease rates, or birth rate

* predicting the profit for a company based on the costs of producing a product or the level of demand for the product

* predicting the effect on the economy of factors such as the unemployment rate or the value of exported goods

* predicting the effect of widening a road on traffic volume

* describing the relationship between the volume of blood flowing through an artery and the pulse rate of a person.

In this course you will use mathematics to create models that explore and explain a wide range of real-world issues. You will also use your imagination to create these models, then use mathematics to test them and see if they make sense. In order to create and test your models tools are needed, such as paper and pencil problem solving, using calculators, and doing research at your library and on the Internet. Most importantly you will need to find good ways to show your model to your teacher and to other students.

This may seem a very different way of learning math, but in this course you will see how mathematical modeling can help you succeed, both in school and in many careers. So give mathematical modeling a chance, you may find it changes how you feel about math.

1
CHAPTER

Science: Modeling with Direct and Inverse Variation

Extra! Extra! Scientists Use Mathematical Modeling!

From ancient times, people have tried to make sense of the world around them. Nomadic Native Americans made observations about the behavior of the buffalo herds in the central plains of North America. These observations led them to make conjectures about the movement of the herd, which was essential to the tribe's survival. If they successfully followed the herd, then food was plentiful. If the herd left them behind, then they starved.

Some civilizations began to use numbers to describe relationships. In ancient Egypt, people began writing down numerals to keep count of things. They began to write simple equations to perform calculations.

These numeric observations prompted early scientists to want to learn more. They noticed that certain quantities are related, such as the length of day and the location of certain stars, and began to use mathematics to describe these relationships. These observations were the early stages of what we now call mathematical modeling.

In this chapter, you will explore some of the work of three notable scientists who used mathematics to describe relationships that they noticed in the natural world.

Archimedes (**Figure 1.1**) was a Greek scientist who lived in Syracuse, Sicily, during the third century BC. Archimedes wrote many books about geometry, mathematics, and physical science and was a good friend of King Hiero of Syracuse. Archimedes was instrumental in defending his home city against the Roman siege in 212 BC, before his death that same year.

FIGURE 1.1.
Archimedes.

Archimedes is perhaps best known for what is today called Archimedes' Principle. This idea describes the forces that interact between a fluid, such as water, and an object that is submerged in that fluid.

FIGURE 1.2.
Robert Hooke.

Robert Hooke (**Figure 1.2**) was an English scientist who lived in London during the 1600s. This was an exciting time to be a scientist in England. Like most of Western Europe, England was enjoying the Age of Enlightenment, a time when scientists and philosophers explored new ideas about the world around them. After a long period of silence, they rediscovered the work of the ancient Greeks and Romans. As technology had become quite advanced for the day, scientists now had many new tools at their disposal, and they began to look for new ways to use them.

Robert Hooke began his work with springs as he searched for a way to build a better clock. Ships had been sailing from Europe to North America and Asia for over 200 years in Hooke's day. Yet, they had difficulty telling time in order to determine their longitude. European clocks at this time used a pendulum that swung back and forth, keeping steady time. However, on long sea voyages, waves disrupted the pendulum. So, Hooke began to explore the use of springs to make clocks tick. Along the way, he discovered a relationship between the length that a spring stretches and the amount of force required to make it stretch to that length. This relationship today is known as Hooke's Law.

Robert Boyle (**Figure 1.3**) was also an English scientist in London during the 1600s. In fact, Robert Hooke was one of his students. Boyle studied religion, chemistry, and physics. Like many of his colleagues, he wanted to take the mystery out of science, and he relied heavily on mathematics to do so.

FIGURE 1.3.
Robert Boyle.

Boyle was keenly interested in the properties of air, which were still largely misunderstood. Boyle's predecessors in Italy had found that air has weight and exerts a force on the ground called air pressure. Boyle learned through a series of experiments that not only did air have weight but also that fire cannot burn without air.

Boyle also studied the relationship between air pressure and volume. In 1662, he wrote in *Touching the Spring of the Air and Its Effects* about his experiments with a vacuum chamber to determine the relationship between pressure and volume of a gas. His findings are today known in chemistry as Boyle's Law.

Scientists continue to use mathematical modeling to describe natural events and to make predictions. Astrophysicists use mathematical modeling to chart the paths of stars and solar systems. Aeronautical engineers use mathematical modeling to build better airplanes and space vehicles. Social scientists use mathematical modeling to make predictions about populations and natural resource management.

Throughout this book, you will study how different people use mathematical modeling to make decisions about everyday life. You will also see how mathematics appears in unlikely places and is used by people from a variety of backgrounds.

In Chapter 1 you will explore some important ideas in science using mathematical modeling.

Archimedes and the Crown

In the third century BC lived a famous mathematician and scientist named Archimedes. Archimedes is famous for many discoveries including an irrigation device, the law of the lever, the formula for the volume of a sphere, and possibly even the odometer. One of his discoveries is the Archimedes Principle, which describes the concept of buoyancy. Vitruvius, a Roman architect, tells a famous story about Archimedes and King Hiero of Syracuse.

King Hiero hired a craftsman to make a crown of gold. The king measured out the exact amount of gold for the craftsman to use. The craftsman later delivered to the king a beautiful crown. The crown weighed the same as the measured amount of gold. Rumors began floating around Syracuse that the crown was not made of pure gold. It was suggested that the craftsman had replaced part of the gold with an equal mass of silver. King Hiero asked Archimedes to prove or disprove the rumors without damaging the crown in any way. (Today this is called nondestructive testing.) As Archimedes began to sit down in a bath pondering the problem, he noticed the water level in the bath rising as he submerged more and more of his body into the bath. Realizing he had found a way to solve the problem he ran down the street, still naked, shouting, "Eureka!" ("I have found it!") The craftsman admitted he was guilty of stealing part of the gold and replacing it with silver.

1. What do you think Archimedes' solution might have been?

2. Gold has greater mass than silver. If a gold crown and a silver crown have the same weight, would they have the same volume? Why?

3. How can the volume of an object be determined by placing it in water?

4. Suppose your teacher places 15 pennies in a film canister and 20 pennies in another. Which canister has greater mass?

5. Which canister, the one with 15 pennies or the one with 20 pennies, would displace more water when submerged?

6. Does mass or volume cause displacement?

Your teacher will do a demonstration with film canisters, pennies, and a graduated cylinder. Answer the following questions as she/he does the demonstration.

7. What did you observe when your teacher placed the film canister into the graduated cylinder?

8. What did you observe when your teacher placed 20 pennies into the film canister?

9. Which canister, one with 15 pennies or one with 20 pennies, has greater mass?

10. Calculate the volume of a film canister.

11. What do you observe about the relationship between the calculated volume of the film canister and the amount of water displaced when the canister is submerged?

Displacement Investigation

In this section you will explore displacement. You have a graduated cylinder filled with a given amount of water. You will record three things: the number of film canisters in the water, the total displacement of the canisters (the change in the volume of water), and the total volume contained in the cylinder.

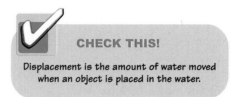

CHECK THIS!

Displacement is the amount of water moved when an object is placed in the water.

1. Fill a large graduated cylinder to the 500 mL mark. In a table, record the amount of displacement when no film canisters have been placed in the cylinder. Also record the total volume contained in the cylinder.

2. Place a film canister with the minimum number of pennies to make it sink into the water in the large graduated cylinder (**Figure 1.5**). Read and record in your table (similar to the table in **Figure 1.4**) the volume of water displaced by 1 film canister and the total volume contained in the cylinder. Repeat this process adding 1 additional canister at a time. Continue until you submerge all 6 of your canisters.

Total Number of Submerged Canisters	Total Volume of Water Displaced (mL)	Total Volume Contained in the Graduated Cylinder (mL)

FIGURE 1.4.
Displacement data.

3. If you place 20 pennies in the film canister, does it displace more water than a film canister with 15 pennies?

FIGURE 1.5.
Displacement illustration.

Your table has three columns. The first step of the mathematical modeling process is selecting a problem. In the rest of this section you will examine the relationship between displacement and the number of submerged canisters. You will examine the relationship between total volume and the number of submerged canisters in a later section.

4. Make a scatterplot of the pairs (displacement, number of submerged canisters) using the data in your table.

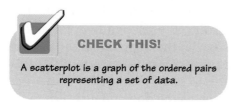

CHECK THIS!

A scatterplot is a graph of the ordered pairs representing a set of data.

5. Describe the pattern of the points that you observe in your scatterplot.

6. Predict the total volume of water displaced if you submerge 8 canisters.

7. Predict the number of canisters that you need to submerge in order to displace 500 mL.

SECTION 1.3

A Question of Variation

In the previous section, you collected and analyzed data regarding the relationship between volume of water displaced by canisters and the number of canisters submerged in water in a graduated cylinder.

You have already collected data and answered some questions about what you found. Now you will look at some important ideas about collecting data and building models based on that data.

The number of film canisters in the water and the total volume of water displaced are variables because their values change. A **variable** is a quantity that changes. Letters of the alphabet can be used to label variables. For example, c is a natural choice for the total number of film canisters in the water, and w is a good choice for the total volume of water displaced. The variable that you want to use to make predictions in your investigation is called the input or **independent** variable. The variable that you want to predict is called the output or **dependent** variable. Another way to think about this is that the dependent variable responds to changes in the independent variable or that changes in the independent variable explain changes in the dependent variable. In an experiment such as the one you just did, the independent variable is the one that you control.

When making a table of data in an experiment, it is customary to place the values of the independent variable in the first (left) column.

There are other variables in this situation, but in order to keep the modeling simple you will consider only two of them: the total number of canisters in the water (c) and the volume of water displaced (w). In modeling, variables have **units** that describe the kind of quantity the variable uses. For c, the units are numbers of canisters, for w, the units are milliliters

1. In the Displacement Investigation in Section 1.2, which variable is the independent variable? Why? Which variable is the dependent variable? Why?

2. The set of possible values of the independent variable is called the **domain of the situation**. What is a reasonable domain in this situation? Why?

3. The set of possible values of the dependent variable is called the **range of the situation**. What is a reasonable range for this situation? Why?

4. What patterns do you observe in your collected data?

5. One important aspect of mathematical modeling is the way the variables change in relation to each other. In the table where you recorded the number of submerged film canisters and the total displacement of the volume, find the value of the total displacement divided by the total number of film canisters for each row, $\frac{w}{c}$ (as in **Figure 1.6**).

Total Number of Submerged Canisters	Total Volume of Water Displaced (mL)	$\frac{w}{c} = \frac{\text{Total volume of water displaced}}{\text{Total number of film canisters}}$

FIGURE 1.6.
More displacement data.

6. A **proportional relationship** is one in which the ratio $\frac{\text{dependent variable}}{\text{independent variable}}$ is constant. The constant is called the **constant of proportionality**. In a proportional relationship, this constant is also a **rate of change**. A **rate of change** is a ratio that compares the change in the output variable to the change in the input variable. What do you observe in your table?

7. Real-world data are seldom perfect. Is the constant of proportionality the same or does it vary in your table?

One way to visualize a relationship between two variables is with a graph of enough data to get a sense of the pattern they form. In mathematics, a pair of perpendicular **axes** (number lines) creates a **coordinate plane**, in which a pair of numbers locates a point. The two numbers, a value of the independent variable and the corresponding value of the dependent variable, are called the **coordinates** of the point. In a graph, values of the independent variable are located along the horizontal axis (traditionally called the x-axis), and values of the dependent variable are located along the vertical axis (traditionally called the y-axis).

A **scatterplot** (**Figure 1.7**) is a graph of pairs (x, y) where the x-values are the independent values from your data and the y-values are the corresponding dependent values from your data. You created a scatterplot with the number of submerged film canisters on the x-axis and the total displacement of water on the y-axis.

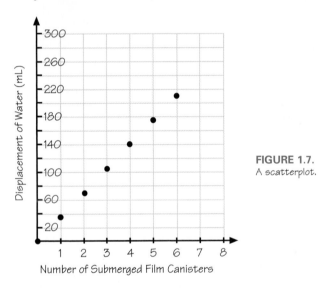

FIGURE 1.7.
A scatterplot.

This graph is called **discrete** because it shows distinct (separated) points. It does not make sense to connect the points since you cannot have a part of a canister. Since you cannot have a fraction of a canister, the domain is restricted to whole numbers. However, to use a scatterplot to make predictions, it is convenient to connect the points with a straight line, which creates a type of **continuous** graph. However, doing so changes the domain shown in the graph from '*some*' values to '*all*' values. Even though it makes mathematical sense, drawing a continuous graph can cause confusion when working with real-world situations.

8. Does it make sense to ask how much water 1.5 film canisters displace? Why or why not?

In a proportional relationship:

❖ The continuous graph is a straight line that passes through the origin;

❖ The ratio $\frac{\text{dependent variable}}{\text{independent variable}}$ is constant (or nearly so) for all data.

A proportional relationship can be described with an equation of the form $y = kx$, which is called a **direct variation function**. When a function is used to describe a relationship among variables, it is sometimes said that the function models the relationship.

9. Do your data demonstrate a proportional relationship between displacement and number of canisters? How do you know?

10. Describe how the constant of proportionality is displayed in the graph.

11. Based on your table or graph, what is the volume of 1 film canister in cubic centimeters?

Two quantities have a **positive relationship** (sometimes called a positive correlation) when the dependent variable increases as the independent variable increases.

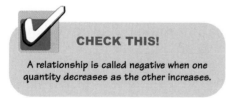

CHECK THIS!

A relationship is called negative when one quantity decreases as the other increases.

12. Is there a positive relationship between the total displacement of the water and the number of canisters submerged? Why or why not?

13. Use a graphing calculator to make a scatterplot of your data from the Displacement Investigation in Section 1.2. Your teacher will give you instructions on how to do this.

Assignment

For their science project, Judy and Jose plant a kudzu vine seed in order to investigate how quickly it grows. Every four days after the seed sprouts, they measure and record the height of their plant. Their results are shown in **Figure 1.8.**

Day Number	Height (cm)
0	0
4	3
8	6
12	9
16	12
20	15

FIGURE 1.8.
Kudzu data.

1. For this situation, what is the dependent variable and what is the independent variable?

2. State a reasonable domain and range for this situation.

3. Make a scatterplot for these data.

4. Is there a proportional relationship between height and day number? Why or why not?

5. What is the constant of proportionality for this situation?

6. Which kind of graph, continuous or discrete, is more appropriate for this situation? Why?

7. What is an appropriate direct variation function to model the relationship between height and day number?

Alexia and Alex collected data by placing marbles in a graduated cylinder partially filled with water and measuring the volume of displaced water. Their data are shown in the scatterplot in **Figure 1.9.**

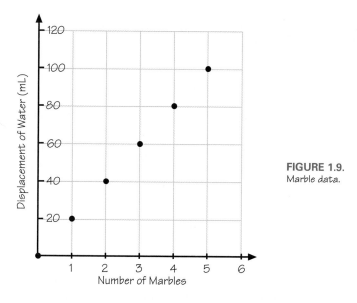

FIGURE 1.9.
Marble data.

8. Make a table for the data displayed in the scatterplot.

9. For this situation, what is the dependent variable and what is the independent variable?

10. State a reasonable domain and range for this situation.

11. Is this a proportional relationship? Why or why not?

12. What is the constant of proportionality for this situation?

13. Which kind of graph, continuous or discrete, is more appropriate for this situation?

14. What is an appropriate direct variation function to model the relationship between displacement and number of marbles?

15. Use the volume of 1 marble to find the approximate radius of a marble.

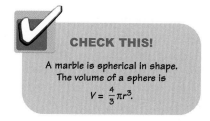

CHECK THIS!

A marble is spherical in shape.
The volume of a sphere is
$$V = \frac{4}{3}\pi r^3.$$

Displacement Investigation Round 2

In Section 1.2 you collected data and recorded the data in a table. You made a scatterplot of the relationship between displacement and number of submerged canisters, and found that the data demonstrated a proportional relationship. The direct variation model that you made involves two variables: the number of submerged film canisters (c) and the amount of water displaced (w).

If you change the variables you examine in a situation, your model may change.

In Section 1.2 you also recorded the total volume of the graduated cylinder. For this next investigation, continue to use c for the number of submerged canisters, your independent variable. Use v for the total volume contained in the graduated cylinder, your dependent variable.

1. Make a table showing the number of submerged canisters and the total volume of the graduated cylinder.

2. Make a scatterplot of the data in your table.

3. What are the domain and range for this situation?

4. When the independent variable has a value of 0, what is the value of the dependent variable?

5. Describe the relationship displayed in your scatterplot.

6. Do the variables appear to be positively related?

7. Do you think there is a proportional relationship between the total volume of the graduated cylinder and the number of submerged canisters?

8. What is the value of the dependent variable when the independent variable is 0?

9. What does your answer to the Question 8 value mean in this situation?

10. What do you predict the total volume contained in the cylinder will be if you submerge 7 film canisters?

11. How many canisters do you need to submerge for the total volume to be 900 mL?

12. When the points in a scatterplot lie along a straight line, the relationship between the two variables is called **linear**. Not all linear relationships are proportional. Do you think the relationship between total volume and number of canisters is linear?

Assignment

Tell whether the relationship in each situation is proportional or not. Justify your answer.

1. Traveling on interstate highway I-10 with data shown in **Figure 1.10.**

Time Elapsed (hr)	Distance Traveled (mi)
0	0
3	180
6	360
9	540

FIGURE 1.10.
Highway travel.

2. Fare in a taxicab: it costs $2.00 to get in the cab and an additional $0.20 for each $\frac{1}{4}$ mile traveled.

(Hint: Make a table!)

3. Temperature conversions shown in **Figure 1.11.**

Celsius Scale (°C)	Fahrenheit Scale (°F)
5	41
10	50
15	59
20	68

FIGURE 1.11.
Temperature conversions.

4. Money spent on many cans of coffee when the sale price is $1.89/can.

A bank savings plan book keeps track of the amount of money in the account at the end of each month. The data are recorded in **Figure 1.12.**

Number of Months	Account Balance
0	$220
1	$250
2	$280
3	$310
4	$340

FIGURE 1.12.
Savings account.

5. Explain how the balance can be something other than $0 after 0 months.

6. Make a scatterplot of the savings account data.

7. What are the domain and range for this situation?

8. When the independent variable has a value of 0, what is the value of the dependent variable?

9. Describe the type of relationship displayed in your scatterplot.

10. Do the variables appear to be positively related? Why or why not?

11. Is the relationship proportional? Why or why not?

12. What does the pair (0, 220) mean in this situation?

13. Is this set of data better represented by a continuous or discrete graph?

14. If the person deposits money into his savings account each month at the same rate, how much money is in the account after 10 months?

15. How many months does it take for this person to save $1000?

16. Make a scatterplot on the graphing calculator of the savings account data.

Mystery Metals

Tom and Tara's teacher gives them one of the metals shown in **Figure 1.13.**

Metal	Density $\left(\dfrac{g}{cm^3}\right)$
Aluminum	2.70
Zinc	7.13
Silver	10.49
Mercury	13.55
Gold	19.32

FIGURE 1.13.
Mystery metals.

Tom and Tara collect the following data (**Figure 1.14**) in the science lab on their metal. They use a graduated cylinder to find the volume and a balance to find the mass.

Volume (cm³)	Mass (g)
10	135
20	270
30	410
50	680
100	1350

FIGURE 1.14.
Metal data.

1. Use three different methods (table, graph, and equation) to examine the relationship between the mass of the metal and its volume. Then use the results of your investigation to determine the volume of 500 grams of the metal. Justify your answer.

2. Which metal do you think Tom and Tara were given? Why?

SUMMARY

In these sections you learned that proportional relationships have certain characteristics.

1. Continuous graphs of proportional relationships are linear and contain the point (0, 0).

2. The ratio $\frac{y}{x}$ is a constant in a proportional relationship and is also called the **constant of proportionality.**

3. Proportional relationships can be described by a function of the form $y = kx$, which is called a **direct variation function.**

You also saw that there are relationships that are linear, but not proportional.

This is Really a Stretch

In this section your teacher will conduct a class demonstration. Be sure to observe the demonstration carefully as you answer the following questions.

1. What do you observe when your teacher holds up the Slinky® with an empty film canister attached?

2. What observations can you make when your teacher holds up the Slinky with the attached film canister containing 5 pennies?

3. What observations can you make when your teacher holds up the Slinky with the attached film canister containing 10 pennies?

4. What observations can you make when your teacher holds up the Slinky with the attached film canister containing 15 pennies?

5. What patterns do you notice?

6. What are the input and output variables for this situation?

7. Do you think that the relationship between the amount of stretch of the Slinky and the number of pennies in the film canister is a proportional relationship? Why or why not?

8. Do you think that the amount of stretch of the Slinky and the number of pennies in the film canister are positively related? Why or why not?

9. What experiment could you do to further investigate the relationship between the stretch of a Slinky and the amount of weight attached to it?

Hooke's Law

Robert Hooke (1635–1703) was an English scientist. He grew up during the Age of Enlightenment, a time of much scientific discovery. Hooke spent his life studying astronomy, geometry, mathematics, mechanics, and physics. He worked with such famous colleagues as Robert Boyle and Isaac Newton and served as the chief assistant to Christopher Wren, the famous architect who designed the rebuilt London after the Great Fire of 1666.

Today Hooke is known for his work with springs. In the 1600s, most people kept time with pendulum clocks. These clocks use a large pendulum that swings with a regular period to drive a wheel and turn the clock's hands. They work well on land. However, on a ship the large waves of the ocean disrupt the pendulum. Since determining a ship's longitude requires knowing the time in Greenwich, England when the sun is directly overhead, the ship's navigator needs an accurate way to keep time.

Hooke recognized this problem. In 1658, he began experiments using springs instead of a pendulum to control the wheel of a clock. By 1660, he made two significant improvements on spring clock design. While refining these improvements, he made many observations about the stretch of springs. One of these is a relationship between the amount of force applied to a spring and the length the spring stretches as a result. This relationship is known as Hooke's Law.

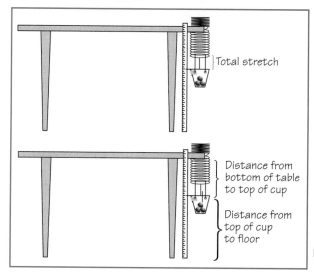

Total stretch

Distance from bottom of table to top of cup

Distance from top of cup to floor

HOOKE'S LAW EXPERIMENT

Place paper clips through three holes in the sides of a cup and hang the cup from the bottom of a Slinky. Suspend the Slinky and cup from a desk to allow the cup to move up and down freely. Tape a bent paper clip to the top of the cup to use as a pointer. Tape a meter stick vertically to the table (see **Figure 1.15**).

FIGURE 1.15. Slinky set-up.

In this experiment, measure the stretch that is explained by the marbles, but not the stretch that is explained by the cup or the weight of the Slinky. Place a mark or a piece of tape on the table or the meter stick at the level of the top of the empty cup and measure the stretch from this mark.

1. You will be adding one object at a time to the cup and measuring the total stretch of the Slinky as the objects are added. What is the independent variable? What is the dependent variable? What are a reasonable domain and range for this situation? Why?

2. You will also be measuring the distance from the bottom of the table to the top of the cup. What is the independent variable? What is the dependent variable? What are a reasonable domain and range for this situation? Why?

3. The third measurement that you will take is the distance from the top of the cup to the floor. What is the independent variable? What is the dependent variable? What are a reasonable domain and range for this situation? Why? Record and keep these data. You will need them in Section 1.9.

4. Sketch what you predict a scatterplot of total stretch versus number of objects placed in the cup would look like. Explain why you made the scatterplot the way you did.

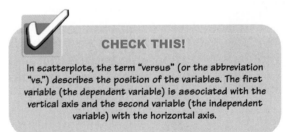

CHECK THIS!

In scatterplots, the term "versus" (or the abbreviation "vs.") describes the position of the variables. The first variable (the dependent variable) is associated with the vertical axis and the second variable (the independent variable) with the horizontal axis.

5. Sketch what you predict a scatterplot of the distance from the bottom of the table to the top of the cup versus the number of objects placed in the cup would look like. Explain why you made the scatterplot the way you did.

6. Add objects to the cup one at a time. After each object is added, record the total stretch of the Slinky, the distance from the bottom of the table to the top of the cup, and the distance from the top of the cup to the floor (see **Figure 1.16**).

Number of Objects in the Cup	Total Stretch of the Slinky® (cm)	Distance from the Bottom of the Table to the Top of the Cup (cm)	Distance from the Top of the Cup to the Floor (cm)
0	0		
1			
2			
3			
4			
5			

FIGURE 1.16.
Slinky data.

7. Is the relationship between the total stretch and the number of objects placed in the cup a proportional relationship? Use your table to justify your answer.

8. Use the data in your table to create a scatterplot of total stretch versus number of objects placed in the cup. Record your window. Sketch and describe your graph.

9. Do you think that your scatterplot shows a positive relationship between the total stretch and the number of objects placed in the cup? Why?

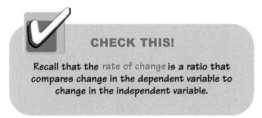

CHECK THIS!

Recall that the rate of change is a ratio that compares change in the dependent variable to change in the independent variable.

10. What characteristics of your graph verify that the relationships between total stretch and number of objects placed in the cup is or is not a proportional relationship?

Mathematicians use Δ, the Greek letter delta, for the change in a variable. Thus, Δs means "the change in the variable named s," or simply "the change in s." For example, between $s = 3$ and $s = 5$, $\Delta s = 2$.

You can calculate a rate of change between any two pairs of values in your table. To do so, divide the change in the dependent variable by the change in the independent variable. That is, find the ratio $\frac{\Delta s}{\Delta c}$, where s is the total stretch in the spring and c is the number of objects in the cup.

11. Find the rate of change between two pairs of values in your table. How does the rate compare to the constant of proportionality? What does the rate mean in this situation?

CHECK THIS!

A proportional relationship can be modeled with a direct variation function. The function's equation is in the form $y = kx$ where k, the constant rate of change, is called the constant of proportionality.

12. What is an appropriate function rule for a direct variation function that models the relationship between total stretch and the number of objects placed in the cup?

A **function rule** is a symbolic equation that describes a relationship between two variables. For example, if each value of the independent variable is triple the corresponding value of the dependent variable, then a function rule is $y = 3x$.

13. Graph your function rule over your scatterplot. Sketch your results. Does the graph show that your function models the relationship well?

14. Use your function rule to determine the total stretch of the Slinky when 12 objects are added to the cup.

15. How many objects should it take to make the Slinky stretch a total of 32 cm?

16. Is the relationship between the distance from the bottom of the table to the top of the cup to the number of objects placed in the cup a proportional relationship? What characteristics in your table justify your answer?

17. Use the data in your table to create a scatterplot of the distance from the bottom of the table to the top of the cup versus the number of objects placed in the cup. Record your window. Sketch and describe your graph.

18. What characteristics of your graph show that the relationship between the distance from the bottom of the table and the top of the cup versus the number of objects placed in the cup is or is not a proportional relationship?

19. Find the rate of change between two pairs of values in your table. Do the same for another two pairs. What is the meaning of the rate in this situation?

20. How does the rate of change for the relationship between the distance from the bottom of the table to the top of the cup and the number of objects placed in the cup compare to the rate of change for the relationship between total stretch and the number of objects placed in the cup? How are the graphs related?

Assignment

For Questions 1 and 2, decide whether the relationship between the two variables is or is not a proportional relationship. Explain how you made your decision.

1.

x	0	0.2	0.6	2.5	6.1
y	0	1.2	3.6	15.0	36.6

2.

t	0	1.6	2.4	3.0
d	0	3.2	4.2	5.1

For Questions 3 and 4, decide whether the function rule describes a direct variation function. Explain how you made your decision.

3. $x \cdot y = 12$

4. $y = 0.3875x$

For Questions 5 and 6, decide whether the graph depicts a proportional relationship between the two variables. Explain how you made your decision.

5. The graph shown in **Figure 1.17**

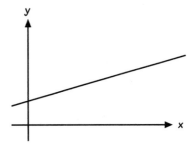

FIGURE 1.17.
A graph.

6. The graph shown in **Figure 1.18**

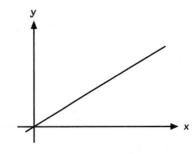

FIGURE 1.18.
A graph.

For Questions 7 and 8, let the relationship between x and y be a proportional relationship, and let $y = 12$ when $x = 5$.

7. What is the constant of proportionality?

8. If $x = 11$, what is the value of y?

Use the following information for Questions 9–17. Marbles were placed on a scale and weighed. The collected data are shown in **Figure 1.19.**

Number of Marbles (m)	Mass in Ounces (w)
1	1.5
2	3.0
4	6.0
8	12.0
10	15.0

FIGURE 1.19.
Mass of marbles.

9. What is the independent variable in this situation? Why?

10. What is the dependent variable in this situation? Why?

11. What are a reasonable domain and range for this situation?

12. Create a scatterplot of mass in ounces versus number of marbles.

13. Is this a proportional relationship? How do you know?

14. Find the rate of change between two pairs in the table. Do the same for two other pairs. What do you notice?

15. What is a function rule that models this relationship?

16. Predict the weight of 27 marbles.

17. Predict the number of marbles that have a mass of 54 ounces.

Variation on a Theme

In the previous section, you collected and analyzed data for the relationship between the amount of stretch in a Slinky and the number of marbles in a plastic cup.

You have already collected data and answered some questions about what you found. Now you will look at some important ideas about data collection and building models based on those data.

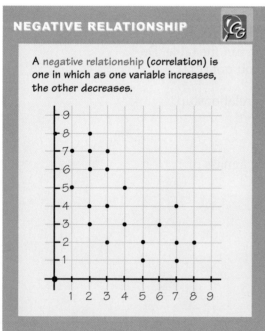

1. How did you decide which is the independent and which is the dependent variable for this situation?

2. How did you decide on a reasonable domain and range for this situation?

3. Why did you sketch your predicted scatterplots the way you did?

4. How did you use your table to determine if the relationship between total stretch and the number of objects in the cup is a proportional relationship? What happens when you divide w by n?

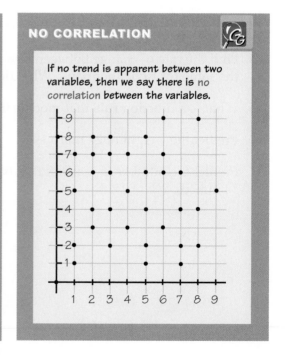

NEGATIVE RELATIONSHIP

A negative relationship (correlation) is one in which as one variable increases, the other decreases.

NO CORRELATION

If no trend is apparent between two variables, then we say there is no correlation between the variables.

5. Why do you think that there is a positive relationship between the total stretch of the Slinky and the number of objects in the cup?

6. What do you think is meant by a negative relationship?

7. What do you think is meant by no relationship?

8. How did you determine rates of change in your table?

To find the rate of change $\frac{\Delta w}{\Delta n}$ for any two pairs of values in the table, subtract the values of the dependent variable and divide by the corresponding difference in the values of the independent variable.

9. Find the rate of change for the pairs (2 objects, 4 cm) and (5 objects, 10 cm).

10. Explain how the rate of change for pairs of values in the table appears in the graph of this relationship.

11. In a proportional relationship, how can you use the rate of change and the values of the independent variable to find the values of the dependent variable?

12. Write a function rule to model the relationship between the total stretch of the Slinky, w, and the total number of objects in the container, n.

For a linear function including direct variation functions, the rate of change is also the slope of the line. In terms of x and y, the formula for the slope of the line through (x_1, y_1), (x_2, y_2) is $m = \frac{\Delta y}{\Delta x} = \frac{y_2 - y_1}{x_2 - x_1}$. In Question 12, you used your table to write a direct variation function rule, $w = 2n$, to relate the variables. In terms of x and y, the equation of the line is $y = 2x$.

13. Show how you can use the slope formula to determine the slope of the line that relates the total amount of stretch to the number of objects in the cup.

Another way to find the equation of a line through (x_1, y_1) and (x_2, y_2) is to use the **point-slope formula**: $y - y_1 = m(x - x_1)$.

14. Show how you can use the point-slope formula to determine the equation of the line that relates the total amount of stretch to the number of objects in the cup.

15. How can you predict the total stretch of the Slinky when 12 objects are added to the cup?

16. How can you predict the number of objects it takes to stretch the Slinky 32 cm?

Now, consider the situation where you compared the number of objects in the cup with the distance from the bottom of the table to the top of the cup. Data that one group gathered are in **Figure 1.20.** Use these data to answer the remaining questions.

Number of Objects in the Cup (n)	Distance (cm) from the Bottom of the Table to the Top of the Cup (d)
0	17
1	19
2	21
3	23
4	25
5	27

FIGURE 1.20.
More Slinky data.

17. How can you decide if this relationship is or is not proportional?

18. How can you find the slope of a function that models this relationship?

19. The **y-intercept** of a function's graph is the point where the graph crosses the y-axis. For the function that models this relationship, where do you find this point's coordinates in the table?

20. What is the meaning of the y-intercept in this situation?

Another representation for a linear function is called **slope-intercept form**: $y = mx + b$. This general form of a linear function expresses the dependent variable, y, in terms of the independent variable, x, the slope of the line (m), and the y-intercept of the line whose coordinates are $(0, b)$.

The slope-intercept form of a linear function is useful when you know the rate of change, or slope, and the starting point, or y-intercept, for a relationship that can be described with a linear function.

21. Use your answers to Questions 18 and 19 to write a function rule that can be used to find the distance between the bottom of the table and the top of the cup for n marbles.

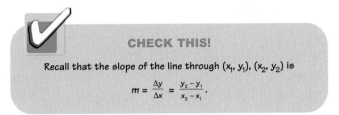

CHECK THIS!

Recall that the slope of the line through (x_1, y_1), (x_2, y_2) is

$$m = \frac{\Delta y}{\Delta x} = \frac{y_2 - y_1}{x_2 - x_1}.$$

22. How does the function relating the distance from the table to the cup and the number of objects in the cup (Question 21) compare to the function relating the total stretch of the Slinky and the number of objects in the cup (Question 14)?

 Assignment

Predicting values from a proportional relationship can be done using a **proportion** (two fractions that are equal to each other), by writing an equation that looks like this:

$$\frac{12}{5} = \frac{y}{11}.$$

In this proportion 12 and 5 are corresponding values of y and x. The y-value that corresponds to the x-value 11 is not known.

1. Why must the two fractions be equal?

One algebraic method to solve a proportion involves "cross-multiplying" in the manner shown in **Figure 1.21**, and setting the two products equal to each other.

FIGURE 1.21.
Cross-multiplying.

$$\frac{12}{5} \diagtimes \frac{y}{11}$$

2. In this case, what are the two products formed?

3. What equation do you get when you set the products equal to each other?

4. How do you solve that equation for y?

Another way to solve the equation $\frac{12}{5} = \frac{y}{11}$ is to multiply both sides of the equation by 11.

5. Why does that one step *solve* the equation?

6. In order to find the answer using this method, what arithmetic steps must you do? How does this compare to the arithmetic you did in Questions 2 through 4?

Solve each of the following proportions:

7. $\frac{4}{x} = \frac{15}{23}$

8. $\frac{7}{6} = \frac{y}{25}$

9. x and y form a proportional relationship. When $x = 13$, $y = 5$. Find x, when $y = 13$.

Write a direct variation function rule to model each of the following situations. Be sure to list the constant of proportionality and its units. Then use the rule to solve the problem.

10. On a map scale, 1 cm represents a distance of 25 miles. Two cities on the map are 3.2 cm apart. What actual distance separates the two cities?

11. On a typing test, Jane typed 98 words correctly in 2 minutes. Assuming she can type for longer periods of time without losing her concentration, how many minutes would it take her to type an essay that contains 343 words?

12. Hanging 3 washers on a spring stretches it a total of 4.5 cm. If 13 washers are placed on it instead, how far will the spring stretch? (Assume that the spring can be stretched several feet without problems.)

A local theme park charges $15 for admission. The amount of revenue generated by admission sales can be found using the function rule $R = 15n$, where R is the total revenue and n is the number of admissions sold.

13. Complete the table in **Figure 1.22**, and then use that information to answer Questions 14–15.

n	2	20		1000	
R			3000		30,000

FIGURE 1.22.
Theme park admissions.

14. For each of the five pairs in the table, calculate the ratio $\frac{R}{n}$. What do you notice?

15. Find $\frac{\Delta R}{\Delta n}$ (the rate of change of the revenue compared to the number of tickets sold) between the first and second entries of the table. What units does your answer have?

In Questions 16–18, find the slope of the line.

16. The line whose equation is $y = \frac{4}{3}x + 12$

17. The line that goes through the points $P(4, 9)$ and $Q(7, 21)$

18. The line that goes through the points $P(12, 5)$ and $Q(2, 8)$

This Floors Me

Recall that in Section 1.7 you took three measurements during the Hooke's Law experiment. You measured the total stretch of the Slinky, the distance from the bottom of table to the top of cup, and the distance from the top of the cup to the floor (**Figure 1.23**). In this section you will investigate the relationship between the number of objects placed in the cup and the distance from the top of the cup to the floor.

FIGURE 1.23.
Slinky stretch.

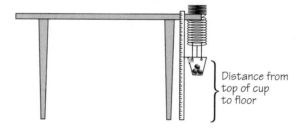

Distance from top of cup to floor

Copy your data from Section 1.7 into a table like **Figure 1.24.**

Number of Objects in the Cup	Distance from the Top of the Cup to the Floor (cm)
0	
1	
2	
3	
4	
5	

FIGURE 1.24.
Distance from cup to floor data.

1. In the relationship between the distance from the top of the cup to the floor and the number of objects in the cup, what is the independent variable? What is the dependent variable? What are a reasonable domain and range for this situation? Why?

2. Is the relationship between the distance from the top of the cup to the floor and the number of objects in the cup a proportional relationship? Use your table to justify your answer.

3. Suppose the starting position (empty cup) is 10 cm. How would this change your table?

4. Sketch what you predict a scatterplot of the distance from the top of the cup to the floor versus the number of objects in the cup would look like. Explain why you made the scatterplot the way you did.

5. Use the data from your table to create a scatterplot of the distance from the top of the cup to the floor versus the number of objects in the cup. Record your window, sketch and describe your graph.

6. Does your scatterplot show a positive, negative, or no correlation between the distance from the top of the cup to the floor and the number of objects in the cup? How do you know?

7. What characteristics of your graph verify that distance from the top of the cup to the floor versus the number of objects in the cup is or is not a proportional relationship?

8. Suppose the top of your cup is 10 cm higher. How would this change your graph?

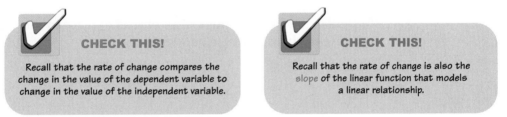

CHECK THIS!

Recall that the rate of change compares the change in the value of the dependent variable to change in the value of the independent variable.

CHECK THIS!

Recall that the rate of change is also the slope of the linear function that models a linear relationship.

9. Find the rate of change between successive pairs of values in your table. To estimate the slope of a linear model for this relationship, find the average of these rates of change. What is the meaning of the slope in this situation?

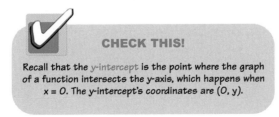

CHECK THIS!

Recall that the y-intercept is the point where the graph of a function intersects the y-axis, which happens when x = 0. The y-intercept's coordinates are (0, y).

10. What is the *y*-intercept of the graph of a linear function that models the relationship between the distance from the top of the cup to the floor and the number of objects in the cup? What is the meaning of the *y*-intercept in this situation?

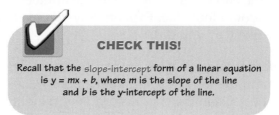

CHECK THIS!

Recall that the slope-intercept form of a linear equation is y = mx + b, where m is the slope of the line and b is the y-intercept of the line.

11. Write the slope-intercept form of a function rule that models the relationship between the distance from the top of the cup to the floor and the number of objects in the cup.

12. Suppose the top of your cup is 10 cm higher. Write the new function rule.

13. Graph your function rule on your scatterplot. Sketch your results. Do you think your function models the data well?

14. Predict the distance from the top of the cup to the floor when 9 objects are added to the cup.

15. Predict the smallest number of objects to place in the cup to make the bottom of the cup touch the floor.

Assignment

In Questions 1–3, an equation in slope-intercept form is provided. Use the equation to fill in the table. Then calculate Δx, Δy, and the ratio $\frac{\Delta y}{\Delta x}$ for successive pairs. (In these questions, x and y have no units.)

1. $y = 3x - 8$

x	y
4	
8	
12	
16	

2. $y = 1.2x + 15$

x	y
5	
7	
9	
11	

3. $y = 4.1x - 12$

x	y
13	
19	

Use the tables from Questions 1–3 to answer Questions 4–6.

4. In a table, do the values of the input variable (x) <u>have</u> to increase by a constant amount?

5. What is the smallest number of ordered pairs needed to calculate the ratio $\frac{\Delta y}{\Delta x}$?

6. What is the relationship between the rate of change ratio $\frac{\Delta y}{\Delta x}$ and the equation given?

7. The following functions were graphed with a computer drawing utility: $y = 1.2x + 5$, $y = 0.8x + 5$, $y = 2.3x - 5$, $y = -0.5x + 10$, and $y = -1.4x + 10$. The graphs are shown in **Figure 1.26.**

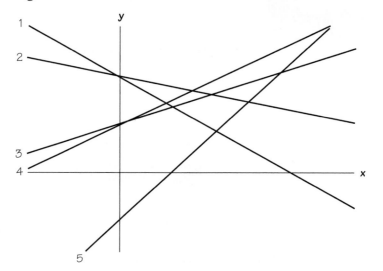

The order in which the lines were drawn is unknown, and the axes don't show a scale. Explain how you can identify the graph of each equation.

For Questions 8–11, find the equation of the line that goes through the two points given. Express your answer in slope-intercept form.

8. $P(-4, 12)$ and $Q(2, 3)$

9. $P(3, 8)$ and $Q(7, 15)$

10. $P(5, 12)$ and $Q(9, 14)$

11. $P(4, 14)$ and $Q(8, 4)$

Recall that the equation for a line in point-slope form looks like this: $y - k = m(x - h)$.

12. Graphs of direct variation functions always go through the origin (0, 0). What does $y = mx$ look like if written in point-slope form?

13. If a function is written in slope-intercept form, like $y = 2x + 5$, you already know one point on its graph, the y-intercept. What are the coordinates of that point? What does the point-slope form of that same equation look like?

14. Suppose that Garth Brooks can sell out the Cotton Bowl, which has 25,704 seats, when the ticket price is set at $50, but a crowd of 16,000 is estimated when the admission is raised to $80. Assume that ticket sales drop off in a linear pattern as the price increases. Find a function rule to model the relationship between the ticket sales and ticket price.

Use the following information for Questions 15–17.

A concert promoter keeps track of advance ticket sales. Those sales can be used to estimate the attendance at the performance and to help determine how much help is needed in planning for the event. The data shown in **Figure 1.27** compares ticket sales 4 weeks in advance of several concerts with the actual attendance.

Advance Ticket Sales (A)	Actual Attendance (n)
5628	13,581
7043	15,902
8912	19,873
9117	21,683
9741	22,705

FIGURE 1.27.
Ticket sales.

15. Use the grid in **Figure 1.28** to make a scatterplot that shows the relationship between the actual attendance and the advance ticket sales.

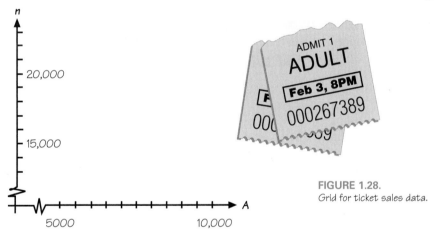

FIGURE 1.28.
Grid for ticket sales data.

16. When the pattern in a scatterplot is nearly linear, but not perfectly so, you can estimate a linear model that you can use to make fairly accurate predictions. Draw a line on the scatterplot you made in Question 15 that you think captures the trend of the data fairly well. Then find an equation for the line. Explain how you found the equation.

17. If a performance features a popular act, would you expect the data point to be above the line or below it? Explain.

Distance vs. Ramp Height

After investigating the relationship between the number of objects in a cup and the stretch of a Slinky, the students in the Math Club decided to roll a tennis ball down a ramp and measure how far it travels. To see if there is a relationship between the distance that a tennis ball rolls and the steepness of the ramp, they stacked books beneath one side of the ramp (**Figure 1.29**). As they changed the number of books, they rolled the ball and measured the distance of the roll.

FIGURE 1.29.
Changing ramp height.

The data from their experiment are in **Figure 1.30.**

Ramp Height in Books	Distance Traveled from the End of the Ramp (in)
1	27
2	53
3	84
4	110
5	129
6	160
7	180

FIGURE 1.30.
Ramp height data.

1. Is there a proportional relationship between the distance traveled and the number of books? Justify your answer.

2. Use three different methods (table, graph, and function rule) to predict the distance a tennis ball travels if the ramp is 10 books high.

SUMMARY

In this lesson you learned about different methods to get the value of m in $y = mx$, function rules that model proportional relationships.

* Find the constant of proportionality by dividing each y-value by its corresponding x-value.

* Find the rate of change.

You also learned about methods to write symbolic rules for functions that model non-proportional, linear relationships.

* From a table, find the rate of change (slope) and the y-intercept. Then use the slope-intercept formula, $y = mx + b$.

* If you know the coordinates of two points, (x_1, y_1), (x_2, y_2), use the slope formula, $m = \frac{\Delta y}{\Delta x} = \frac{y_2 - y_1}{x_2 - x_1}$, to find the slope. Then use the point-slope formula, $y - y_1 = m(x - x_1)$.

Two variables can have a positive relationship, a negative relationship, or no relationship at all.

Positive Relationship:

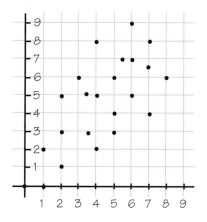

Negative Relationship:

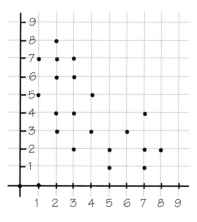

No Relationship:

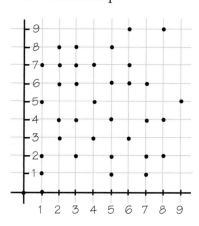

If one variable increases as the other variable increases, then there is a **positive relationship (correlation)** between the two variables.

If one variable decreases as the other variable increases, then there is a **negative relationship (correlation)** between the two variables.

If there is no apparent trend in the scatterplot, then there is **no relationship (correlation)** between the two variables.

Apparent Size

In this section you will mark the apparent size of a meter stick that your teacher has attached to a wall of the room. You will mark the apparent size on a pencil that you hold a short distance from your eyes.

1. Hold a pencil a few inches from your eyes. Align one end of the pencil with the top of the stick. Use your thumb to mark the bottom of the stick. Move the pencil farther from your eyes and repeat. What do you notice?

2. What are the variables in this situation?

3. Which is the independent variable? Why?

4. How are these variables related?

5. Again, mark the apparent size of the meter stick by holding the pencil a few inches from your eyes. After you have done so, keep the distance between your eyes and the pencil the same. This time move farther away from the meter stick and mark the apparent size. What do you notice?

6. What are the variables in this second situation?

7. Which is the independent variable? Why?

8. How are the variables related?

9. What experiment could you do to investigate the relationship between an object's apparent size and the distance that an observer is from the object?

The Farther You Go

In this section you will conduct an experiment or use data provided by your teacher to further examine a relationship that you discussed in Section 1.11. The variables are the distance that an observer stands from a meter stick taped to a wall and the apparent length of the meter stick.

To do the experiment, begin by taping a meter stick vertically to one of your room's shorter walls or use a meter stick that your teacher taped to the wall in advance. The middle of the ruler should be about eye level.

Use a tape measure to measure a distance of 8 feet from the wall or use an 8-foot mark made by your teacher. Stand with your toes on the mark and hold a ruler vertically at arm's length. Align the top of the ruler with the meter stick. Use your thumb to mark the place on the ruler that is aligned with the bottom of meter stick (see **Figure 1.31**). Record this apparent length of the meter stick.

FIGURE 1.31.
Apparent length of a meter stick.

1. Continue taking measurements, moving an additional 2 feet from the meter stick each time. Record the measurements in a table like the one in **Figure 1.32.**

Distance from Meter Stick (ft)	Apparent Length of Stick (in)
8	
10	
12	
14	
16	
18	
20	
22	
24	
26	
28	
30	

FIGURE 1.32.
Meter stick data.

2. Enter the data points from the table into a graphing calculator and make a scatterplot. Record your viewing window and sketch the graph.

3. What happens to apparent length as distance from the meter stick increases?

4. Can the distance from the meter stick equal 0? Why or why not?

5. Do you think a decreasing linear function would be a good model for the relationship between apparent length and distance from the meter stick? Why?

6. Add a column to your table for the products of the apparent length and the distance from the meter stick. Calculate the product of each pair. What do you notice?

7. How can you use your observation in Question 6 to write a function rule for the relationship between apparent size and distance from the meter stick?

8. Use your equation to predict the distance you should stand from the meter stick for its apparent size to be 2 inches.

9. Change your viewing window to include negative values of x and y. (For example, if your scatterplot had Xmin = 0 and Xmax = 35, change Xmin to –35.) How does the graph change? Do you see more or fewer data points?

10. Enter your function from Question 7 into your calculator and graph it over your scatterplot. Use the same window you used in Question 9. Sketch your graph.

11. The domain and range of the mathematical function you just graphed are different from the domain and range of the situation shown in your table. Explain the differences.

For each table of values determine an appropriate viewing window, create a scatterplot, write a function rule, and graph your function rule over your scatterplot.

1.

x	y
−3	−2
−2	−3
−1	−6
1	6
2	3
3	2

2.

x	y
−3	−3
−2	−4.5
−1	−9
1	9
2	4.5
3	3

3.

x	y
−3	$-\frac{2}{3}$
−2	−1
−1	−2
1	2
2	1
3	$\frac{2}{3}$

4.

x	y
−3	−4
−2	−6
−1	−12
1	12
2	6
3	4

5. A group of senior citizens is planning a trip from Houston to Seattle. The cost to charter a private airplane is $10,000. The plane holds a maximum of 80 passengers.

Number of Passengers	Cost per Passenger
10	
20	
30	
40	
50	
60	
70	
80	

a) Fill in the table for the cost per passenger.

b) Which is the independent variable? Why?

c) Which is the dependent variable? Why?

d) What is a reasonable domain for this situation?

e) What is a reasonable range for this situation?

f) Indicate an appropriate viewing window, create a scatterplot, write a function rule, and graph your function rule over your scatterplot.

g) If 52 people buy tickets on the flight, what is the cost per person?

6. In some situations, it is not clear which variable is independent. For example, consider a rectangle that has a fixed area of 20 square centimeters. If the length is 10 centimeters, then the width must be 2 centimeters. But neither the length nor the width is truly independent of the other. So you can choose either to be the independent variable.

a) Use x and y to write a function rule that describes the relationship between the length and the width in this 20 square centimeter rectangle.

b) What are a reasonable domain and range for this situation?

c) Graph your function rule on a graphing calculator and record the viewing window you used.

d) If the length of the rectangle is 13 cm, what is the width?

One Goes Up, One Goes Down

In the last section you investigated the relationship between the distance from an object and its apparent size. You found a decreasing non-linear relationship.

1. What function rule describes the relationship between the distance from a meter stick and its apparent size?

2. What function rule describes the relationship between the length and width of a rectangle that has an area of 20 square units?

3. What do these function rules have in common? How do they differ?

4. Graph the functions on separate axes. Sketch your graphs.

5. What do the graphs have in common? How do they differ?

6. As the independent variable increases, what happens to the dependent variable in each situation? Does this change happen at a constant rate?

7. Think back to the apparent size situation in Section 1.12. The table in **Figure 1.33** contains some sample data that one student group collected.

Distance from Meter Stick (x)	Apparent Length of Stick (y), in cm	xy
8	24.5	
10	20.0	
12	16.3	
14	13.5	
16	12.3	
18	11.3	

FIGURE 1.33.
Sample data.

For each pair, multiply the apparent length of the stick by the distance from it. Record your results in a table like Figure 1.33.

8. What is the average of the products of the distance from the meter stick and its apparent length?

9. In a proportional relationship, $y = kx$, or $k = \frac{y}{x}$. This means that $\frac{y}{x}$ is a constant value. Add a fourth column to your table and use it to find $\frac{y}{x}$ for each of your data points. Is this ratio constant? Are these ratios close to each other?

10. Is the relationship between distance from the meter stick and apparent size a proportional relationship? How do you know?

11. Use your graphing calculator to make a scatterplot of apparent size versus distance from the stick. Sketch your graph and identify your window.

12. If $xy = 196.8$, solve this equation for y in terms of x. Graph your equation on this scatterplot. Based on your graph, how well do you think this function models the relationship between apparent size and distance from the meter stick? Explain.

SUMMARY

In some relationships, the product of the values of the independent variable and the corresponding values of the dependent variable is a constant. In other words, xy equals (or is close to) a constant, k. These relationships are called **inverse variation** or **indirect variation**. In these situations, the variables are said to be **inversely proportional**.

The general form of an inverse variation function rule is $y = \frac{k}{x}$. The parent function for inverse variation functions is $y = \frac{k}{x}$, and the graphs of this family of functions have two branches (see **Figures 1.34 and 1.35**).

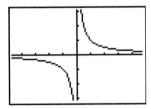

FIGURE 1.34. Graph of two branches of inverse functions.

FIGURE 1.35. Table of family of inverse functions.

When k is positive, one branch of the graph is in the first quadrant where small x-values yield large y-values and large x-values yield small y-values. This branch is commonly used to model inverse variation situations in the real world, such as the relationship between the apparent size of an object and distance from the object (see **Figure 1.36**).

Direct Variation	Inverse Variation
$\frac{y}{x}$ is a constant value, k	xy is a constant value, k
$y = kx$	$y = \frac{k}{x}$
x and y are positively related	x and y are negatively related
Linear graph	Non-linear graph

FIGURE 1.36. Traits of direct and inverse variation.

Assignment

For each inverse function, complete the table and graph the
function using the ordered pairs from the table.

1. $y = \dfrac{1}{x}$

x	y
–4	
–2	
–1	
–0.5	
–0.25	
0.25	
0.5	
1	
2	
4	

2. $y = \dfrac{2}{x}$

x	y
–4	
–2	
–1	
–0.5	
–0.25	
0.25	
0.5	
1	
2	
4	

3. $y = \dfrac{5}{x}$

x	y
–4	
–2	
–1	
–0.5	
–0.25	
0.25	
0.5	
1	
2	
4	

4. $y = \dfrac{-1}{x}$

x	y
–4	
–2	
–1	
–0.5	
–0.25	
0.25	
0.5	
1	
2	
4	

5. Compare the graphs in Questions 1, 2, and 3. In what ways are they alike, and in what ways do they differ? How does the equation of each support your answers?

6. Compare the tables in Questions 1, 2, and 3. In what ways are they alike, and in what ways do they differ? How does the equation of each support your answers?

7. How do the graph and table in Question 4 differ from those in Questions 1, 2, and 3? How does the equation of each support your answers?

8. For each table, is the relationship an inverse variation, a direct variation, or neither?

a)

x	y
3	1
6	2
9	3
12	4
15	5

b)

x	y
2	12
7	32
11	48
13	56
14	60

c)

x	y
3	8
4	6
6	4
8	3
12	2

d)

x	y
1	5
2	$\frac{5}{2}$
3	$\frac{5}{3}$
4	$\frac{5}{4}$
5	1

9. Describe a method for determining if a direct variation function is a good model for a relationship in a table.

10. Describe a method for determining if an inverse variation function is a good model for a relationship in a table.

Boyle's Law

In 1662, Robert Boyle and an assistant found a way to increase the pressure on a quantity of air and measure both the volume of the air and the pressure exerted on it. They did these things by pouring mercury into a large U-shaped tube containing air. As more mercury was added, the air compressed. Boyle measured the volume of the air by measuring its height in the tube. He measured the pressure on the air by measuring the height of the mercury in the tube.

Some of Boyle's original data are shown in **Figure 1.36.**

Volume (height of air in inches)	Pressure (height of mercury in inches)
12	117.5625
16	87.875
20	70.6875
24	58.8125
28	50.3125
32	44.1875
36	39.3125
40	35.3125
44	31.9375
48	29.125

FIGURE 1.36.
Boyle's data.

1. Enter the data from the table into your graphing calculator and make a scatterplot. Sketch your graph and record your viewing window.

2. As volume increases, what happens to pressure?

3. Based on the scatterplot, do you think a direct variation function is a good model for the relationship between volume and pressure? Why?

4. Does the scatterplot appear to represent an inverse variation relationship? How do you know?

5. Add a third column to the table and label it *product*. Calculate and record the product for each pair.

6. Find the average product of volume and pressure.

7. Use the mean (average) product as the constant of variation and write an inverse variation function rule to model the relationship between pressure and volume for a gas.

8. Graph this function on your scatterplot. Based on the graph, does the function rule appear to model the relationship well? Explain.

Graphing a function rule on a scatterplot is one way to assess how well a function models a relationship. Another way is to compare numerical values. For example, you could use your rule to predict the pressure for a volume value of 12 and compare the prediction to the actual pressure that Boyle measured, 117.5625.

9. Use your function rule to calculate a predicted value for each volume value in your table. Compare the actual pressure values to the predicted ones. How well do you think the function models this relationship?

In the seventeenth century, most Europeans did not understand the nature of air. In 1644, Evangelista Torricelli, an Italian scientist and colleague of Galileo Galilei, correctly identified the concept of air pressure and built the first mercury barometer to measure it.

Robert Boyle, a prominent English chemist, set up a series of experiments with his research assistant, Robert Hooke (whom you met in Section 1.6), to further investigate properties of air. Among other things, Boyle and Hooke proved in the 1660s that air is necessary for sound, fire, and life.

The proof that fire needs air to exist and that sound cannot travel in a vacuum were radical at the time. Many scientists and philosophers insisted there was no such thing as a vacuum, or absence of air. Thus, the work of Boyle and Hooke was groundbreaking. Boyle's Law continues to be used as one of the fundamental principles of branches of science such as fluid dynamics and meteorology.

In 1662, Boyle published an appendix to his 1660 textbook *New Experiments Physio-Mechanicall, Touching the Spring of the Air and its Effects*. In this appendix, Boyle wrote about the mathematical relationship between the volume of air and its pressure.

10. Based on your work in this section and Boyle's ideas about the relationship between the volume of a gas and its pressure, make a conjecture about a function rule that could model this relationship. How can this function rule be generalized to model the pressure and volume in any data set? Explain your answer.

11. Boyle's Law is one example of inverse variation. Can you think of some others?

SUMMARY

Inverse variation can be used to describe many relationships in the natural world. In 1662, Robert Boyle established an inverse variation relationship between the pressure and volume of a gas when it is kept at a constant temperature. This relationship is known as Boyle's Law and is represented mathematically by the equation $P = \frac{k}{V}$, where P is the pressure, V is the volume, and k is the constant of variation.

 Assignment

1. A group of students decide to conduct an experiment to verify Boyle's law. They use a CBL and a pressure sensor attachment to vary the volume and record the resulting pressure. Their data are in **Figure 1.38.**

Volume (cubic cm)	6	8	10	12	14	16	18
Pressure (atmospheres)	3.94	3.00	2.41	2.00	1.67	1.44	1.26

FIGURE 1.38.
Student data.

a) Which is the independent variable? Why?

b) Which is the dependent variable? Why?

c) What is a reasonable domain for this situation?

d) What is a reasonable range for this situation?

e) Decide an appropriate viewing window, create a scatterplot, write a function rule, and graph this function rule on your scatterplot.

f) Predict the pressure that results from a volume of 2 cubic centimeters.

g) Predict the volume when the pressure is 1 atmosphere.

2. In a recent experiment, Javier used a 9-volt battery to test a circuit. He set various current levels and measured the resulting resistance. The data are in **Figure 1.39.**

Current (I)	Resistance (R)
2	4.5
5	1.8
6	1.5
10	0.9
12	0.75
15	0.6
20	0.45

FIGURE 1.39.
Javier's data.

a) Which is the independent variable? Why?

b) Which is the dependent variable? Why?

c) What is a reasonable domain for this situation?

d) What is a reasonable range for this situation?

e) Decide an appropriate viewing window, create a scatterplot, write a function rule, and graph your function rule on your scatterplot.

f) If the current is 7, predict the resistance.

g) Predict the current when the resistance is 1.75.

Using Inverse Variation

1. Pete's Construction Company has hired a team of engineers to study the company's policy for buying cement. Pete's foreman always orders 108 cubic feet of cement to pour a 12-foot wide driveway. The engineers conducted an experiment. They collected data by changing the length of a driveway, while keeping the width constant at 12 feet, and measuring the depth of cement after pouring 108 cubic feet of cement. Their data are in the table in **Figure 1.40.**

Width (feet)	Length (feet)	Depth (feet)	Volume of Cement (cubic feet)
12	1	9.00	108
12	2	4.50	108
12	3	3.00	108
12	4	2.25	108
12	5	1.80	108

FIGURE 1.40.
Pete's Construction data.

City code requires that driveways be 4 inches deep. What is the longest 12-foot wide driveway that can be constructed using the foreman's order? Justify your answer.

Modeling Project Scope It Out

When you look through a telescope, the amount you can see depends on several variables.

In this project, you will investigate the relationship between the size of a telescope's viewing circle and two other variables.

You will need several paper towel rolls, masking tape, a meter stick, a tape measure, and scissors.

Make a simple telescope by cutting a paper towel roll from one end to the other so that another paper towel tube can fit inside of it. Do the same with a third paper towel roll. Put the uncut tube inside one of the cut tubes. Then put these two inside the other cut tube. You can now vary the length of your scope from one tube to nearly three.

Next, tape a meter stick to a wall horizontally. Back off and look at the stick through your scope. If you align the left edge of your viewing circle with the left end of the meter stick, you can estimate the viewing circle's diameter. Now change the length of the scope. The diameter of the viewing circle should change.

There are several variables in this situation:

❖ The diameter of the viewing circle;

❖ The length of the scope;

❖ The distance you are standing from the meter stick.

In mathematical modeling, it can be difficult to analyze the relationship between several variables at once. So mathematical modelers use a simple trick: they keep all but two of the variables constant and examine just those two. To do this, they make changes in one variable and record the effect on the other. After they have figured out how these two variables are related, they do something similar with a different pair of variables.

So here is an approach to this situation:

❖ Keep the distance from the meter stick constant and examine the relationship between viewing circle diameter and telescope length;

❖ Keep telescope length constant and examine the relationship between viewing circle diameter and distance from the meter stick.

Conduct an investigation into these two relationships. Use the scope you have made to gather data. Prepare a report on your findings.

Practice Problems

1. A concert promoter is considering setting the ticket price at $30. **Figure 1.41** shows a table, function rule, and graph for revenue (R) based on number of tickets sold (n).

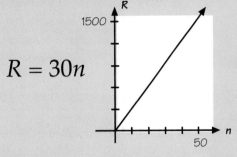

n	R
10	$300
20	$600
30	$900
40	$1200
50	$1500

$$R = 30n$$

FIGURE 1.41.
Data for Question 1.

Explain how to tell if the relationship between R and n is a proportional relationship from the

a) table of values.

b) function rule.

c) graph.

2. For each linear relationship, find the slope (m). That is, find the constant rate of change $\frac{\Delta y}{\Delta x}$.

a) The table in **Figure 1.42**

x	y
5	23
9	29
13	35
17	41
21	47

FIGURE 1.42.
Data for Question 2a.

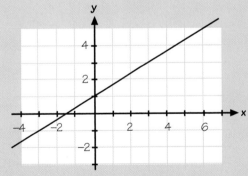

FIGURE 1.43.
Graph for Question 2c.

b) The line going through the points $P(5, 13)$ and $Q(10, 10)$

c) The line shown in **Figure 1.43**

3. Solve each of the following equations for the indicated variable:

a) $\frac{5}{12} = \frac{x}{18}$, for x.

b) $4.20n + 67000 = 76030$, for n.

c) $C = 2.45 \cdot n + 108000$, for n.

4. Two long-distance telephone carriers have quoted costs shown in **Figure 1.44**:

FIGURE 1.44.
Comparison of phone
company rates.

Company	Monthly Service Charge	Rate (per min)
NCO	$5.00	$0.20
Jog	$3.00	$0.25

Write equations describing the total cost associated with each company plan for one month. Use t as the variable to represent the amount of time (number of minutes) spent on the phone.

5. Sam gathered data on the advertising costs and ticket sales from concerts at the Cotton Bowl. The data are shown in **Figure 1.45**. Sam is interested in the relationship between advertising costs and ticket sales.

Advertising Costs	Ticket Sales
$10,000	12,478
$15,000	16,395
$20,000	19,882
$25,000	22,043
$30,000	25,512
$40,000	25,704
$50,000	25,704

FIGURE 1.45.
Advertising costs
vs. ticket sales.

a) The pattern in the table shows increasing ticket sales as advertising costs go up. However, when the large sums are spent, there isn't an increase in ticket sales. What could explain this?

b) On a copy of the grid in **Figure 1.46**, make a scatterplot to show how the ticket sales are related to advertising costs.

Chapter 1 Science: Modeling with Direct and Inverse Variation Practice Problems

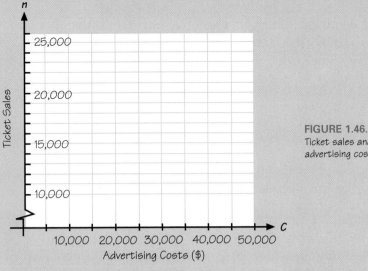

FIGURE 1.46.
Ticket sales and advertising costs.

c) The pattern for the first five data points is fairly linear. Draw a line on the scatterplot that you think captures this linear trend. Find the line's equation.

6. Data collected from ticket sales at the Cotton Bowl are shown in **Figure 1.47.**

Price (p)	Ticket Sales (n)
$10	25,000
$20	24,000
$30	22,000
$40	19,000
$50	16,000
$60	14,000
$70	10,500

FIGURE 1.47.
Price vs. ticket sales.

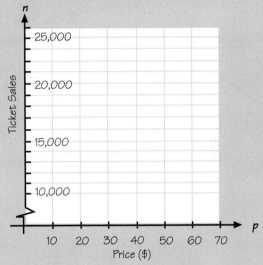

FIGURE 1.48.
A blank grid plot comparing price and ticket sales.

a) Make a scatterplot on a copy of the grid in **Figure 1.48.**

b) Draw a line on the graph that you think captures the trend. Find the line's equation.

c) On a graphing calculator, put the ticket price information in list L1 and the ticket sales information in list L2. Adjust the window settings to match the scatterplot you drew in a. What window settings did you use?

7. Suppose that a concert will have a sell-out attendance of 20,000 when the admission is $25, but the attendance drops 2000 for every $5 added to the ticket price.

a) What is a function rule that models the relationship between attendance and admission price?

b) What is a reasonable domain for this situation?

8. Direct variation functions have graphs that are straight lines, but not all functions with straight-line graphs are direct variations.

a) Compare slope-intercept and point-slope forms of function rules for lines in general with function rules for direct variations.

b) Compare the graphs of direction variations with the graphs of linear functions in general.

9. Data on various attendance projections for a concert are in **Figure 1.49:**

Ticket Price (p)	$10	$20	$30	$40	$50
Ticket Sales (n)	25,000	23,500	22,250	21,100	19,900

FIGURE 1.49. Projection of the ticket sales by ticket price.

a) Draw a scatterplot on a copy of the grid in **Figure 1.50.**

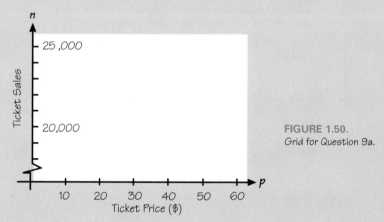

FIGURE 1.50.
Grid for Question 9a.

b) Draw a line on your scatterplot that you think captures the trend of the data. Find the line's equation.

For each table in Questions 10 through 13, determine the constant of variation. Then match the table with a graph (a–d) and an equation (e–h) below.

10.

X	Y₁
.5	32
1	16
2	8
4	4
8	2
16	1

$k =$ _____

graph _____

equation _____

11.

X	Y₁
-16	-.25
-8	-.5
-4	-1
-2	-2
-1	-4
-.5	-8

$k =$ _____

graph _____

equation _____

12.

X	Y₁
-16	-.5
-8	-1
-4	-2
-2	-4
-1	-8
-.5	-16

$k =$ _____

graph _____

equation _____

13.

X	Y₁
-8	.5
-4	1
-2	2
-1	4
-.5	8
-.25	16

$k =$ _____

graph _____

equation _____

a)

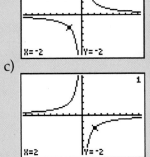

c)

b)

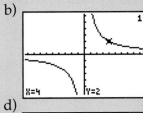

d)

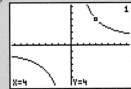

e) $y = \dfrac{4}{x}$

g) $y = \dfrac{16}{x}$

f) $y = \dfrac{-4}{x}$

h) $y = \dfrac{8}{x}$

For Questions 14 and 15, fill in the missing values in the table and write the function rule.

14.

X	Y1
	ERROR
.25	
.5	48
1	
2	12
	6
	4

15.

X	Y1
-10	-10
-5	
	-100
0	
1	
5	20
	10

16. Students studying strengths of materials performed an experiment. They cut Styrofoam into beams of different lengths, all with the same width and thickness. Then they fastened each beam between two desktops and gradually placed one-ounce weights on it until it broke. Their data are shown in **Figure 1.51**.

Length of Beams (inches)	Breaking Weight (ounces)
4	28
5	22
6	19
7	16
8	14
9	13

FIGURE 1.51.
Data on length of beams vs. breaking weight.

a) Examine the relationship between beam length and breaking weight. What kind of relationship do you think it is?

b) Which is the independent variable in this situation? Why?

c) What function rule would you use to model this relationship? Explain.

17. The students in Question 16 conducted another experiment. This time they kept the length and thickness of the beams constant, but varied the width. Their data are shown in **Figure 1.52**.

Width of Beams (inches)	Breaking Weight (ounces)
0.5	6
1.0	13
1.5	19
2.0	22
2.5	29
3.0	37

FIGURE 1.52.
More data on width of beams vs. breaking weight.

Investigate the relationship between breaking weight and beam width. Give a function rule that models the relationship.

Glossary

KEY CONCEPTS

Axes: Number lines drawn at right angles used to locate points. Axes is the plural of axis.

Boyle's Law: A law that states that the pressure of a gas is inversely related to the volume of the gas.

Constant of proportionality: The constant ratio of y/x for (x, y) values of a direct variation function.

Continuous graph: A graph with the data points connected. For example, the relationship between the amount of hamburger purchased and the amount paid at a supermarket has a continuous graph. A shopper can order any amount of hamburger and pays more as the amount of hamburger increases.

Coordinate plane: A system for finding the location of points (x, y) in two dimensions, using axes with scales.

Coordinates: A pair of numbers that describes the location of a point in a coordinate plane. The first number is the x-coordinate, the second number is the y-coordinate.

Δ: The Greek capital letter, delta, used to show "the change in." The notation Δy means the change in the y variable.

Dependent variable: The output variable. In modeling, the dependent variable is the one you want to predict.

Direct variation function: A function with an equation of the form $y = kx$. Direct variation functions are used to describe proportional relationships.

Discrete graph: A graph with the data points unconnected. For example, the relationship between the number of oranges purchased at a supermarket and the price paid has a discrete graph. You cannot order 4.5 oranges, so connecting lines between 4 and 5 does not make sense.

Domain: The set of values that the input variable in a mathematical function can have.

Domain of the situation (or model): The set of reasonable values of the independent variable for a given situation.

Function: A set of ordered pairs of real numbers in which no two pairs with the same first coordinates have different second coordinates.

Function rule: A symbolic equation that describes a relationship between two variables.

Hooke's Law: A law that states that the force applied to a spring is directly proportional to the stretch of the spring.

Independent variable: The input variable. In modeling, the input variable is the one that is used to make predictions.

Inverse variation or indirect variation: A relationship in which one variable decreases as the other increases and the product of corresponding values of the variables is a constant. In other words, xy equals a constant, k.

Inversely proportional: Variables in an inverse variation relationship are said to be inversely proportional. That is, as one variable increases the other decreases, and the product of corresponding values of the variables is constant.

Linear relationship: When the points in a scatterplot lie along a straight line, the relationship between the two variables is called linear.

Mass: In science, mass is the amount of matter in an object. It is common to use weight and mass as the same.

Negative relationship: Two variables have a negative relationship (sometimes called a negative correlation) when the dependent variable decreases as the independent variable increases.

Point-slope formula: A method for finding the equation of a line. The formula is $y - y_1 = m(x - x_1)$.

Positive relationship: Two quantities have a positive relationship (sometimes called a positive correlation) when the dependent variable increases as the independent variable increases.

Proportional (relationship):
A relationship is proportional if its continuous graph is a straight line that passes through the origin and the ratio $\frac{y}{x}$ is constant (or nearly so) for all data.

Proportions: Two fractions that are equal to each other.

Range: The values that the output variable in a mathematical function can have.

Range of the situation (or model):
The set of reasonable values of the dependent variable for a given situation.

Rate of change: A ratio that compares the change in the output variable to the change in the input variable.

Scatterplot: A graph of pairs (x, y) where the x-values are the independent values from your data and the y-values are the corresponding dependent values from your data.

Slope: A measure of the steepness of a line: the ratio of the vertical change to the horizontal change between two points on a line, or "rise over run."

Slope-intercept form: A form represented by the equation $y = mx + b$. This general form of a linear function expresses the dependent variable, y, in terms of the independent variable, x, the slope of the line (m), and the y-intercept of the line whose coordinates are $(0, b)$.

Units: Units describe the kind of quantity or information that a variable uses. Inches, centimeters, and milliliters are all units.

Variable: A quantity that changes.

Versus (vs.): When used in the phrase y versus x, it describes a scatter plot in which y is the dependent variable (vertical axis) and x is the independent variable (horizontal axis).

Volume: Generally, refers to the size of an object. That is, volume is a measure of the amount of space that a three-dimensional object occupies.

y-intercept: The point at which a graph crosses the y-axis. The y-intercept is the term b in the slope-intercept form for the equation of a line.

2 CHAPTER

Bones: Linear Functions and Predictions

The Disappearance of Amelia Earhart

Amelia Earhart is one of the most famous pilots of all time. She was the first woman to fly solo across the Atlantic Ocean and later across the Pacific. On June 1, 1937 she set off on a flight around the world along with her navigator. On July 2, their plane vanished between New Guinea and Howland Island. The U.S. Navy searched but did not find a trace of them. To this day their fate is unknown.

A group trying to solve this mystery heard about bones that were found on a Pacific island in 1940. At the time a Dr. D. W. Hoodless examined the bones. He concluded that they were from a male about 5 feet 5 inches tall. Some of his measurements are given in **Figure 2.1**.

Bones	Length (cm)
Humerus	32.4
Tibia	37.2
Radius	24.5

FIGURE 2.1.
Bones analyzed by Dr. Hoodless.

Statements in his report raised doubt about his knowledge of the human skeleton. Lacking the bones, Dr. Karen Burns and Dr. Richard Jantz studied the measurements left by Dr. Hoodless. Using data from a data bank at the University of Tennessee they built models to predict height, gender, and ethnic background. They concluded that the bones were from a white female about 5 feet 7 inches tall, which fits Earhart. Could the bones have been hers? This question can only be answered if the bones are recovered.

In this chapter you will be asked to think like a forensic anthropologist. Given measurements of a set of bones, you will investigate the clues about a dead person. You will also collect data and build models to predict height and gender.

CHECK THIS!

A forensic anthropologist is a scientist who uses information about the human body and its bones to try to identify a dead person based on bones and teeth. This is one of many kinds of work that a forensic anthropologist does.

Mysterious Findings

Archaeologists and forensic scientists often use mathematical models to help investigate human remains found at historical sites and crime scenes. In this section you will explore models that describe the relationship between the length of a person's head and the person's height.

From time to time, bones are found in rugged areas. A hiker in Arizona's Superstition Mountains found a skull, eight long bones, and many bone fragments. He called the local police who sent a team to investigate. The team recorded facts about the bones, including their size. **Figure 2.2** shows some data that are similar to what the team recorded.

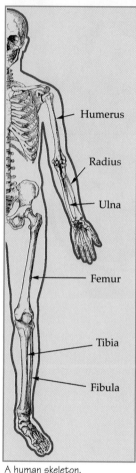

Humerus

Radius

Ulna

Femur

Tibia

Fibula

A human skeleton.

Bone Type	Number Found	Length (cm)
Femur	3	41.5, 41.4, 50.8
Tibia	1	41.6
Ulna	2	22.9, 29.0
Radius	1	21.6
Humerus	1	35.6
Complete Skull (including jaw)	1	23.0
Fragments	More than 10	From 3.0 to 5.0 cm

FIGURE 2.2. Measurements of bones found at Superstition Mountains.

Use all the facts you have so far to answer these questions.

1. Based on the data in the table, what is the precision of the measurements?

2. Study the data in Figure 2.2. The team reports that these bones belong to at least two people. How do they know?

3. Which bones do you think belong to the same person? What assumptions did you make to get your answer? Explain your answer. (To make it easier to classify the bones, refer to the dead people as Skeleton 1, Skeleton 2, and so on.) You will need the answers to this question later on.

4. Do the lengths of the bones make you think they belonged to a male or a female? What did you use to get your answer? (Remember, Dr. Hoodless concluded that the bones found on the island belonged to a male, but Burns and Jantz disagreed with his findings.)

5. Do you think the dead people were children or adults? Defend your answer.

6. Guess the heights of the dead people. How good do you think your guesses are?

A Model for Estimating Height

One way to turn your guess of the dead peoples' heights into a scientific estimate is to explore the relationship between the length of certain bones and a person's height.

In this section you will gather some data to explore a possible relationship between head length and a person's height.

Within your group, measure the length of each person's head (from chin to the top of the head) and then measure their height. Record your data in a table like **Figure 2.3**. Be sure to give the units of measure you used at the top of the second and third columns.

Name	Head Length	Height

FIGURE 2.3. Group head-length and height data.

1. What patterns do you see in this data set?

2. We aren't sure yet that there is a relationship between head length and height, so why does it make sense to consider head length as the independent variable here?

3. What is a reasonable domain for this situation? Why?

4. What is a reasonable range for this situation? Why?

5. On a sheet of chart paper create a scatterplot of height versus head length. Sketch your graph.

TREND LINES:
LINES THAT APPROXIMATE DATA

The plot of height versus head length is fairly spread out, but it appears to have a linear form. This large amount of variability makes it hard to pick a line that you can use to make good predictions for heights. The following two methods will help you choose a line that approximates the pattern of the height versus head-length data from your class:

METHOD 1

1. Pick a point that appears to lie in the middle of the points displayed in your scatterplot. The point doesn't have to be a data point.

2. Using this point as one point on your line, adjust the slope of your line until you find a line that you think best describes the pattern of the data.

3. Find the equation of your line.

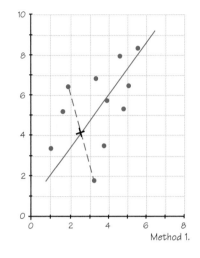

Method 1.

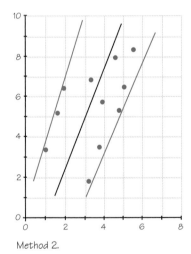

Method 2.

METHOD 2

1. Draw two lines in such a way that the points on your hand-drawn scatterplot are squeezed as tightly as possible between these lines. (The lines don't have to be parallel.)

2. Now draw one line halfway between the two lines that you have drawn.

3. Find the equation of this line.

6. Divide your group in half. Half of your group should use Method 1 and a meter stick to find a trend line for the graphed data. The other half should use Method 2 and two meter sticks to find a trend line. Draw both trend lines over the scatterplot and sketch your graph.

7. Write the equation of your trend line.

8. Find the ratio of head length to height by dividing each person's height by his or her head length. Record your results in a table like **Figure 2.4.**

Name	Height / Head Length

FIGURE 2.4. Ratio of head length to height.

Now you have a ratio of head length to height for each member of the class. You can start using these data to predict a person's height.

You need to find the best constant of proportionality (multiplier) that can be used to predict the height of the whole class.

One way to find the constant of proportionality is to use a measure of central tendency. You may have seen three before: mean, median, and mode. Let's review these and decide which one would be useful in making a prediction.

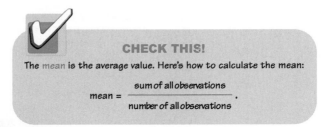

CHECK THIS!

The mean is the average value. Here's how to calculate the mean:

$$\text{mean} = \frac{\text{sum of all observations}}{\text{number of all observations}}.$$

9. What is the mean of the ratios of the head length to height?

CHECK THIS!

The median is the middle value. Here's how to calculate the median:

1. Arrange the data in order from smallest to largest.

2. If the number of data is odd, the median is the middle number. To find it, add 1 to the number of data then divide by 2. Start at the bottom of the ordered data and count up that number of observations.

3. If the number of data is even, the median is the average of the middle two numbers. To find it divide the number of data by 2. Again, start at the bottom and count up that number of observations. Add this number to the next number in the data set. Divide the sum by 2.

10. What is the median of the ratios of the head length to height?

CHECK THIS!

The mode is the most frequent data point in a data set.

11. What is the mode of the data set of ratios of the head length to height?

The question you are trying to answer is which measure of central tendency is the best constant of proportionality (multiplier).

In general, use the mode when you want to know what is the most common, as in the most common shoe size among American men. Use the mean when no values are much larger or much smaller than the rest of the data. Use median when a few relatively large or small values make the mean larger or smaller than most of the data.

Since all of the measures of central tendency are close in this case, it does not really matter which one we use. So, we will use the mean as the constant of proportionality (multiplier).

12. Use the constant of proportionality (multiplier) to write a function rule that could be used to predict a person's height given their head length.

13. Use a graphing calculator to create a scatterplot of height versus head length. Sketch your scatterplot and record your window.

14. Graph your function rule on the scatterplot. If needed, adjust the equation. Write your new equation and sketch your graph.

15. On the same scatterplot, graph the trend line that you found using the meter stick.

16. How does the trend line found using the meter stick compare to the function rule found with the constant of proportionality?

17. Does the relationship of height and head length appear to be a proportional relationship? Why or why not? Give at least two reasons to support your answer.

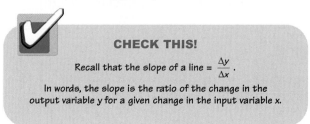

CHECK THIS!

Recall that the slope of a line = $\dfrac{\Delta y}{\Delta x}$.

In words, the slope is the ratio of the change in the output variable y for a given change in the input variable x.

18. What is the equation of a line that you think fits the data well? What is the slope of this line?

19. What meaning does the slope have in this context?

20. Using words, describe the relationship between the length of a person's head and the height of the person.

21. Predict the height of a person whose head length is 25 cm.

22. Predict the head length of a person whose height is 175 cm.

Assignment

1. A class has the following heights (in centimeters):

   168, 178, 161, 155, 156, 155, 171, 188, 166, 161, 178, 180, 155, 167, 155, 157, 160, 158, 152, 152, 159, 155, 172, 188

   a) What is the mean height for this group of students?

   b) What is the median height?

   c) What is the mode of the heights?

2. The line plot in **Figure 2.5** shows the average daily temperature in a city for each day during the month of May. Each dot represents one day when the average daily temperature was that number of degrees Fahrenheit. For example, there were three days when the average daily temperature was 50°F.

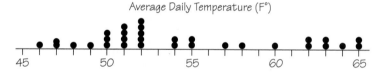

Average Daily Temperature (F°)

FIGURE 2.5. Line plot.

   a) What is the average (mean) daily temperature for the month of May? Explain how you found your answer.

   b) What is the median daily temperature? Explain how you found your answer.

   c) What is the mode daily temperature? Explain how you found your answer.

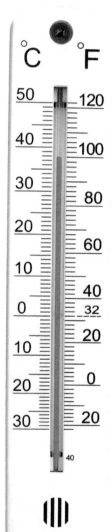

Use **Figure 2.6**, which shows the height of students in Ms. Jaczinko's tenth-grade class, for Questions 3–19.

Female		Male	
Name	**Height (cm)**	**Name**	**Height (cm)**
Alicia	157	Ahmed	173
Bia	166	Brian	177
Christi	164	Jesús	174
Chantalle	164	Davis	192
Coral-Mae	161	José	172
Juanita	164	Kelvin	180
Ji-Hyun	167	Lenny	174
Kim	162	Luis	175
Kristen	175	Mike	185
Maria	166	Pedro	185
Tianna	172	Sang	178
Teresa	176		

FIGURE 2.6.
Height data from Ms. Jaczinko's class.

3. What can you say about the precision of these measurements?

4. Use the table in **Figure 2.7** to find the mean, median, and mode for the male students, the female students, and all students in one class.

	Mean	**Median**	**Mode**
Male students			
Female students			
All students			

FIGURE 2.7. Measures of central tendency for Ms. Jaczinko's class.

5. Look over the data in Figure 2.6. What is the range in heights from the shortest student to the tallest?

6. A student joined Ms. Jaczinko's class. Is it reasonable to predict that the tenth-grader would be between 164 cm and 180 cm tall? Explain your answer.

7. What is the range of girls' heights from shortest to tallest?

8. If you know the new student in Ms. Jaczinko's class is a girl, what would you say about this person's height based on these data?

9. A girl who is 196 cm tall joins Ms. Jaczinko's class. How does this new girl's height compare with the other heights in the class?

10. What effect does this new height have on the mean, median, and mode of the girls' height data?

One way to predict a new student's height is to take the **mean** of all the heights.

11. Use the mean of the students' heights as a prediction of a new student's height. Record the mean student height.

12. If the new student is as short as the shortest student in the class, how far off is the prediction in Question 11?

13. If the new student is as tall as the tallest student in the class, how far off is the prediction in Question 11?

14. Do you think that the mean is a good prediction? Explain. Can you make a better one?

15. A new student, Melissa, joins the class. Does the new student, a girl, change your prediction? Find the mean for girls' heights. Use this average to predict Melissa's height.

16. If Melissa is as short as the shortest girl in Ms. Jaczinko's class, how far off is your prediction? What if Melissa is as tall as the tallest girl?

17. Do you think this is a better prediction than the one made in Question 11? Explain.

18. If the new student turns out to be Martin (a boy), not Melissa, can you choose a way to predict Martin's height? Give your prediction and your method.

19. If the new student's height is between the shortest boy and the tallest boy, what is the largest possible error for your prediction?

Height vs. Bone Lengths

In the last section, you collected and analyzed data on the relationship between a person's height and the length of their head from the bottom of the chin to the top of the skull. This

relationship is important because it allows anthropologists who find skull bones to estimate the height of the person. Forensic scientists, such as those on crime-solving television shows, can also use this relationship to help find whose bones they were.

You have already collected data and answered questions about what you found. Now, let's look at some important ideas about data collection and building linear models based on those data.

1. When you measured the head length of your group members, what method did you use? How did you know that your method would yield good data?

2. How did you decide on a reasonable domain and range here?

3. How did you place your trend line?

4. How did you find the equation of your trend line?

5. When is it best to use mean as a measure of central tendency?

6. When is it best to use median as a measure of central tendency?

7. When is it best to use mode as a measure of central tendency?

8. What are the features of a direct variation function?

9. What effect does changing the value of the multiplier have on the graph of a direct variation function?

10. How might you use your model to make a rough prediction of the height of the person whose skull length is recorded in Figure 2.2?

   a) Recall that the skull measured 23.0 cm in length. Predict the height of the person in centimeters (cm). Describe the process you used to make your prediction.

   b) Does your prediction result in a reasonable height for a person? Explain.

11. How might you use your model to make a rough prediction of the head length of a person whose height was 175 centimeters?

   a) Predict the head length of the person in centimeters. Describe the process you used in making your prediction.

   b) Does your prediction result in a reasonable head length for a person? Explain.

12. What information do you think might give better estimates of the heights of the dead people whose bone lengths are recorded in Figure 2.2? How or where might you get this information?

MODELS OF THE FORM $y = mx$

- The graph of a function in the $y = mx$ family is a line that passes through the origin.

- The steepness and incline or decline of each of these lines is controlled by the value m, which is the slope of the line.

- These are also called direct variation functions, which are used to model proportional relationships.

MODELS OF THE FORM $y = mx + b$

- The graph of a function in the $y = mx + b$ family is a line that intersects the y-axis at $(0, b)$.
- The steepness and incline or decline of each of these lines is controlled by the value of m, which is the slope of the line.
- The vertical shift of the graph is controlled by the value of b, which is the y-intercept of the line.

SUMMARY

In Sections 2.1, 2.2, and 2.3 you explored the relationship between the length of certain bones and a person's height. You then used specific functions to predict a person's height from these bones.

❖ You also gathered data and applied a measure of central tendency—mean, median, or mode—to the data to find a multiplier (constant of proportionality) and a formula to predict height based on the length of the person's head.

❖ Since these models give rough estimates of a person's height, you will need to do more investigating to find a better model that gives better predictions. One way to improve your models is to collect data and use the data to test your model. Analyzing data forms the basis of the next section.

Assignment

1. Which graph(s) in **Figure 2.8** show(s) a trend line that appears to model the given data well? Explain your reasoning.

FIGURE 2.8.
Three graphs of trend lines.

Graph A   Graph B   Graph C

2. Hernando kept a record of his salon sales and tips for one afternoon as shown in **Figure 2.9.** Plot the data on a copy of the grid in Figure 2.9, number and label the graph appropriately. Use a straightedge to draw a trend line. Use this graph to answer the questions that follow.

Sale Amount ($)	Tip Amount ($)
10	2
15	3
20	2
25	4
30	4
35	6
40	5
45	7

FIGURE 2.9. A table of Hernando's tips with a grid to plot the data.

a) Use what you know about slope and y-intercept to write an equation for your trend line.

b) What does the slope mean here? Does this value make sense in this context?

c) What does the y-intercept mean? Does this value make sense in this context?

d) Predict Hernando's tip if his salon sale is $55. Justify your answer.

3. Nedra buys beads in bulk, by the pound, for her jewelry business. She has kept a record of her bead purchases (which are small) for the last 2 months. Use the data in **Figure 2.10** to graph a trend line and to answer the questions that follow.

Pounds of Beads Purchased	Total Amount Paid
1	1
1.25	1.50
2	2
2.25	2.5
2.75	3
3	3.5
3.75	4

FIGURE 2.10. Nedra's data.

a) Use your knowledge of slope and y-intercept to write an equation for your trend line in slope-intercept form.

b) What does the slope mean here? Does this value make sense in this context?

c) What does the y-intercept mean? Does this value make sense in this context?

d) How much would you expect Nedra to pay for 5 lbs of beads? Justify your answer.

4. Ten students' semester grades from Mr. Johnson's last year's class are given in **Figure 2.11.**

First Semester Grade (x)	55	62	64	71	75	78	82	85	95	97
Second Semester Grade (y)	50	54	64	65	60	70	77	72	88	88

FIGURE 2.11. Grades for 10 students.

Chapter 2 Bones: Linear Functions and Predictions

Assignment 2.3

a) Use these data to make a scatterplot. Find an appropriate trend line.

b) What does the slope mean here? Does this value make sense in this context?

c) What does the y-intercept mean? Does this value make sense in this context?

d) If you made a 72 the first semester, what is your predicted score for the second semester?

5. Psychologists are trying to find a relationship between test anxiety and success on a test. Examine the data in **Figure 2.12**, and answer the questions that follow.

X	0	7	14	14	15	20	20	21	23
Y	77	50	59	48	51	52	46	51	43

FIGURE 2.12.
Test anxiety data.

x = score on a test anxiety evaluation.
y = exam grade.

a) Looking at the overall trend in the table, as x-values increase do the y-values increase or decrease?

b) Use these data to create a scatterplot. Find the equation of a good trend line.

c) What does the slope mean here? Does this value make sense in this context?

d) If a person scores an 18 on the anxiety evaluation, what is the predicted exam grade?

e) What is the expected anxiety score if the exam grade is a 60?

SECTION 2.4

I Think We Have Your Thighbones

In Section 2.2 you completed a process known as mathematical modeling, which is similar to using the Scientific Method, to solve problems. The first step in this process is to identify a problem that you need to solve. Collecting and analyzing data to develop a mathematical model and create a hypothesis is often the next step. The model is then used to make predictions. In this section you will analyze data that may have been collected by a famous doctor, develop a mathematical model of the data, and then use that model to make predictions.

Early models (from the late 1800s) that predicted height from the length of long bones were based on ratios. (See Figure 2.2 that shows some of the long bones.) For example, the ratio of the height H and femur length F is given by the formula $H/F = 3.72$.

1. Based on this model, estimate the heights of the people whose femur lengths are given in **Figure 2.13.**

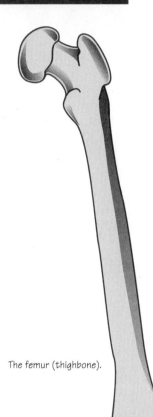

The femur (thighbone).

Bone Type	Number Found	Length (cm)
Femur	3	41.5, 41.4, 50.8
Tibia	1	41.6
Ulna	2	22.9, 29.0
Radius	1	21.6
Humerus	1	35.6
Complete Skull (including jaw)	1	23.0
Fragments	More than 10	From 3.0 to 5.0 cm

FIGURE 2.13. Measurements of bones found at Superstition Mountains.

2. For most adults, femurs range in size from 38 cm to 55 cm. According to this model, what is the range of heights of most adults? Are these reasonable heights for adults? (Recall that 2.54 cm = 1 in.)

3. What function rule would you enter into your graphing calculator in order to graph this model for the relationship between height and femur length?

The function rule that you wrote for Question 3 should be a member of the $y = mx$ family, as were the first models used to predict height from the lengths of long bones.

Dr. Mildred Trotter (1899–1991), a physical anthropologist, was well known for her work in the area of height prediction based on the lengths of long bones.

Dr. Mildred Trotter

During World War II, the armed services sometimes had problems identifying the remains of dead soldiers. Dr. Trotter was asked to help. She decided to measure each person's height and the length of each person's femur. Using these data she refined earlier models by adding a constant, thereby producing models of the form $y = mx + b$.

Data similar to the data she obtained are shown in **Figure 2.14.**

Femur Length (cm)	Height (cm)
45	165
53	190
46	168
38	150
54	188
52	185
39	155
51	186
41	157
42	160
47	178
40	160
55	195
50	175
43	165
48	175
44	166
49	178

FIGURE 2.14.
Adult height versus femur length.

4. Why does it make sense to consider femur length as the independent variable?

5. What is a reasonable domain for this situation? Why?

6. What is a reasonable range for this situation? Why?

7. Use a graphing calculator to make a scatterplot of height versus femur length. Sketch your scatterplot and record your window.

8. Recall that Dr. Trotter's model is of the form $y = mx + b$. Find a function rule for the trend line for these data. So that you can compare your function rule to Dr. Trotter's model, be sure your rule is of the form $y = mx + b$.

9. Graph your function rule on the scatterplot. If necessary adjust the equation. Write your adjusted equation, sketch your graph, and record your window.

Dr. Trotter models the relationship between the height measurements and femur measurements with the equation $H = 2.38F + 61.41$ where height, H, and femur length, F, are in centimeters.

10. Is your function rule similar to Dr. Trotter's model? How do you know?

11. How does the graph of the function rule for the early model ($y = 3.72x$) compare to the graph of the function rule for Dr. Trotter's model?

12. Would the early model or Dr. Trotter's model be the best way to predict a person's height given their femur length? Why?

13. Predict the height of an adult whose femur length is 42.5 centimeters.

14. If an adult is 170 centimeters tall, what is the approximate length of his or her femur?

SUMMARY

To build and test a model, you often need to collect data. In this section you did an analysis of collected data and made predictions. You also compared different models that are used to predict height. Most models used in this lesson are of the $y = mx$ family. Sometimes a model contains a non-zero constant such as those in the $y = mx + b$ family. These models often are used due to the variability of real-world data.

Assignment

1. Jackson's femur measures 39 cm and his brother's measures 40 cm. Based on Dr. Trotter's first formula, $H = 2.38F + 61.41$ where H is the person's height (cm) and F is the length of the femur (cm), predict the difference in the brothers' heights.

2. Femurs that belong to two women are found. One femur is one centimeter longer than the other. Predict the difference in their heights. Explain how you were able to get your answer even though the lengths of the two women's femurs were not given. In addition, tell how you could get your answer from Dr. Trotter's first formula.

3. If a man is 178 cm (about 5 ft 10 in) tall:

   a) Explain how you could use your graph to estimate the length of his femur. What is your estimate?

   b) Write a set of algebraic steps to solve Dr. Trotter's first formula, $H = 2.38F + 61.41$, for F. (A medical doctor might use such an equation to check that the length of a person's femur is normal for a person of that height.)

   c) Use your equation in b to predict the length of a man's femur if the man is 178 cm tall. Compare your answer to the femur length you estimated in a.

4. Another of Dr. Trotter's equations predicts height, H, from a known tibia length, T (this is called the second formula): $H = 2.52T + 78.62$ where H and T are measured in cm.

   a) The length of the tibia listed in Figure 2.13 is 41.6 cm. Use Dr. Trotter's second formula to predict the person's height. Is your answer a reasonable height for a person?

   b) Use your predicted height from 4a and your formula from 3b to predict the length of the femur of a person with the 41.6-cm tibia. Which femur length from Figure 2.13 is closest to your prediction?

c) Write a set of algebraic steps to solve Dr. Trotter's second formula, $H = 2.52T + 78.62$, for T. (A medical doctor might use such an equation to check that the length of a person's tibia is normal for a person of that height.)

5. In a third formula, Dr. Trotter used both the tibia and the femur to predict height:
$H = 1.30(F + T) + 63.29$. (All measurements are in cm.)

a) A group of students measure the femur and tibia of a skeleton. They find that the femur is 42 cm long and the tibia is 43 cm long. Predict the height of the person using Dr. Trotter's third formula, $H = 1.30(F + T) + 63.29$.

b) Compare the prediction in a with the predicted height using Dr. Trotter's equation, $H = 2.38F + 61.41$.

c) Compare the predictions in a and b with the predicted height using Dr. Trotter's second formula, $H = 2.52T + 78.62$.

d) You should have found a clear difference between your predictions in a–c. If a man is 175 cm tall (about 5 ft 9 in), based on Dr. Trotter's equations in b and c, would you expect his tibia or his femur to be longer and by how much?

Height vs. Forearm Length

Let's apply what you have learned thus far about building and using linear models to a new situation.

The table in **Figure 2.15** shows the heights and forearm lengths of students in Ms. Jaczinko's class.

Female			Male		
Name	Forearm Length (cm)	Height (cm)	Name	Forearm Length (cm)	Height (cm)
Alicia	24	157	Ahmed	26.5	173
Bia	24.5	166	Brian	27	177
Christi	27	164	Jesús	27	174
Chantalle	24	164	Davis	31	192
Coral-Mae	23	161	José	28	172
Juanita	27.5	164	Kelvin	29	180
Ji-Hyun	27	167	Lenny	27	174
Kim	26	162	Luis	28	175
Kristen	26	175	Mike	32	185
Maria	28.5	166	Pedro	30	185
Tianna	26.5	172	Sang	30	178
Teresa	25.5	176			

FIGURE 2.15. Heights and forearm data from Ms. Jaczinko's class.

1. Two new students will be added to the class next Monday. Each new student will get a made-to-fit class shirt. Ms. Jaczinko finds the sleeve lengths of shirts she orders by doubling the student's forearm length. Student A is 160 centimeters tall. Student B is 182 centimeters tall. Based on the class data, what sleeve lengths should Ms. Jaczinko order for the two students? Should she order only boys' shirts, only girls' shirts, or one of each? Justify your answer.

Manatees and Powerboats

On the coast of Florida lives the manatee, a large and friendly marine mammal. However, the gentle Florida manatee does not live an easy life. It is one of the most endangered marine mammals in the United States. One major threat to the manatee is the large number of them killed each year by powerboats.

Should the Florida Department of Environmental Protection limit the number of registered boats in order to protect the manatee population? Before they decide, they will have to present a convincing argument to the public.

In a later section you must make a good case for whether or not to restrict powerboats. These are the main steps to present a good case to the authorities:

❖ Find a model that describes the relationship between manatee deaths and powerboat registrations.

❖ Show that the model does a good job of describing the data.

❖ Use the model to make your prediction.

Figure 2.16 contains data on the number of powerboats registered in Florida (in thousands) and the number of manatees killed.

1. Does there appear to be a relationship between powerboat registrations and manatee deaths? Explain why.

2. To make a recommendation about the number of powerboat registrations, you must find a model that represents the relationship between manatee deaths and powerboat registrations. To investigate this relationship, choose which variable—powerboat registrations or manatee deaths— should be the independent variable and which should be the dependent variable. Explain why.

Year	Powerboat Registrations (in thousands)	Manatees Killed
1977	447	13
1978	460	21
1979	481	24
1980	498	16
1981	513	24
1982	512	20
1983	526	15
1984	559	34
1985	585	33
1986	614	33
1987	645	39
1988	675	43
1989	711	50
1990	719	47

FIGURE 2.16. Powerboat registrations and manatee deaths in Florida, 1977–1990.

Assignment

1. The table in **Figure 2.17** lists the weights at birth for two groups of babies. The first group is babies whose mothers never smoked. The second group is babies whose mothers smoked at least ten cigarettes per day. From this small data set, does it appear that smoking affects a baby's birth weight? Explain your answer.

FIGURE 2.17.
Babies' birth weights.

Never Smoked	6.3	7.3	8.2	7.1	7.8	9.7	6.1	9.6	7.4	7.8	9.4	7.6
Smoked Ten or More Cigarettes per Day	6.3	6.4	4.2	9.4	7.1	5.9	6.8	8.2	7.8	5.9	5.4	6.3

2. Two groups of high school students were asked how much they typically spend on a date. The first group includes 12 students who did not exercise. Students in the second group exercised at least twice a week. **Figure 2.18** shows the results.

FIGURE 2.18.
Cost of a date (in dollars).

Does Not Exercise	10	5	20	4	20	20	15	0	8	40	8	15
Does Exercise	15	15	15	5	10	5	5	6	30	25	30	60

a) Find the mean, median, and mode for the Does Not Exercise group.

b) Find the mean, median, and mode for the Does Exercise group.

c) Based on this information, which of the two groups of students spends more on a date?

d) Make a scatterplot of the Does Not Exercise group vs. the Does Exercise group.

e) Is it valid to claim that there is a relationship between the exercise and non-exercise groups? Could you use the typical amount spent by someone in the Does Exercise group to predict how much a person in the Does Not Exercise group would spend? Explain.

CHECK THIS!

If the relationship between two variables is strong and has linear form, then the points in a scatterplot fall very close to a line. For weaker relationships, the data are more scattered.

A Scatterplot of Manatees Killed vs. Registrations

The last section established a problem: More manatees (an endangered species) are being killed as the number of powerboat registrations in the state of Florida rises. In this section, you will use the data comparing the number of manatee deaths and the number of powerboat registrations in order to build a mathematical model. You will use this model to make predictions in preparation for your report to the Florida Department of Environmental Protection on this issue.

1. Make a scatterplot of manatee deaths versus powerboat registrations on a sheet of graph or chart paper, and then make a scatterplot on your graphing calculator.

2. Are the two variables positively or negatively related? What does this mean?

CHECK THIS!

- If one variable increases as the other variable increases, then the two variables are positively related. This is sometimes called positive correlation.

- If one variable increases as the other variable decreases, then the two variables are negatively related. This is sometimes called negative correlation.

3. With your group, find an equation of a trend line that approximates the pattern of the data in your scatterplot. Draw the trend line on your scatterplot.

4. Use your model to predict the number of manatee deaths when 500,000 powerboats are registered. Does your prediction make sense?

5. Did all groups have the same prediction? Why or why not?

Assignment

In this assignment you will make scatterplots of some data sets, and in some cases fit a line to the scatterplot and make predictions. Pay particular attention to the features of the relationship between the variables.

Do the points in the scatterplot appear to be scattered close to the straight line? Then the scatterplot has linear form and it makes sense to describe it with a linear equation (a member of the $y = mx + b$ family).

Does the pattern made by the points move upward as you look from left to right? If so, the two variables are positively related (as one variable increases the other tends to increase). If the pattern drifts downward, then the two variables are negatively related (as one variable increases the other tends to decrease).

1. Linda heats her house with natural gas. She wonders how her gas consumption is related to the weather. The table in **Figure 2.19** shows the average outside temperature (in degrees Fahrenheit) each winter month and the average amount of natural gas Linda used (in hundreds of cubic feet) each day that month.

Month	Sep	Oct	Nov	Dec	Jan	Feb	Mar	Apr	May
Outdoor Temperature F	48	46	38	29	26	28	49	57	65
Gas Used Per Day (x100 ft³)	5.1	4.9	6.0	8.9	8.8	8.5	4.4	2.5	1.1

FIGURE 2.19. Gas usage and temperature data.

a) Make a scatterplot of these data. Which is the independent variable and which is the dependent variable? How did you decide?

b) Describe the features of the relationship between outside temperature and natural gas consumption. Why does the relationship have this direction?

c) Draw a trend line that you think best describes the pattern of these data. What is the equation of your line?

d) Use your equation from c to predict the gas used during a month when the average temperature is 60°F.

2. The 11 members of a college women's golf team play a practice round, then the next day play a round in competition on the same course. Their scores appear in **Figure 2.20.** (A golf score is the number of strokes required to complete the course, so low scores are better.)

Player	1	2	3	4	5	6	7	8	9	10	11
Practice	89	90	87	95	86	81	105	83	88	91	79
Competition	94	85	89	89	81	76	89	87	91	88	80

FIGURE 2.20. *Golf scores.*

a) Make a scatterplot of competition score versus the practice score.

b) Describe the relationship between practice and competition scores. Is there a positive or negative relationship? Explain why you would expect the scores to have a relationship like the one you observe.

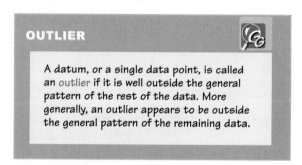

OUTLIER

A datum, or a single data point, is called an outlier if it is well outside the general pattern of the rest of the data. More generally, an outlier appears to be outside the general pattern of the remaining data.

c) One point falls clearly outside the overall pattern. Circle this point in your plot. A good golfer can have a bad round, or a weak golfer can have a good round. Can you tell from the given data whether the unusual point is produced by a good player or a poor player? What other data would you need to distinguish between the two possibilities?

d) You might expect a player to have about the same score on two rounds played on the same course. Draw on your graph the line that represents the same score on both days. Does this line fit the data well when you ignore the unusual point? If you don't like this line, draw a line that you would prefer to use to predict the competition score from the practice score.

e) Another golf team member shot a 95 in practice. Predict her score in competition.

3. **Figure 2.21** contains two scatterplots that might show the relationship between human height and ulna length (forearm-bone length). In both displays, a line describing the pattern of the data has been added.

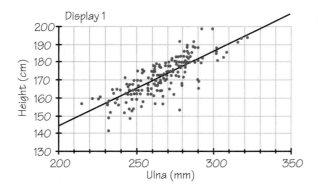

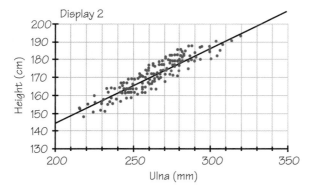

FIGURE 2.21. Two scatterplots showing height versus ulna length.

a) Both scatterplots have a linear form. Which of the two shows a stronger linear relationship? Explain.

b) A scientist used the model $y = 60.2 + 4.2x$ (where x is ulna length in cm and y is height in cm) to predict the height of a dead person whose ulna length of 29.0 cm is shown in Figure 2.21. What did the scientist predict as his or her height?

c) How close is the scientist's prediction if Display 1 shows the real data? How close is the scientist's prediction if Display 2 shows the real data? Which display better supports the scientist's prediction?

d) Describe the connection between a scatterplot and the predictions you can make using a trend line.

Residuals and Least-Squares Regression Lines

Previously, you learned methods for finding a trend line that describes a pattern of data. You used the equations of the functions you found to make predictions. In this section you will learn about a method used to find a line that approximates the pattern of data.

Whenever you make predictions based on data, you want to check the accuracy of your predictions. One way to evaluate your predictions is to calculate what are called the residual errors.

CHECK THIS!

Residual error: When a prediction is made from data, the difference between the actual value and the predicted value is called the residual error.

Residual error = Actual value − Predicted value.

You can represent the residuals graphically by drawing a vertical line from each point on the scatterplot to the line that represents your model as shown in **Figure 2.22.**

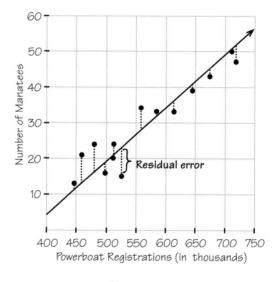

FIGURE 2.22.
Residuals for the plight of the manatee.

A good line should meet a few tests. One test is that the sum of the residual errors should be close to 0. The sum of the residual errors is often found with a calculator or computer software. At times, the graph allows you to see that the sum of the residuals is fairly close to 0, but often it is easier to use a table, such as **Figure 2.23,** where you can total the residuals.

Registrations (in thousands)	Manatees Killed	Predicted Number of Manatees Killed ($y = 0.15x - 56$)	Residual Error
447	13	11	2
460	21	13	7
481	24	16	8
498	16	19	-3
513	24	21	3
512	20	21	-1
526	15	23	-8
559	34	28	6
585	33	32	1
614	33	36	-3
645	39	41	-2
675	43	45	-2
711	50	51	-1
719	47	52	-5
Total			2

FIGURE 2.23. Residual table for manatee deaths.

As you can see in Figure 2.23, the sum of the residual errors can be close to zero even if most of the residual errors are not. This happens because some of the residuals errors are positive and others are negative. To give more emphasis to values that deviate from the overall pattern, the residual errors are squared and then totaled. The squares of the residuals are shown in **Figure 2.24.** The goal is then to find a line that makes the sum of the squared residual errors as small as possible.

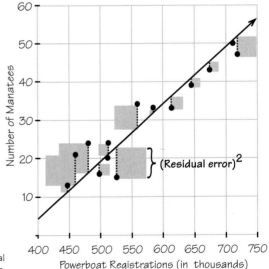

FIGURE 2.24. Squared residual errors for the plight of the manatee.

To try and find the "line of best fit" by trial and error might take you a while. **Figure 2.25** shows some examples of equations that you might investigate as a trend line and the sum of squares for each line.

Equation	Sum of Squares
$y = 0.14x - 56$	745
$y = 0.13x - 50$	670
$y = 0.13x - 45$	228
$y = 0.12x - 45$	783
$y = 0.12x - 40$	246
$y = 0.125x - 41$	223

FIGURE 2.25.
Sum of the squared residual errors.

Your graphing calculator has built-in commands that calculate the equation of the **least-squares regression line**. Statisticians also call this line the **line of best fit**. To find the model that fits the data the best, they look for several criteria:

❖ The pattern of data in the scatterplot is randomly scattered close to the line.

❖ The sum of the residual errors is close to 0.

❖ The sum of the squared residual errors is as small as possible.

The general name for finding an equation that fits the data is **regression**. Since you are looking for a linear relationship, the technique used in fitting the "best" line is called **linear regression**.

1. Use your calculator (or spreadsheet) to calculate the values of the slope and y-intercept of the least-squares line. Write its equation.

2. What do the slope and y-intercept of the linear regression line tell you about boats and manatees?

3. Plot both the data and the least-squares line so that you can see both graphs in the same window. Does the least-squares line appear to fit the data well? Support your answer.

SUMMARY

After you collect data on two variables and display the data in a scatterplot, you may describe a relationship between the two variables by finding a line of best fit. Statisticians often use the least-squares regression line as the best model linear relationship. Criteria for a good regression line include the following:

* The line appears to go through the middle of the points in the scatterplot.

* The sum of the residual errors is close to 0.

* The sum of the squared residual errors is as small as possible.

Graphing calculators (and spreadsheets) can calculate the least-squares regression line for you. However, you should check your linear regression model to see if it fits the criteria above. If it does not fit, you should look for a different model to describe your data.

Assignment

1. On graph paper, make a scatterplot of Ms. Jaczinko's class data (see **Figure 2.26**). Let forearm length be the independent variable and height be the dependent variable. Remember to label each axis and use an appropriate scale. To distinguish the boys from the girls, use two colors (or different shapes), one to represent the boys' data and the other to show the girls'.

FIGURE 2.26.
Height and forearm data from Ms. Jaczinko's class.

	Female			Male	
Name	**Forearm Length (cm)**	**Height (cm)**	**Name**	**Forearm Length (cm)**	**Height (cm)**
Alicia	24	157	Ahmed	26.5	173
Bia	24.5	166	Brian	27	177
Christi	27	164	Jesús	27	174
Chantalle	24	164	Davis	31	192
Coral-Mae	23	161	José	28	172
Juanita	27.5	164	Kelvin	29	180
Ji-Hyun	27	167	Lenny	27	174
Kim	26	162	Luis	28	175
Kristen	26	175	Mike	32	185
Maria	28.5	166	Pedro	30	185
Tianna	26.5	172	Sang	30	178
Teresa	25.5	176			

2. Find a linear regression model to predict a girl's height from her forearm length. Find a second linear regression model to predict a boy's height from his forearm length.

3. Use your scatterplot and least-squares model to make these predictions.

   a) If a girl the same age as the students in Ms. Jaczinko's class has a forearm that measures between 25 cm and 27 cm, what would you predict for her height?

b) Predict the height of a tenth-grade boy with a 28.5-cm forearm. Explain your answer.

c) What would be the forearm length of a student who is 163 cm tall? Explain your answer.

The 16% Model

Next you will use the data from Ms. Jaczinko's class to examine and refine a model that represents the relationship between height and forearm length.

4. Archaeologists study ancient human life. They use general rules of proportions. So an archaeologist might use the rule of thumb that the forearm of a typical female teenager is 16% of her height.

   a) Write this rule as an equation that predicts height, y, from forearm length, x. We call this equation the "16% model." Test a few pairs. Does this model make sense?

   b) Sketch a graph of the 16% model on the same set of axes as your scatterplot.

   c) Compare the 16% model with the data from Ms. Jaczinko's class. Is the model true for all the people in the class? Justify your answer based on your graph.

5. Use the 16% model to make the following predictions.

   a) Predict the height of a student whose forearm is 27 cm. Use the data from Ms. Jaczinko's class to check your prediction.

   b) Predict the height of a student whose forearm is 33 cm.

   c) The forearm lengths of two students differ by 1 cm. Use the 16% model to predict how much their heights differ. What if their forearm lengths differed by 2 cm? Justify your answers.

What is Your Recommendation?

Now that you have a model for the relationship between manatee deaths and powerboat registrations, you are ready to make your recommendation to the Florida Department of Environmental Protection.

1. Present to the class, using your scatterplot and the equation of the least-squares regression line, a convincing case for whether or not to restrict powerboat registrations. Your argument should include the three main steps listed in Section 2.6:

   ❖ Find a model that describes the relationship between manatee deaths and powerboat registrations.

   ❖ Show that the model does a good job of describing the data.

   ❖ Use the model to make your prediction.

2. Say you want to reduce the number of manatee deaths to about 30 per year. How many powerboat registrations should there be? Explain how you can use your model and algebra to answer this question. What number of powerboat registrations do you recommend?

3. Say, instead, that you recommend 700,000 powerboat registrations (slightly below the number of registrations in 1989). Predict the number of manatees that would be killed each year, on average, if this proposal were adopted. Use your scatterplot to see how good your prediction is.

4. Fill in the blank: Every time the number of boat registrations is raised by 50,000, one can predict that, on average, an additional _____ manatees would be killed by powerboats each year. Justify your response.

5. It is possible that the Florida Department of Environmental Protection did not follow your recommendations back in 1991. In 2002, powerboats killed 95 manatees, and there were 923,000 powerboat registrations. Even though the least-squares model should only be used to predict the number of manatee deaths when the number of powerboat

registrations is between 447,000 and 719,000, how well does the least squares model predict the number of manatees killed in 2002?

6. The year 2002 had more manatees killed than the model predicts. **Figure 2.27** shows data for the years 1996 through 2003. Add these data to the previous data.

Year	Powerboat Registrations (in thousands)	Actual Number of Manatees Killed
1996	751	60
1997	797	54
1998	806	66
1999	805	82
2000	841	78
2001	903	81
2002	923	95
2003	978	73

FIGURE 2.27.
Data on powerboats and manatees from 1996–2003.

*These data are from the Florida Fish and Wildlife Research Institute and the United States Coast Guard.

a) What is an equation of a new line of best fit?

b) Graph both the old and new lines of best fit on the calculator scatterplot.

c) What does the new slope tell you?

d) What is the predicted number of manatee deaths with the new model?

e) Is the new prediction closer to the actual number than the old model?

In this section, you used the least-squares model that you calculated in Section 2.8 to make predictions. In the process, you were given additional data to test how well your model predicted future events. You observed that a model that fits one data set may or may not fit an expanded data set. A line that fits a set of data well cannot always be trusted to predict outside the range of the data.

Hence, often when you gather additional data, you may need to refine your mathematical model. The more data points that you can collect, the more accurate your model will be.

Not every data set can be modeled well with a linear regression equation. There are many other types of relationships between variables. We will explore some of these relationships in the following chapters.

Assignment

How would you choose which of two models makes better predictions? Let's explore some data to help you decide. The data in **Figure 2.28** were collected from a ninth grade class. The asterisks (*) indicate missing values.

Height (cm)	Stride Length (cm)	Forearm Length (cm)
166.0	58.2	28.5
164.5	55.9	27.2
175.0	59.1	28.6
184.0	68.9	30.5
161.0	72.5	26.5
164.0	*	28.2
171.0	*	29.0

FIGURE 2.28.
Data on height, stride length, and forearm length.

1. a) Make a scatterplot of height versus stride length. Make a second scatterplot of height versus forearm length. (For both plots, height should be on the vertical axis. Use the same scale on the vertical axis for each plot.) Which of the two scatterplots shows the stronger relationship? How can you tell?

   b) Find the least-squares line that represents each of these relationships.

   c) Use the equations of your two least-squares lines to predict the height of a person whose stride is 73 cm and whose forearm length is 27 cm. Which of the two estimates is more reliable? Explain.

   d) State, in your own words, how you would choose, in general, between two different models that predict the same quantity.

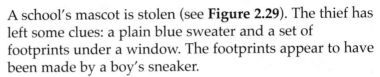

Our Mascot
Call 1-555-626-2833

FIGURE 2.29.
The missing manatee.

A school's mascot is stolen (see **Figure 2.29**). The thief has left some clues: a plain blue sweater and a set of footprints under a window. The footprints appear to have been made by a boy's sneaker.

The distance between the footprints, from the back of the heel on the first footprint to the back of the heel on the second, reveals that the thief's stride is approximately 58 cm. The length of the thief's forearm can be estimated by measuring the sweater from the center of a worn spot on the elbow to the turn where the cuff meets the sleeve. The thief's forearm is between 26 cm and 27 cm.

School officials suspect that the thief is a student from a rival high school. **Figure 2.30** contains data from a 1st period class about students' genders, heights, stride lengths, and forearm lengths. Use these data to answer the following questions.

2. Find the mean, median, and mode for the whole class and then find the mean, median, and mode for the boys and the girls.

   a) Is there a difference between the mean stride length for a boy and the mean stride length for a girl?

3. The footprint was made by a boy's sneaker. However, sometimes girls wear boys' sneakers. So you'll need to decide whether or not the thief was male. Use what you know about the thief's stride length and forearm length.

   a) Do the class stride length data tend to confirm that the footprints belonged to a boy and not a girl? Use the data you gathered to support your answer.

   b) Do the forearm data tend to confirm that the sweater belonged to a boy and not a girl? Use the data you gathered to support your answer.

Next you will predict the height of the thief. You have two possible independent variables you can use for your prediction: stride length and forearm length. You will try to decide which is better. Divide the work in Questions 4 and 5 among the members of your group.

Name	Gender	Height (in cm)	Stride Length (in cm)	Forearm Length (in cm)
Scott	Male	166.0	58.25	28.5
John	Male	178.0	68.5	29.0
Matt	Male	171.0	58.5	27.2
Will	Male	165.0	50.125	28.0
Michael	Male	177.5	58.75	31.3
Jeffrey	Male	166.0	62.875	28.3
Even	Male	175.5	59.125	28.6
Brad	Male	171.0	67.75	31.5
Lonnie	Male	184.0	68.875	30.5
William	Male	184.5	66.25	30.8
Robert	Male	183.5	79.5	30.5
Karim	Male	172.0	70.5	30.3
Meredith	Female	164.5	55.875	24.2
Lee	Female	166.0	52.375	27.3
Pilar	Female	168.0	55.375	28.0
Ansley	Female	178.5	59.75	29.1
Julie	Female	166.0	48.375	27.9
Becton	Female	159.0	57.125	28.0
Elizabeth	Female	166.0	64.0	27.4
Shannon	Female	154.5	57.75	25.8
Janie	Female	161.0	63.5	27.0
Jeris	Female	177.0	69.75	30.1
Kat	Female	161.0	72.5	26.5
Blaie	Female	164.0	75.25	28.2
Frances	Female	174.0	58.5	28.4
Eliz	Female	164.0	59.75	26.8
Baily	Female	168.0	55.25	26.4

FIGURE 2.30. Height, stride length, and forearm length for students in 1st period class.

4. a) Use your data to find models for the relationship between height and forearm length. First find a model based on the entire data set. Then use the girls' data to find a second model, and finally use the boys' data to find a third model.

b) Compare the three models. Is there much difference? Explain.

c) Which model gives a better prediction if, in fact, the thief were male? Justify your answer.

d) Which model gives a better prediction if, in fact, the thief were female? Justify your answer.

5. Repeat Question 4 for the relationship between height and stride length.

6. Select the best model for the job of predicting the height of the thief. Support your choice.

7. Use this model to predict the height of the thief. Explain your answer.

8. **Figure 2.31** shows the winners of the Indianapolis 500 Auto Race and their average speed every 4 years from 1912 to 1972. No race was run in 1944 due to World War II.

Year	Number of Years Since 1912	Winner	Winner's Average Race Speed (mph)
1912	0	Joe Dawson	79
1916	4	Dario Resta	84
1920	8	Gaston Cheverolet	89
1924	12	L. L. Corum & J. Boyer	98
1928	16	Louis Meyer	99
1932	20	Fred Frame	104
1936	24	Louis Meyer	109
1940	28	Wilbur Shaw	114
1944	32	—	—
1948	36	Mauri Rose	120
1952	40	Troy Ruttman	129
1956	44	Pat Flaherty	128
1960	48	Jim Rathmann	139
1964	52	A. J. Foyt	147
1968	56	Bobby Unser	153
1972	60	Mark Donohue	163

FIGURE 2.31. Indianapolis 500 Auto Race results.

Finding a linear regression equation is easier if you use the number of years since 1912 as the independent variable. This also gives meaning to the y-intercept.

a) Make a scatterplot of the data.

b) Find the equation of a linear regression model.

c) What do the slope and y-intercept in this model show?

d) The speed of the winner in 1957 was 136 mph. How well does the linear regression model predict this value?

e) Even though you know that 200 mph is outside the range of the data, you would like to use your model to predict when a driver will reach a race speed of 200 mph. Based on the linear regression model, when would you expect a driver to average 200 mph in the Indianapolis 500 race?

f) The actual race speed of the winner, Buddy Rice, in 2004 was 139 mph. Use your line of best fit to predict the speed in 2004. Is the least-squares line a good predictor? Why or why not?

Line Fitting with Domain Restrictions

Let's take what we have learned about building linear models thus far, and apply it to a new situation.

Marietta has been working as a waitress for 7 weeks. Since she earns an hourly wage plus tips, there is no set amount she makes per hour. However, after examining her 7 pay stubs she notices an apparent trend. **Figure 2.32** shows how many hours she worked and how much money she makes per week.

FIGURE 2.32.
Marietta's data table.

Time (T) (in hours)	8	15	23	21	16	20	22
Money (M) (in dollars)	53	101	155	131	124	138	157

1. Label the axes appropriately and draw a scatterplot of money (M) versus time (T).

2. Use a straightedge to approximate a trend line for the data. Write an equation for your trend line.

3. Use a graphing calculator to make a scatterplot, and then find the line of best fit using linear regression.

4. How are your trend line and the calculator's line of best fit alike and how are they different?

5. What do the slope and y-intercept of the line of best fit mean in this context?

6. Marietta's boss tells her that she must work at least 10 hours every week in order to keep her job. Furthermore, state law says that a restaurant employee cannot work more than 60 hours during any week. Considering these restrictions, sketch a more appropriate trend line. Do not re-plot the data. Number and label your axes appropriately.

7. Use the second graph to predict how much Marietta will make if she works for 30 hours. Explain your answer.

8. Use the second graph to predict how many hours Marietta needs to work to make $75. Explain your answer.

Modeling Project Who Am I?

You are an anthropologist that finds bones of two or more individuals. The table in **Figure 2.33** contains the information about those bones.

Skeleton 1 (possibly female)	Skeleton 2 (taller of the two)	Uncertain
Femur: 413, 414	Femur: 508	Skull: 230
Ulna: 228	Ulna: 290	Humerus: 357
		Radius: 215
		Tibia: 416

FIGURE 2.33. Classification of bones, measurements in millimeters.

Figure 2.34, on the following page, contains actual data from the Forensic Anthropology Data Bank (FDB) at the University of Tennessee. The FDB contains metric, nonmetric, demographic, and other kinds of data on skeletons from all over the United States. These individuals most likely are unidentified bodies that went to forensic anthropologists for analysis and identification.

Use the data in Figure 2.34 to answer the following items. Present your findings in a formal report. All of your conclusions must be supported by statistical analysis of the data in Figure 2.34.

1. Determine two models to predict people's height from the lengths of various long bones in their arms and legs. Explain which of these models you would prefer to use and why.

2. Based on these data, do you agree that Skeleton 1 is female? Do the data provide any information that would help you decide whether Skeleton 2 is male or female?

3. Find models for relationships between pairs of long bones that would help you decide whether the bones in the uncertain column belong to Skeleton 1 or Skeleton 2. (Or is there strong evidence that one of these bones belongs to a third person?)

4. Predict the heights of Skeleton 1 and Skeleton 2. Explain why you chose the model that you used to make your predictions.

Sex	Height	Humerus	Radius	Ulna	Femur	Tibia	Fibula	Sex	Height	Humerus	Radius	Ulna	Femur	Tibia	Fibula	Sex	Height	Humerus	Radius	Ulna	Femur	Tibia	Fibula
1	168	307	240	258	448	384	368	1	165	307	230	248	452	363	355	2	178	337	272	272	475	393	390
1	178	336	247	261	463	404	390	1	163	297	240	260	435	356	356	2	172	344	255	281	470	400	393
1	161	294	213	227	413	335	322	1	143	282	216	233	398	334	318	2	188	360	269	283	510	422	416
1	155	324	262	279	465	395	375	1	154	297	228	248	423	344	334	2	189	347	272	283	547	432	445
1	165	314	243	258	432	364	364	1	171	342	272	290	485	418	407	2	177	330	246	262	462	386	370
1	168	303	223	244	441	355	342	1	162	303	237	262	433	367	364	2	166	322	242	258	442	373	374
1	165	311	231	254	436	362	360	1	150	308	220	247	383	352	341	2	186	332	267	283	478	391	388
1	173	312	248	266	483	405	401	1	157	288	201	215	429	363	350	2	177	322	245	265	457	397	395
1	165	322	229	246	448	368	352	1	158	314	239	263	432	371	358	2	176	332	259	274	458	382	378
1	163	298	221	245	443	355	361	1	162	306	250	268	444	355	352	2	180	323	251	275	448	390	387
1	153	280	218	234	410	345	344	1	159	310	238	255	449	362	352	2	173	335	253	273	497	404	389
1	165	294	220	235	448	354	353	2	169	337	254	273	460	396	385	2	175	330	253	274	470	384	382
1	170	311	235	253	440	360	347	2	153	296	223	243	407	337	338	2	169	313	252	265	472	391	385
1	160	316	214	226	437	356	348	2	175	339	256	271	470	390	381	2	175	336	256	274	464	388	377
1	159	292	223	233	419	346	336	2	179	343	242	263	464	378	371	2	181	390	284	303	521	440	435
1	163	315	228	251	438	356	347	2	179	352	253	269	484	407	397	2	193	356	297	318	522	451	433
1	165	303	237	249	451	356	348	2	198	354	263	292	508	417	412	2	182	362	275	293	499	424	405
1	165	308	234	248	439	348	344	2	173	327	256	276	463	383	387	2	169	322	249	266	426	366	356
1	165	315	227	240	448	363	353	2	180	357	268	278	494	401	390	2	180	337	265	281	482	412	399
1	175	316	244	260	473	390	374	2	178	344	254	269	464	371	366	2	185	363	286	302	520	429	420
1	180	333	256	278	475	391	381	2	175	339	245	272	456	374	366	2	180	355	274	292	490	422	424
1	168	321	230	248	450	365	362	2	177	343	250	266	483	361	365	2	170	378	272	291	512	404	390
1	163	299	219	236	435	357	339	2	180	353	260	281	490	420	415	2	180	370	278	292	523	429	420
1	165	304	246	264	467	392	383	2	170	303	235	249	435	366	361	2	175	333	260	273	484	398	386
1	160	309	236	248	432	364	358	2	191	364	263	278	511	430	417	2	168	342	262	280	484	404	385
1	158	319	246	268	442	371	364	2	188	349	269	288	498	427	423	2	170	347	269	291	476	396	393
1	165	325	242	250	448	378	365	2	179	323	256	276	486	398	400	2	166	315	240	260	456	377	362
1	170	335	248	263	474	400	382	2	180	350	263	280	480	419	418	2	185	363	295	309	524	446	427
1	182	334	254	273	514	420	407	2	181	350	263	282	488	391	381	2	191	382	299	316	537	479	466

FIGURE 2.34. Data from Forensic Anthropology Data Bank (FDB).

Key to Data (in order from left to right): sex (1 = female, 2 = male), height (cm), humerus (mm), radius (mm), ulna (mm), femur (mm), tibia (mm), fibula (mm)

Practice Problems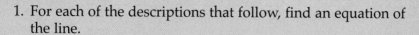

1. For each of the descriptions that follow, find an equation of the line.

    a) The line through the point (2, 3) that has slope $\frac{1}{2}$.

    b) The line that has y-intercept 3 and slope $-\frac{1}{2}$.

    c) The line passing through points (3, 2) and (2, 5).

    d) The line has y-intercept 5 and is parallel to the line $y = 7x - 1$.

2. On December 18, 1994, three amateur spelunkers (cave explorers) found a cave in France, now known as Chauvet Cave, that had ancient paintings. In later explorations, human footprints were found. According to prehistorian Michel-Alain Garcia, the footprints belonged to a boy who was about 4.5 feet tall.

    a) Scientists have used simple models to predict height from footprints since the mid-1800s. One model, still in use today, predicts height by dividing the maximum foot length by 0.15. Write an equation for this model.

    b) The model in a can be expressed as a member of the $y = mx$ family. What is the value of m?

    c) Use this model to predict the maximum length of the footprints found in Chauvet Cave. Give your answer in centimeters. (Remember 2.54 cm = 1 in.)

    d) Suppose that another footprint was found and it measured 1 cm more than the one discussed by Garcia. By how much would you increase your estimate for height? (Be careful of the units you use to report your answer.)

3. Anthropologists have refined early models for estimating a person's height from the length of a footprint. One revision suggests different models depending on whether a footprint is from the right foot or from the left. Here are two models designed for use with adult footprints.

For right foot: $H = 3.641L + 72.92$
For left foot: $H = 4.229L + 56.49$
(where all measurements are in cm)

a) Suppose a footprint measures 22 cm. Predict the person's height, first by assuming the print is from the right foot and then by assuming it is from the left foot.

b) Use your calculator to graph each function. Based on your graphs, what footprint length gives the same height prediction from both models? How can you determine this value using algebra? Try it and check to see if you get the same result.

c) Both the right-foot and left-foot models are from the $y = mx + b$ family. For each of the models, interpret the meaning of m in the height-footprint context. What does b mean in this context?

4. a) Solve the right-foot equation in Question 3 for L in terms of H. Then do the same for the left-foot equation.

b) Suppose a person is 153 cm tall. Use your equations from a to predict the lengths of the person's right and left footprints. How much longer is the larger foot than the shorter foot?

5. Regular Chips Ahoy® chocolate chip cookies boast "1000 chips in every bag." You can also buy reduced fat Chips Ahoy cookies. Do you think both types of Chips Ahoy cookies contain roughly the same number of chips? To find out, a statistics class opened bags of regular Chips Ahoy and reduced fat Chips Ahoy cookies, randomly selected 15 cookies from each bag, and counted the number of chips in each cookie. Their data appear in **Figure 2.35**.

Reduced Fat	13	15	14	12	15	17	13	10	15	18	19	18	20	21	16
Regular	18	20	17	22	20	16	21	18	16	19	27	22	19	16	24

FIGURE 2.35. Chip counts in reduced fat and regular Chips Ahoy cookies.

a) From the data in Figure 2.35, make two dot plots using the same scaling on each. Place one dot plot directly above the other.

b) Suppose you select a cookie from the regular Chips Ahoy bag. Predict the number of chips in the cookie. How far off might your prediction be?

c) Suppose instead, you select a cookie from the reduced fat bag. Predict the number of chips in the cookie. How far off might your prediction be?

d) Does it appear that the number of chips is changed in order to produce a lower fat product? Explain.

e) George wants to make a scatterplot of the row 1 data in Figure 2.35 versus the row 2 data. Do you think his scatterplot would reveal useful information about these two types of cookies? Explain.

6. A newspaper article in the *Worcester Sunday Telegram* reported that scores on intelligence tests are going up at a rate of 3 IQ points per decade.

a) In 1932 the average IQ test score for Americans was 100 points. Use the information given in the article to write a function rule that predicts the average IQ score for years after 1932. Let $x = 0$ represent 1932 to simplify your model.

b) **Figure 2.36** provides data on the average IQ scores of Americans. Make a scatterplot of these data. (Let $x = 0$ represent 1932.)

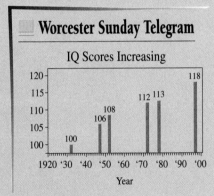

FIGURE 2.36. Average IQ scores from 1932 to 1997.

c) Based on these data, do IQ scores and years have a positive or negative relationship? Explain.

d) Fit a least-squares line to these data. What is the equation for this line? Add this line to your scatterplot in b.

e) Based on the least-squares equation from d, was the newspaper correct in reporting that IQ scores are rising at a rate of 3 points per decade? Explain.

f) A genius is a person with an IQ over 140. If the rate of increase continues, in what year will the average IQ be at the level of genius? Do you believe this? Explain.

The Boston Marathon is the world's oldest and best-known marathon. The first Boston Marathon was held in 1897. Fifteen men participated. Over 17,000 people entered the 104th Boston Marathon held April 17, 2000. Questions 7–8 are based on the first-place times in **Figure 2.37**.

Men's		Women's	
Marathon Number	**Time (hr: min: sec)**	**Marathon Number**	**Time (hr: min: sec)**
31	2:40:22	82	2:34:28
36	2:33:36	83	2:26:46
41	2:33:20	84	2:29:33
46	2:26:51	85	2:22:42
51	2:25:39	86	2:29:28
56	2:31:53	87	2:34:6
61	2:20:5	88	2:24:55
66	2:23:48	89	2:25:21
71	2:15:45	90	2:24:30
76	2:15:30	91	2:24:33
81	2:14:46	92	2:25:24
86	2:8:51	93	2:24:18
91	2:11:50	94	2:23:43
96	2:8:14	95	2:25:27
		96	2:21:45
		97	2:25:11
		98	2:27:13
		99	2:58:0
		100	2:40:10

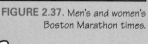

FIGURE 2.37. Men's and women's Boston Marathon times.

7. The men's data in Figure 2.37 contain first-place times for selected marathons from 1927, marathon 31, to 1992, marathon 96.

a) Make a scatterplot of the men's times versus the marathon number. (What unit did you use for time?)

b) Fit a least-squares line to the data in your scatterplot. What is the equation? Add a graph of the least-squares line to your scatterplot.

c) Interpret the slope of your linear model in the context of the Boston Marathon.

d) Use your model to predict the time of the first-place finisher for the 104th Boston Marathon. The actual winning time was 2:09:47. How close is your prediction?

8. Figure 2.37 shows women's times for marathons 82–100, held in years 1980–1996.

a) Fit a least-square's line to these data. Interpret the slope in the context of the marathon. Does this seem reasonable? Explain.

b) Make a scatterplot of the women's data. Add the least-squares line to your plot. Does the least-squares equation do a good job of describing the women's data?

c) Remove the times corresponding to the 99th and 100th marathons. Refit the least-squares line to the remaining data. What affect did the removal of these points have on the slope?

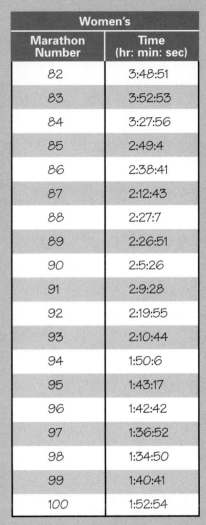

Men's		Women's	
Marathon Number	Time (hr: min: sec)	Marathon Number	Time (hr: min: sec)
82	2:40:10	82	3:48:51
83	2:26:57	83	3:52:53
84	2:38:59	84	3:27:56
85	1:55:0	85	2:49:4
86	2:0:41	86	2:38:41
87	1:51:31	87	2:12:43
88	1:47:10	88	2:27:7
89	2:5:20	89	2:26:51
90	1:45:34	90	2:5:26
91	1:43:25	91	2:9:28
92	1:55:42	92	2:19:55
93	1:43:19	93	2:10:44
94	1:36:4	94	1:50:6
95	1:29:53	95	1:43:17
96	1:30:44	96	1:42:42
97	1:26:28	97	1:36:52
98	1:22:17	98	1:34:50
99	1:25:59	99	1:40:41
100	1:30:11	100	1:52:54

FIGURE 2.38. Men's and women's wheelchair times in the Boston Marathon.

9. a) Make scatterplots for the men's and women's wheelchair times in **Figure 2.38**. So that you can compare the men's and women's data, use the same scale on the axes of both plots.

   b) Is there a positive or negative relationship between marathon number and times for the men's data? What about for the women's data? Interpret what this means in the context of the marathon.

   c) Comment on the form of the data. Does the pattern of the data appear linear or nonlinear? Explain.

The data in **Figure 2.39** provide information on the heights of people as children and again as adults. Use the data in this figure to answer Questions 10–13.

Girl's Height at 1.5	Girl's Adult Height	Boy's Height at 2	Boy's Adult Height
78.0	157.0	89.0	178.0
79.4	158.4	89.9	177.1
80.4	161.4	90.3	179.6
81.3	164.7	90.8	181.8
81.3	160.4	90.9	184.0
82.1	163.7	91.0	180.5
83.2	164.4	91.1	182.0
83.2	170.2	91.2	183.1
83.9	170.5	91.4	180.1
84.9	166.5	91.5	185.1
86.2	171.3	92.9	182.0
87.9	170.7	93.3	186.3
88.2	179.7	94.7	187.4
89.4	176.9	95.4	187.9
90.1	176.9	96.1	189.4

FIGURE 2.39.
Height data on children and adults.

10. Suppose one of the people from this study plans to visit your school.

   a) If you find out the visitor is a woman, predict her height. How did you decide on your prediction?

   b) What if the visitor is a man?

11. Create a display that compares the men's heights with the women's heights. Write a description of the information your display conveys.

12. Suppose you want to predict how tall a 1 1/2-year-old girl will be when she reaches adulthood.

   a) Which is the independent variable and which is the dependent variable?

   b) Make a scatterplot of women's adult heights versus their heights when they were 1 1/2 years old.

c) Would you describe the relationship between women's heights and girls' heights as linear or nonlinear? Does this relationship appear to be positive or negative?

d) Fit a least-squares line to the data. Write its equation, and sketch its graph on your scatterplot.

e) Use your equation to predict the adult height of a 1 1/2-year-old girl who is 82.5 cm tall.

13. a) Determine the least-squares line for predicting men's heights from their heights when they were 2 years old.

b) If two 2-year-old boys differ in height by 1 cm, predict how much their heights will differ when they are adults.

c) What if their heights as 2-year-olds differ by 2 cm?

d) Does the y-intercept of the least-squares line have any meaning in this context? Explain.

e) Does the slope of the least-squares line have any meaning in this context? Explain.

14. The grades in **Figure 2.40** are from a high school statistics class.

a) What is the average grade on the midterm exam? On the final exam?

b) Make a scatterplot of these data.

c) Does the pattern in your scatterplot appear to have linear form? Does there appear to be a positive or negative relationship between students' midterm grades and students' final grades?

d) Fit a least-squares line to the data.

Name	Midterm exam grade	Final exam grade
	50	54
	53	52
	57	59
	62	70
	62	68
	68	70
	69	68
	73	79
	73	82
	74	83
	74	80
	75	82
	78	88
	79	89
	79	90
	81	88
	81	89
	81	92
	82	91
	85	94
	87	98
	100	99
	100	100

FIGURE 2.40.
Midterm and final exam grades.

e) Add a graph of your model from d to your scatterplot. Do you think your line does a good job in describing these data? Explain.

f) One student missed the final exam and had to take it at a later date. She got 77 on the midterm. Predict her grade on the final exam.

Glossary

KEY CONCEPTS

Average: To find the average of a data set, sum the data and divide by the number of data in the set.

Dot plot: Display in which dots are placed above a number line to represent the values of a single variable. (Also called line plot.)

Least-squares line: The line with the smallest sum of squared residual errors.

Linear equation: An equation relating two variables, x and y, that can be put in the form $y = mx + b$.

Linear form: The form of a scatterplot for which it is possible to draw a line that describes the general trend of the data.

Linear regression: The process of fitting a line to data using the least-squares criterion.

Mean: To compute the mean, sum the data and divide by the number of data. Sometimes mean and average are used interchangeably.

Median: The middle value in a set of data.

Mode: The value in a set of data that appears most often.

Nonlinear form: The form of a scatterplot for which the general pattern of the data is not well described by a straight line.

Outlier: In a collection of data, an individual data point that falls outside the general pattern of the other data.

Residual error: Actual value of the dependent variable minus the predicted value.

Strong linear relationship: A scatterplot of the data that lies in a narrow band.

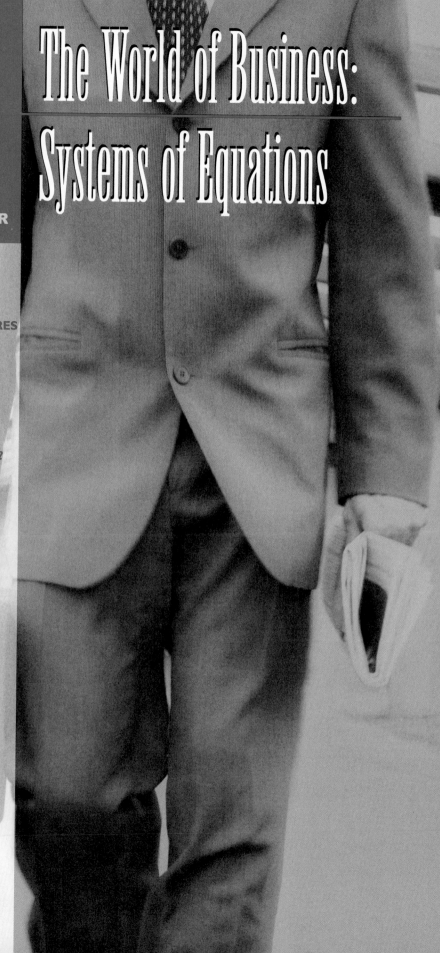

3

CHAPTER

The World of Business: Systems of Equations

Running a Business

Four years ago, Warren Brown left his job as a lawyer to bake cakes. It all started when he decided to become an expert baker. After work, he tried his hand cake making. Then he had dessert parties for his friends. His friends loved his cakes. This made him want to see if he could support himself as a baker. He rented a small kitchen and found customers mostly by word of mouth. His business went so well that he moved into a storefront that he called Cake Love. At first he used his credit cards to get the business started. Then he got a $125,000 loan from the Small Business Administration. Now, Cake Love sells around 40 cakes per day at about $55 each. Cake Love was often very crowded, so Warren opened the Love Cafe across the street. The café serves sandwiches and soups as well as cake.

Warren plans to open more stores this year. Even though managing takes most of his time, he still bakes most mornings. He also works on new types of cakes. His business is now so successful that he has the same salary he used to make as a lawyer.

People start their own businesses for lots of reasons. They know that if they succeed the rewards will be great. Also this gives them a way to make more money than if they worked for someone else, and they can be the person in charge.

Of course there is no guarantee that all businesses will be successful. In fact, for every successful business, there are many that fail. Often a business fails not because it makes a poor product but because of poor financial decisions.

Founder/Owner: Warren Brown
Company: Cake Love and Love Café
Location: Washington, D.C.
Industry: Retail baked goods

In this chapter you will examine a start-up business that makes and sells athletic wear. You will have the opportunity to create mathematical models that can be used to make good financial decisions.

Do You Have Issues?

In this section you will assume the role of a businessperson like Warren Brown. Imagine that last year you started making baseball caps in your house. You gave them to a few close friends as birthday gifts. Your friends liked the caps and offered to pay you to make caps for a few of their friends. Soon you were getting hundreds of requests from people wanting to buy caps. Seeing this response as a great opportunity, you decide to start a business. There is not enough room in your house or time for you to make all these caps on your own. What issues, both practical and financial, do you need to consider before you start your business and agree to produce the caps?

Talk with your group members and make a list of issues that need to be considered before starting the business.

Comparing Pay Structures

One important issue a businessperson must consider is employee pay. After doing some research you find that there are two companies in your city that make caps. Hats, Inc., pays its employees $1000.00 a month plus $5.00 for every hat they complete in the month. Caps, Inc., pays its employees $500.00 a month plus $10.00 for every hat they complete in the month.

In the next activity you will compare these pay structures and see if one will fit your company.

1. Use the description of the pay structure from Hats, Inc., to complete a table like **Figure 3.1.** Then use the process column to develop an algebraic rule for this pay structure.

Number of Caps Completed During the Month (*c*)	Process Column	Pay (*p*)

FIGURE 3.1.
Hats, Inc., pay structure.

2. What algebraic rule models the pay structure for Hats, Inc.?

3. Enter your rule into your graphing calculator. Set the table to begin at 0 and increase by 10. Compare the table generated by the calculator to the table you created for Hats, Inc. Do the tables have the same values? What does this tell you about your algebraic rule?

If the tables do not have the same values, adjust them to match.

4. Use the description of the pay structure from Caps, Inc., to complete a table like **Figure 3.2.** Then use the process column to develop an algebraic rule for this pay structure.

Number of Caps Completed During the Month (c)	Process Column	Pay (p)

FIGURE 3.2.
Caps, Inc., pay structure.

5. What algebraic rule models the pay structure for Caps, Inc.?

6. Enter your rule into your graphing calculator. Set the table to begin at 0 and increase by 10. Compare the table generated by the calculator to the table you created for Caps, Inc. Do the tables have the same values? What does this tell you about your algebraic rule?

7. Look at the table values for both companies. What patterns do you observe?

8. If an employee makes 97 hats in one month, how much will she earn under each pay structure?

9. If an employee makes 103 hats in one month, how much will she earn under each pay structure?

SOLVE THE SYSTEM OF EQUATIONS USING A TABLE

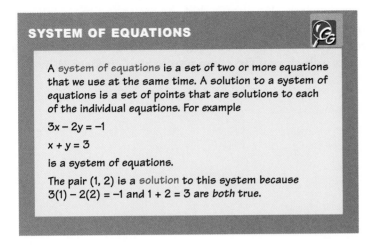

SYSTEM OF EQUATIONS

A system of equations is a set of two or more equations that we use at the same time. A solution to a system of equations is a set of points that are solutions to each of the individual equations. For example

3x − 2y = −1

x + y = 3

is a system of equations.

The pair (1, 2) is a solution to this system because 3(1) − 2(2) = −1 and 1 + 2 = 3 are both true.

10. Use the table feature on your calculator to solve the system of equations. In other words, for what number of hats will two employees, who are on different pay structures, make the same amount of money?

11. As a businessperson, you want to keep the cost of doing business as low as possible. So, which pay structure is best for you? Why?

12. If you were an employee, which pay structure would you prefer? Why?

13. If it takes somewhere between one and three hours for an employee to complete one hat, what is a reasonable domain for this situation? Why?

14. What is a reasonable range for this situation? Why?

15. Use your calculator. Find an appropriate viewing window then graph both functions on the same grid. Sketch your graph and record your window.

SOLVE THE SYSTEM OF EQUATIONS GRAPHICALLY

16. What are the coordinates of the point where the lines intersect? What does this point tell us?

17. If you sell hats for $20 each, which pay structure would you select? Why?

18. If you sell hats for $10 each, which pay structure would you choose? Why?

19. Your research also shows that the average time it takes an employee to finish one hat is two hours. If every employee works forty hours a week and a month has four complete weeks, which pay structure would you choose? Why?

Dolly Wagner plans to open a T-shirt shop in Galveston, Texas. She plans to sell each of her T-shirts for the same low price of $15.00. Use a table like **Figure 3.3** to find her income from T-shirt sales. Then use the process column to write an algebraic rule to represent her total income (y) in terms of the number of T-shirts sold (x).

Number of T-Shirts Sold (x)	Process Column	Total Income (y)
10		
20		
30		
50		
100		
x		

FIGURE 3.3.
Income from T-shirt sales.

1. Write the algebraic rule that models the amount of income earned as a function of the number of T-shirts sold.

2. How much income will Dolly earn for selling 200 T-shirts?

3. How many T-shirts would she have to sell to earn $1050?

As a businesswoman, Dolly knows that it takes money to make money. She needs $525 to get her business started. She also knows that each T-shirt costs $8 to produce. Use a table like **Figure 3.4** to find the cost of producing the T-shirts. Then use the process column to write an algebraic rule to represent her total cost (y) in terms of the number of T-shirts produced (x).

Number of T-Shirts Produced	Process Column	Total Cost
10		
20		
30		
50		
100		
x		

FIGURE 3.4.
Cost of producing T-shirts.

4. Write the algebraic rule that models the cost of producing T-shirts as a function of the number of T-shirts produced.

5. What is the total cost of producing 60 T-shirts?

6. Has Dolly made a profit yet if she has only produced 60 T-shirts and sold them all? Why or why not?

7. Use your graphing calculator to determine an appropriate viewing window, then graph both the income and the cost functions on the same grid. Sketch your graph and record your window.

CHECK THIS!

Remember here an ordered pair is made up of the variables x and y, or the input and output variables. We write the ordered pair as (x, y).

8. What are the coordinates of the point of intersection of the two lines? Write this point as an ordered pair.

9. Use words to describe the meaning of this point in terms of Dolly's business.

Do the Combo!

In the last section you made decisions about employee pay structures by solving systems of equations using tables and graphs. Solving systems of equations is important because it helps make decisions when there are several things to think about.

Let's take another look at the pay structure equations for Hats, Inc., and Caps, Inc.

1. In the algebraic rule for Hats, Inc., $1000 + 5c = p$, what does 1000 represent? What does 5 represent?

2. In the algebraic rule for Caps, Inc., $500 + 10c = p$, what does 500 represent? What does 10 represent?

3. How did you use your table to solve (find the number of hats and the pay where both pay structures are the same) the system of equations $1000 + 5c = p$ *and* $500 + 10c = p$?

4. How did you decide on a reasonable domain and range for this situation?

5. How did you use your graph to solve (determine the number of hats and the pay where both pay structures are the same) the system of equations $1000 + 5c = p$ and $500 + 10c = p$?

There are two other methods to consider when solving systems of equations: linear combination and substitution.

LINEAR COMBINATION METHOD

A system of equations can be solved by the **linear combination** method. This method uses the following steps to eliminate or *cancel out* one of the variables by adding the equations together.

Write the equations one above the other.

$$500 + 10h = p$$
$$1000 + 5h = p$$

Decide what to multiply by, so that when the equations are added one variable is eliminated.	$500 + 10h = p$ $-2[1000 + 5h = p]$
Multiply every term in the equation by that number.	$500 + 10h = p$ $-2000 + (-10h) = -2p$
Add the equations and solve for the remaining variable.	$-1500 = -p$ $1500 = p$

Substitute that value into one of the original equations and solve.	$500 + 10h = p$ $500 + 10h = 1500$ $-500 + 500 + 10h = 1500 - 500$ $10h = 1000$ $\dfrac{10h}{10} = \dfrac{1000}{10}$ $h = 100$

Use words to describe the meaning of your answer.	The solution to this system of equations is (100, 1500). This means if an employee completes 100 hats in a month, he or she will make $1500 on either pay structure.

SUBSTITUTION METHOD

A system of equations can be solved by the substitution method. This method uses the following steps to isolate one of the variables in one equation and then substitute into the other equation.

Isolate one variable. (Note: In the pay structure system of equations, p is already by itself on one side of the equal sign.)	$500 + 10h = p$
Substitute the expression that is equivalent to that variable into the other equation.	$1000 + 5h = 500 + 10h$

Solve the equation.

$$1000 + 5h = 500 + 10h$$
$$1000 + 5h - 5h = 500 + 10h - 5h$$
$$1000 = 500 + 5h$$
$$-500 + 1000 = 500 + 5h - 500$$
$$500 = 5h$$
$$\frac{500}{5} = \frac{5h}{5}$$
$$100 = h$$

Substitute that value into one of the original equations and solve.

$$1000 + 5h = p$$
$$1000 + 5(100) = p$$
$$1500 = p$$

Use words to describe the meaning of your answer.

The solution to this system of equations is (100, 1500). This means if an employee completes 100 hats in a month he or she will make $1500 on either pay structure.

After you have made decisions and hired workers, one of your workers comes to you with a question. She has a box containing 144 silver stars. Her job is to complete each hat by attaching 2 stars to every red hat and 6 stars to every green hat. She must complete 50 hats and use all of the stars. She wants to know how many of each color hat she will need to complete.

6. Write a system of equations to determine the solution to this problem.

7. Solve the system using a table.

8. Solve the system graphically.

9. Solve the system using linear combination.

10. Solve the system using substitution.

Assignment

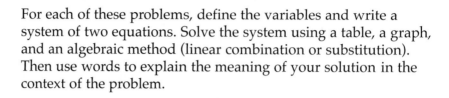

For each of these problems, define the variables and write a system of two equations. Solve the system using a table, a graph, and an algebraic method (linear combination or substitution). Then use words to explain the meaning of your solution in the context of the problem.

1. Jed's market has a total of 26 employees. Each full-time employee makes \$275/week, and each part-time employee makes \$140/week. Jed pays a total of \$5935 in wages each week. How many full-time and part-time employees does he have?

2. Tony has \$100 in the bank and is spending it at a rate of \$3 each day. Kai has \$20 in the bank and is adding to it by saving \$5 each day. How many days will it take for the two boys to have the same amount of money?

3. A wildlife manager has rabbits and pheasants in a cage. All together there are 35 heads and 94 feet in the cage. Every rabbit has 4 feet and every pheasant has 2 feet. How many rabbits and how many pheasants are in the cage?

4. A carnival booth has small stuffed bears and large stuffed bears that it uses for prizes. Each small bear is worth \$2.50 and each large bear is worth \$5. If the booth contains a total of 200 bears with a total value of \$625, how many bears are there of each size?

5. An order of MP3 players and CD players totals \$4003 without any taxes or other charges. The cost of each MP3 player is \$194.50 and the cost of each CD player is \$159.50. The shipment contains a total of 24 players, how many of each is in the order?

Buyer Beware!

Now that you've explored how to pay your employees, you have to decide where to buy the materials for your hats.

There are several options. First, you can buy the materials from Cloth City, a retail store in your town where you have been buying them up to this point. Since it is local, Cloth City must charge 8.25% sales tax. Another option is ordering your materials from Discount Fabrics, a wholesaler in another state. By doing so, you avoid paying sales tax. However, the wholesaler charges a processing fee of $13 per order, and 5% of the cost of materials for shipping and handling.

You must decide which option is the most cost-effective way to purchase your materials.

1. Define your variables.

2. Write a system of equations in terms of x and y.

3. Solve the system using a table, a graph, and an algebraic method of your choice.

4. What is the intersection point, or solution to the system? What does it mean in this context?

5. Which option is the most cost-effective way to buy your materials?

6. While shopping on the Internet, you discover Textile City, a textile factory in another state that charges a $37 processing fee, but only 1% of the cost of materials for shipping and handling. In light of this new option, where should you buy your materials?

   To answer this question, write an equation in terms of x and y for the Textile City offer.

7. Use a graph, a table, and the algebraic method of your choice to compare Cloth City with Textile City. Between these two, who has the better offer?

8. Use a graph, table, and the algebraic method of your choice to compare Discount Fabrics with Textile City. Who has the better offer and why?

9. If you plan to order $300 worth of materials, who has the best offer?

10. If you plan to order $450 worth of materials, who has the best offer?

11. If you plan to order $550 worth of materials, who has the best offer?

12. If you plan to order $700 worth of materials, who has the best offer?

13. What are the intersection points where the companies with the best offer change?

14. Which of the three options is the most cost-effective way to purchase your materials?

Assignment

For each of these situations, define variables and write a system of two equations. Solve the system using a table, a graph, and an algebraic method (linear combination or substitution). Then use words to explain the meaning of your solution in the context of the problem. Also state how the solution could be used to help decide which option to select in each situation.

1. The Zippy Photo Store charges $1.60 to develop a roll of 35mm film plus $0.10 for each print, while SuperPIX charges $1.20 for development plus $0.15 for each print. For how many prints is the cost the same?

2. Carlo is trying to decide between two used cars. The sports car costs $5000, but the insurance is $2300 per year. The SUV costs $8000, and the insurance is $800 per year. After how many years would the cost of owning either car be the same?

3. Rita is moving to a new apartment. She can rent a truck to move for $59.88 a day plus $0.49 a mile. Strong Men Movers would charge $81 a day plus $0.38 a mile. It will take one day to move. How many miles will make the costs of the two options (renting a truck or hiring Strong Men Movers) the same?

4. Flash Rent-a-Car rents a compact car for $24.95 per day plus $0.23 per mile. King Car rents the same car for $22.95 per day plus $0.31 per mile. For a one-day rental, how many miles would make the cost of renting the car from either company the same?

What About Those Bills?

Let's apply what you have learned thus far about solving systems of linear equations to a new situation.

1. Sometimes a businessperson needs to find creative ways to sell merchandise quickly.

   You just realized that in two days, you must pay a bill for supplies in the amount of $12,750. Your bank account is empty but you have 1000 hats in stock. You decide to have a two-day tent sale. You sell plain hats for $10 and logo hats for $12. At the end of the first day you sell a total of 500 hats and collect $5750.

   You realize that if you sell the remaining 500 hats at the same prices you will not make enough money. Thus, for the second day, you decide to sell plain hats for $11 and logo hats for $15. Assuming that you sell exactly the same number of each hat as the day before, will you make enough money to pay your bill? Justify your answer.

SUMMARY

In these sections we used the solutions to systems of linear equations to make a variety of business decisions. These decisions involve understanding costs and pay scales, choosing suppliers, and developing pricing.

Cracking the Code

Guarding plans and ideas is important in business. If another company discovers what you plan to do, they can steal your ideas. People try to create codes to hide information. Baseball coaches have elaborate methods for giving signs to keep the opposing team from knowing their plans.

Military leaders also need to keep their plans secret. During World War II, the Germans developed a machine called Enigma that coded messages. The ability of the Allies to break this code contributed to their winning the war. Navajo code talkers contributed to the success of the armed forces in the Pacific by translating messages into the Navajo language, which was impossible for the Japanese to crack. One of the first military leaders to use coded messages was Julius Caesar. His code involved shifting the letters of the Roman alphabet. He shifted the letters three spaces forward as shown in **Figure 3.5** ($x + 3$). Each letter is assigned a number based on its position in the alphabet. So, if you add 3 to the position number of a letter you will get the position number of the coded letter. X, Y and Z (the 24th, 25th and 26th) loop around to the beginning of the alphabet, so these letters are coded A, B, and C (1, 2, and 3).

CHECK THIS!

A shift transformation moves every point the same distance in the same direction.

x	1	2	3	4	5	6	7	8	9	10	11	12	13	14	15	16	17	18	19	20	21	22	23	24	25	26
Original Letter	A	B	C	D	E	F	G	H	I	J	K	L	M	N	O	P	Q	R	S	T	U	V	W	X	Y	Z
Coded Letter	D	E	F	G	H	I	J	K	L	M	N	O	P	Q	R	S	T	U	V	W	X	Y	Z	A	B	C
$x + 3$	4	5	6	7	8	9	10	11	12	13	14	15	16	17	18	19	20	21	22	23	24	25	26	1	2	3

FIGURE 3.5. An $x + 3$ shift code.

The following quotation from Julius Caesar,

"As a rule men worry more about what they can't see than about what they can,"

would be coded as,

"Dv d uxoh phq zruub pruh derxw zkdw wkhb fdq'w vhh wkdq derxw zkdw wkhb fdq."

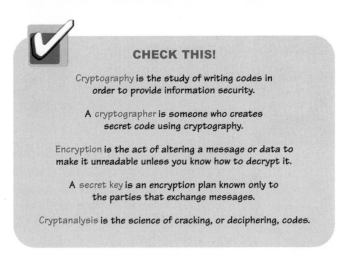
Since it is difficult to keep a key secret, you can make a shift transformation more secure by changing the number of spaces or the direction in which the letters are shifted, giving the secret key only to the person to whom you are sending the message.

In Dan Brown's book *Digital Fortress,* the two main characters send notes to each other using a variation of the Caesar code. They use a shift transformation, moving the letters one space forward, $(x + 1)$. Since both of them know the secret key, they decode each other's messages without anyone else knowing what they are saying.

I LOVE YOU is written as J MPWF ZPV.

You can make your own shift cipher device (like the one shown in **Figure 3.6**) by inserting a sliding slip of paper into a "mask" upon which the letters of the alphabet have been written. You can slide the slip of paper back and forth for different shift transformations.

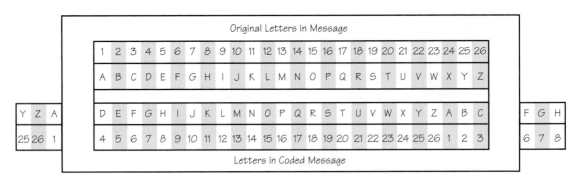

FIGURE 3.6.
A shift cipher device like this one is sometimes called a St. Cyr Strip.

Assignment

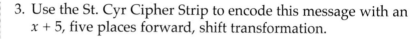

1. Caesar might have used the shift three spaces forward $(x + 3)$ code to send this secret message to one of his generals. Translate the message back into its original form.

   Dwwdfn Yhuflqjhwrula dw gdzq.

2. Use your St. Cyr Cipher Strip to decode this coded message. The message was encrypted with a shift transformation of $x - 10$, ten places backward.

   Dusuiiyjo yi jxu cejxuh ev ydludjyed.

3. Use the St. Cyr Cipher Strip to encode this message with an $x + 5$, five places forward, shift transformation.

   HAVE INVENTED SELF CLEANING FOOTBALL UNIFORM.

   MEET ME AT NOON TO DISCUSS SALES TO TEXANS.

4. Write a school-appropriate note to someone in your group using the shift one forward $(x + 1)$ code. Trade notes with someone in your group and decode their message.

5. Interview at least one adult and some of your friends; ask them why encryption techniques are important in today's world. Write down their answers.

The Matrix Code

Shift codes have a big problem: They are easy to crack. Players on the Wheel of Fortune game show guess letters based on how common they are. Code breakers work in much the same way. For example, if they notice that *h* has a high **frequency** (the number of times the letter is used) in a coded message, they might guess that it represents a letter such as *e* or *a* that is common in English. Once code breakers know the shift of one letter, they can decode a message quickly.

So it makes sense to find a way to code that is harder to crack. A matrix can be used to make code cracking more difficult.

CHECK THIS!

A matrix is a rectangular arrangement of numbers. The numbers are arranged in rows and columns and appear to make a rectangular shape. A row is a horizontal group of numbers. A column is a vertical group of numbers.

1. Write the message LOOK BEFORE YOU LEAP as a matrix using the pattern A = 1, B = 2, C = 3, and so on. Use 0 for the blanks between words.

   Number form of message:

   Matrix A =

You are scrambling your message by multiplying by the coding matrix $C = \begin{bmatrix} 2 & 5 \\ 1 & 3 \end{bmatrix}$. The coding matrix has 2 rows and 2 columns. You are going to use the matrix feature of a graphing calculator to multiply these two matrices. Your teacher will explain to you how to find the product of matrices A and C by entering the matrices into your graphing calculator.

2. Find the product of the two matrices and write it in the space below.

Scrambled message:

Matrix B =

Note that the first time O is coded it is a 30 and the next time it is 155. This means that code breaker needs more than the frequency of a letter to break the code.

3. Does the order in which you multiply the message and coding matrix to get matrix B matter and why?

The message in matrix B was coded with matrix C. That is, if A is a matrix containing the original message, the coding was done with this equation:

$$[C] \cdot [A] = [B]$$

Scrambled message:

Matrix B = $\begin{bmatrix} 24 & 49 & 15 & 40 & 69 & 4 & 43 & 9 & 70 & 8 \\ 43 & 76 & 25 & 62 & 113 & 6 & 71 & 14 & 115 & 16 \end{bmatrix}$

4. How do you think you would find matrix A, the original message, when you know matrices B and C?

5. Matrix equations are solved in much the same way as algebraic equations. How do you use multiplication to solve the equation $2x = 7$?

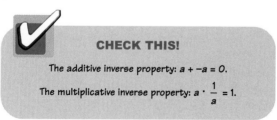

CHECK THIS!

The additive inverse property: $a + -a = 0$.

The multiplicative inverse property: $a \cdot \dfrac{1}{a} = 1$.

You can use multiplicative inverses of matrices to solve matrix equations on a graphing calculator. Your teacher will show you how to do this.

6. Will it matter in which order we multiply the inverse matrix by the coded matrix?

7. Write your product matrix.

Number form of the message:

Matrix A =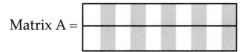

8. Write your decoded message below.

Assignment

Blank	0
A	1
B	2
C	3
D	4
E	5
F	6
G	7
H	8
I	9
J	10
K	11
L	12
M	13
N	14
O	15
P	16
Q	17
R	18
S	19
T	20
U	21
V	22
W	23
X	24
Y	25
Z	26

Create and code a secret message. Record your work on Handout 3.2. Follow the instructions below.

1. Your message must be 20 characters (letters or blanks) or less. Write your message in a table like the one below. Place one letter or a blank in each square.

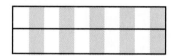

2. Assign each letter in your message a number from the chart at the right. Write the number message in a table like the one below.

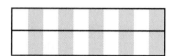

3. Create a 2 × 2 coding matrix. Write your coding matrix on the paper titled Secret Message.

Coding matrix: $\begin{bmatrix} a & b \\ c & d \end{bmatrix}$

To avoid problems with fractions, be sure that $ad - bc$ is equal to 1.

4. Multiply your coding matrix times your message matrix. Record the coded message on the Secret Message paper.

5. Exchange your secret message with another student. They will decode your message while you decode theirs. Write the matrix equation you used to decode the message.

6. Translate the message matrix into letters and write it on the Secret Message paper.

What's in a Matrix?

Tables are a common way to show data. **Figure 3.7** shows a table of the average times in minutes for the national physical fitness test endurance run in 1989 (U.S. Department of Education, 2001). The runs were 3/4 mile for ages 10 and 11 and 1 mile for ages 12 through 17:

	Boys	Girls
10–11-year-olds	7.3	8.0
12–13-year-olds	9.1	10.5
14–17-year-olds	8.6	10.7

FIGURE 3.7.
1989 times (in minutes).

When you remove the labels, in this case the boys and the girls and their ages, you have a group of numbers called a **matrix**. The plural of this word is **matrices**. Matrices are often represented by a capital letter. Here is the matrix for the table above:

$$T = \begin{bmatrix} 7.3 & 8.0 \\ 9.1 & 10.5 \\ 8.6 & 10.7 \end{bmatrix}$$

Here T is the label for the matrix, *times*. Matrices are often described by their size or their **matrix dimensions**, the number of rows and columns. This is a 3 × 2 (read "3 by 2") matrix because it has 3 rows and 2 columns. Each entry in a matrix is called an **element or a component**. The symbol $t_{2,1}$ points to the element in the second row, first column. In this table that is 9.1.

Corresponding elements are in the same position (row and column) in each matrix.

	Boys	Girls
10–11-year-olds	7.5	8.2
12–13-year-olds	9.4	10.4
14–17-year-olds	8.8	10.9

FIGURE 3.8.
2000 times (in minutes).

If you take the matrices from the 1989 table and the 2000 table you get:

$$T = \begin{bmatrix} 7.3 & 8.0 \\ 9.1 & 10.5 \\ 8.6 & 10.7 \end{bmatrix} \qquad U = \begin{bmatrix} 7.5 & 8.2 \\ 9.4 & 10.4 \\ 8.8 & 10.9 \end{bmatrix}$$

Matrix U is the student times in 2000.

Matrices can be labor saving tools when you have a graphing calculator or a spreadsheet program. Suppose you want to compare how fast students ran in 1989 to how fast they ran in 2000 (Figure 3.7 to Figure 3.8). This involves performing a **matrix operation.** A matrix operation allows you to perform a process such as multiplication, addition, or subtraction with one or more matrices.

If you want to see how students' times have changed you could do **matrix subtraction.** Matrix subtraction allows us to subtract elements of one matrix from those of another. To subtract two matrices, subtract the corresponding elements.

$$T = \begin{bmatrix} 7.3 & 8.0 \\ 9.1 & 10.5 \\ 8.6 & 10.7 \end{bmatrix} \quad U = \begin{bmatrix} 7.5 & 8.2 \\ 9.4 & 10.4 \\ 8.8 & 10.9 \end{bmatrix} \quad D = T - U = \begin{bmatrix} -0.2 & -0.2 \\ -0.3 & 0.1 \\ -0.2 & -0.2 \end{bmatrix}$$

Values from matrix D, or *difference*, can then be put in a table:

	Boys	Girls
10–11-year-olds	−0.2	−0.2
12–13-year-olds	−0.3	0.1
14–17-year-olds	−0.2	−0.2

FIGURE 3.9.
Times 1989 vs. 2000 (in minutes).

This table allows you to see that student times, except for 12- and 13-year-old girls, are slower than in 1989.

In this case it made sense to use matrix subtraction. Sometimes it makes sense to add elements of matrices. This is called **matrix addition.**

For example:

$$\begin{bmatrix} 2 & 3 \\ 1 & 0 \end{bmatrix} + \begin{bmatrix} -3 & 5 \\ 7 & -3 \end{bmatrix} = \begin{bmatrix} -1 & 8 \\ 8 & -3 \end{bmatrix}$$

For matrix addition and subtraction, both matrices must be the same size. This means that they have same number of rows and columns.

There are other operations you can perform on matrices. You can multiply a matrix by a number called a **scalar**. To perform **scalar multiplication**, multiply every element in the matrix by the scalar.

EXAMPLE:

$$-5\begin{bmatrix} 3 & 0 \\ -10 & 8 \end{bmatrix} = \begin{bmatrix} -15 & 0 \\ 50 & -40 \end{bmatrix}$$

You can use the definition of equal matrices to solve **matrix equations**. **Equal matrices** have the same dimensions and corresponding elements are equal. To solve for x and y, write the following equations and solve each equation.

EXAMPLE:

Solve for x and y.

$$\begin{bmatrix} 2x-5 & 4 \\ 3 & 3y+12 \end{bmatrix} = \begin{bmatrix} 25 & 4 \\ 3 & y+18 \end{bmatrix}$$

$$2x - 5 = 25 \qquad\qquad 3y + 12 = y + 18$$
$$2x - 5 + 5 = 25 + 5 \qquad\qquad 3y - y + 12 = y - y + 18$$
$$2x = 30 \qquad\qquad 2y + 12 = 18$$
$$\frac{2x}{2} = \frac{30}{2} \qquad\qquad 2y + 12 - 12 = 18 - 12$$
$$\boxed{x = 15} \qquad\qquad 2y = 6$$
$$\boxed{y = 3}$$

To multiply two matrices, the number of columns in the first matrix must be the same as the number of rows in the second matrix.

Each element in row 1 of the first matrix is multiplied by an element of column 1 in the second matrix, and the products are added together. The result becomes the row 1, column 1 element in the answer matrix. The process is continued until every row of the first matrix is paired with a column of the second matrix.

EXAMPLE:

Multiply.

$$\begin{bmatrix} 2 & -1 & 5 \\ 7 & 3 & -2 \end{bmatrix} \cdot \begin{bmatrix} 0 & -3 \\ -4 & 2 \\ 5 & 9 \end{bmatrix}$$

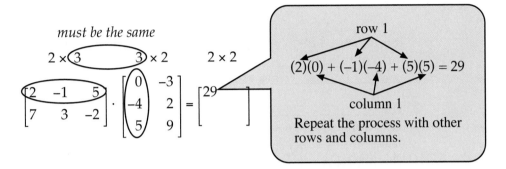

In general, when you pair row m of the first matrix with column n of the second matrix in this way, you get the row m, column n element of the product matrix.

Let's see if you get the same answer when you multiply matrix P by matrix Q as you do when you reverse the order of multiplication.

$$P = \begin{bmatrix} 2 & 3 \\ 0 & -1 \end{bmatrix} \qquad Q = \begin{bmatrix} -3 & 1 \\ 2 & 0 \end{bmatrix}$$

$$P \cdot Q = \begin{bmatrix} 2 & 3 \\ 0 & -1 \end{bmatrix} \cdot \begin{bmatrix} -3 & 1 \\ 2 & 0 \end{bmatrix} = \begin{bmatrix} 2(-3) + 3(2) & 2(1) + 3(0) \\ 0(-3) + (-1)(2) & 0(1) + (-1)(0) \end{bmatrix} = \begin{bmatrix} 0 & 2 \\ -2 & 0 \end{bmatrix}$$

$$Q \cdot P = \begin{bmatrix} -3 & 1 \\ 2 & 0 \end{bmatrix} \cdot \begin{bmatrix} 2 & 3 \\ 0 & -1 \end{bmatrix} = \begin{bmatrix} -3(2) + 1(0) & -3(3) + 1(-1) \\ 2(2) + 0(0) & 2(3) + 0(-1) \end{bmatrix} = \begin{bmatrix} -6 & -10 \\ 4 & 6 \end{bmatrix}$$

Multiply $P \cdot Q$ and $Q \cdot P$ with your calculator to check your answers.

Does order matter when multiplying matrices?

Yes. $P \cdot Q = \begin{bmatrix} 0 & 2 \\ -2 & 0 \end{bmatrix}$, but $Q \cdot P = \begin{bmatrix} -6 & -10 \\ 4 & 6 \end{bmatrix}$, so $P \cdot Q \neq Q \cdot P$.

Therefore, multiplication of matrices is not commutative.

Assignment

Fill in each blank with an appropriate word or number.

1. A _____ is a rectangular arrangement of numbers. It is arranged in _____ and _____. The plural form of this is _____. They are labeled with a _____ and are written within brackets.

2. The _____ of a matrix define the size of the matrix. The number of rows is always stated _____.

3. The matrix A = $\begin{bmatrix} 27 & -3 & 14 \\ 3.8 & -9 & 45 \end{bmatrix}$ is referred to as a ___ × ___ matrix.

4. Each number in a matrix is called an _____.

5. Two matrices are _____ matrices if and only if they have the same dimensions and their corresponding elements are equal. _____ are the elements in the same position (row and column) of each matrix.

6. You can multiply a matrix by a number called a _____ by multiplying every element in the matrix by it.

7. You can use the definition of equal matrices to solve a _____.

8. If two matrices have the _____ dimensions, you can _____ or _____ the corresponding elements to find the sum or difference of the matrices.

9. To multiply two matrices, the number of _____ in the first matrix must be the same as the number of _____ in the second matrix.

Use matrices A, B, C, D, or E for Questions 10–16.

$$A = \begin{bmatrix} 5 & -2 \\ 1 & 7 \end{bmatrix} \qquad B = \begin{bmatrix} 12 & 4 \\ -3 & -1 \end{bmatrix} \qquad C = \begin{bmatrix} 1 & 0 & 5 \\ 7 & 2 & 4 \end{bmatrix}$$

$$D = \begin{bmatrix} -3 & 9 & -1 \\ 5 & 0 & 12 \end{bmatrix} \qquad E = \begin{bmatrix} 0 & 1 & 2 \\ 3 & 4 & 5 \\ 6 & 7 & 8 \end{bmatrix}$$

10. What are the dimensions of matrix C?

11. Which matrix is a 3×3 matrix?

12. If matrix A is equal to $\begin{bmatrix} 5 & 3y - 11 \\ 2x + 9 & 7 \end{bmatrix}$, solve for x and y.

13. Multiply -3B.

14. Add C + D.

15. Simplify 5A − B.

16. Multiply A · D.

Using Matrices to Solve Systems of Equations

A square matrix with ones along the diagonal that goes from the upper left corner to the lower right corner and with zeros in every other position is called an **identity matrix**.

2×2 identity matrix:

$$I = \begin{bmatrix} 1 & 0 \\ 0 & 1 \end{bmatrix}$$

3×3 identity matrix:

$$I = \begin{bmatrix} 1 & 0 & 0 \\ 0 & 1 & 0 \\ 0 & 0 & 1 \end{bmatrix}$$

EXAMPLE:

What is the product of the identity matrix and matrix L?

$$L = \begin{bmatrix} -5 & 4 & 3.2 \\ -1 & 0 & 6 \end{bmatrix}$$

$$\begin{bmatrix} 1 & 0 \\ 0 & 1 \end{bmatrix} \cdot \begin{bmatrix} -5 & 4 & 3.2 \\ -1 & 0 & 6 \end{bmatrix} = \begin{bmatrix} & & \end{bmatrix}$$

If you multiply a matrix by the identity matrix, the product is the original matrix.

If the product of two matrices is the identity matrix then the matrices are __inverses__ of each other.

EXAMPLE:

$$A = \begin{bmatrix} -3 & 5 \\ 5 & -8 \end{bmatrix} \qquad A^{-1} = \begin{bmatrix} 8 & 5 \\ 5 & 3 \end{bmatrix}$$

$$A^{-1} \cdot A = I$$

$$\begin{bmatrix} 8 & 5 \\ 5 & 3 \end{bmatrix} \cdot \begin{bmatrix} -3 & 5 \\ 5 & -8 \end{bmatrix} = \begin{bmatrix} 8(-3)+5(5) & 8(5)+5(-8) \\ 5(-3)+3(5) & 5(5)+3(-8) \end{bmatrix} = \begin{bmatrix} 1 & 0 \\ 0 & 1 \end{bmatrix}$$

$$A \cdot A^{-1} = I$$

$$\begin{bmatrix} -3 & 5 \\ 5 & -8 \end{bmatrix} \cdot \begin{bmatrix} 8 & 5 \\ 5 & 3 \end{bmatrix} = \begin{bmatrix} -3(8)+5(5) & -3(5)+5(3) \\ 5(8)+(-8)(5) & 5(5)+(-8)(3) \end{bmatrix} = \begin{bmatrix} 1 & 0 \\ 0 & 1 \end{bmatrix}$$

If you do not know the inverse of a matrix, you can find it with a graphing calculator. This is especially helpful for matrices that are larger than 2 × 2. Your teacher will give you instructions on how to find the inverse matrix with the graphing calculator.

EXAMPLE:

Use a graphing calculator to find the inverse of matrix W.

$$W = \begin{bmatrix} 3 & 1 \\ 4 & 2 \end{bmatrix}$$

Check to be sure that the two matrices are inverses by multiplying them on the calculator.

EXAMPLE:

Use a graphing calculator to find the inverse of matrix F.

$$F = \begin{bmatrix} 4 & 3 & 0 \\ 5 & 2 & -3 \\ -3 & -1 & 2 \end{bmatrix}$$

Multiply $F \cdot F^{-1}$ (and $F^{-1} \cdot F$) to see if the product is the identity matrix.

You have already learned several methods for solving a system of equations: graphing, tables, substitution, and linear combinations. Inverse matrices are an additional method to help you find the solution.

EXAMPLE:

$$2x + y = 9$$
$$-2x - 3y = -7$$

If we look at the coefficients of x and y in the two equations above, we can represent them with a matrix called the **coefficient matrix**.

$$A = \begin{bmatrix} 2 & 1 \\ -2 & -3 \end{bmatrix}$$

The variables are represented with a different matrix called the **variable matrix**.

$$X = \begin{bmatrix} x \\ y \end{bmatrix}$$

Finally, the constants on the right side of each equation also have their own matrix called the **constant matrix**.

$$B = \begin{bmatrix} 9 \\ -7 \end{bmatrix}$$

You can rewrite the equations as the product of two matrices:

$$\begin{bmatrix} 2 & 1 \\ -2 & -3 \end{bmatrix}\begin{bmatrix} x \\ y \end{bmatrix} = \begin{bmatrix} 2x+y \\ -2x-3y \end{bmatrix} \text{ and is equal to } \begin{bmatrix} 9 \\ -7 \end{bmatrix}.$$

So, the equations could be written as

$$\begin{bmatrix} 2 & 1 \\ -2 & -3 \end{bmatrix}\begin{bmatrix} x \\ y \end{bmatrix} = \begin{bmatrix} 9 \\ -7 \end{bmatrix}$$

[A][X] = [B].

Multiply each side of the matrix equation by the inverse of matrix A.

[A]⁻¹[A][X] = [A]⁻¹[B]

Remember that matrix multiplication is not always commutative, so you must left-multiply on both sides of the matrix equation.

Don't forget that the product of a matrix and its inverse is the identity matrix, commonly labeled matrix I.

[I][X] = [A]⁻¹[B]

If you multiply a matrix by the identity matrix the product is the original matrix.

[X] = [A]⁻¹[B]

Let's do the same steps with the actual numbers in the matrix.

$$\begin{bmatrix} 2 & 1 \\ -2 & -3 \end{bmatrix}\begin{bmatrix} x \\ y \end{bmatrix} = \begin{bmatrix} 9 \\ -7 \end{bmatrix}$$

$$\begin{bmatrix} 2 & 1 \\ -2 & -3 \end{bmatrix}^{-1}\begin{bmatrix} 2 & 1 \\ -2 & -3 \end{bmatrix}\begin{bmatrix} x \\ y \end{bmatrix} = \begin{bmatrix} 2 & 1 \\ -2 & -3 \end{bmatrix}^{-1}\begin{bmatrix} 9 \\ 7 \end{bmatrix}$$

$$\begin{bmatrix} 1 & 0 \\ 0 & 1 \end{bmatrix}\begin{bmatrix} x \\ y \end{bmatrix} = \begin{bmatrix} 2 & 1 \\ -2 & -3 \end{bmatrix}^{-1}\begin{bmatrix} 9 \\ -7 \end{bmatrix}$$

$$\begin{bmatrix} x \\ y \end{bmatrix} = \begin{bmatrix} 5 \\ -1 \end{bmatrix}$$

So, the solution to the system of equations is $x = 5$ and $y = -1$.

Inverse matrices are especially useful when solving systems of equations with three variables.

EXAMPLE:

Solve the system of equations using inverse matrices on the graphing calculator.

$$2x - 3y + z = -7$$
$$x + 2y + 3z = 0$$
$$-3x - 5y + 9z = 1$$

$$\begin{bmatrix} x \\ y \\ z \end{bmatrix} = \begin{bmatrix} 2 & -3 & 1 \\ 1 & 2 & 3 \\ -3 & -5 & 9 \end{bmatrix}^{-1} \begin{bmatrix} -7 \\ 0 \\ 1 \end{bmatrix}$$

$$\begin{bmatrix} x \\ y \\ z \end{bmatrix} = \begin{bmatrix} -2 \\ 1 \\ 0 \end{bmatrix}$$

So the solution set is $x = -2$, $y = 1$, and $z = 0$.

EXAMPLE:

This month, Franco's checking account had a total of 24 checks written and ATM withdrawals. The bank charges $0.30 for each check and $1.50 for each ATM withdrawal. If his service charge was $12.00, how many of each type of activity did Franco carry out this month? Write a system of equations to represent this situation. Clearly define your variables.

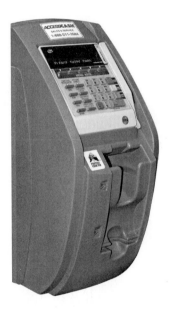

This problem can be represented with the system:

$$x + y = 24$$
$$0.30x + 1.50y = 12$$

where x is the number of checks written and y is the number of ATM withdrawals.

Solve the system using inverse matrices.

$$\begin{bmatrix} x \\ y \end{bmatrix} = \begin{bmatrix} 1 & 1 \\ 0.30 & 1.50 \end{bmatrix}^{-1} \begin{bmatrix} 24 \\ 12 \end{bmatrix}$$

$$\begin{bmatrix} x \\ y \end{bmatrix} = \begin{bmatrix} 20 \\ 4 \end{bmatrix}$$

Franco wrote 20 checks and had 4 ATM withdrawals.

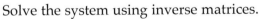

Assignment

1. Are these matrices inverses of each other? Why or why not?

$$A = \begin{bmatrix} 3 & -5 \\ -3 & 6 \end{bmatrix}$$

$$B = \begin{bmatrix} 2 & \frac{5}{3} \\ 1 & 1 \end{bmatrix}$$

2. Use a graphing calculator to find the inverse of this 2 × 2 matrix.

$$C = \begin{bmatrix} -4 & -2 \\ 5 & 2 \end{bmatrix}$$

3. Use a graphing calculator to find the inverse of this matrix.

$$D = \begin{bmatrix} 1 & 1 & 0 \\ -3 & -2 & 2 \\ 3 & 1 & -3 \end{bmatrix}$$

4. A softball team bought 24 jerseys and 15 hats for a total cost of $1713. Later, they bought 5 more jerseys and 12 more hats for a total cost of $490. If the cost per item was the same for each order, what was the cost of each jersey and each hat?

5. A collection of nickels, dimes, and quarters has a value of $3.40. There are twice as many dimes as quarters, and there are 32 coins in all. How many of each kind are there?

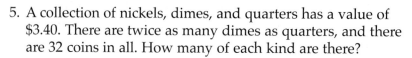

6. A lawn and garden factory makes rakes, shovels, and clippers at a monthly cost of $6850 for a total of 2150 items. It costs $2 to make a rake, $3 to make a shovel, and $4 to make a clipper. Wholesale, a rake sells for $3, a shovel sells for $4.50, and a clipper sells for $5.50. If the total income is $9825, how many of each item did the factory make?

7. A college student earned $177.50 last week working three part-time jobs. During the 30-hour workweek, she spent twice as many hours babysitting at $5 an hour as she did tutoring at $12 an hour. If she earned $4.50 an hour working in her grandmother's garden, how many hours did she spend at each job last week?

Opening Day

The promotions manager for the Texas Rangers is planning a special opening day giveaway. Each of the first 5000 fans will receive either a souvenir cap or a Rangers blanket. The manager knows that the caps cost $5 each and the blankets cost $12 each. What combination of caps and blankets can he purchase for a cost of $32,000?

After deciding how many caps and blankets to buy, the manager must also find the shipping costs. If the cost is $0.25 to ship each cap and $0.60 to ship each blanket, what will be the total cost for the opening day giveaway (including purchase price and shipping costs)?

Play Ball!

A LOOK AHEAD

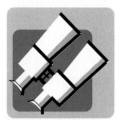

In 1965 the world's first sports stadium with a domed roof was built. The Astrodome in Houston, Texas, was the home of the Houston Astros. It was originally built with glass windows as ceiling tiles. However, during the first game, outfielders discovered that the sunlight shining through the windows made it difficult to see fly balls. Thus, the glass was painted in order to let some light in yet reduce glare. Without direct sunshine, the grass died. To solve this problem, engineers created an artificial grass called Astroturf, and artificial turf was born.

After the construction of the Astrodome, other cities built domed stadiums such as the Metrodome in Minneapolis, Minnesota, or the Superdome in New Orleans, Louisiana. During the 1990s, the people of Houston decided to build a new baseball stadium in downtown Houston. The new stadium, now known as Minute Maid Park, has a retractable roof. When the weather is nice, the Astros can play baseball with an open roof. However, if it is hot or rainy, the roof can be closed, and baseball can be played indoors.

Your sporting goods company plans to sell merchandise at a local baseball stadium. In this section, you will examine information regarding prices and expenses and make decisions about selling your merchandise.

At the stadium souvenir stand, you will sell hats with the home team's logo for $12, and T-shirts with the home team's logo for $20. The stadium charges $500 to rent the space to sell items during a home game, and the team charges $1.50 per item with their logo in royalties. Each hat costs $7 in materials and labor to produce, and each T-shirt costs $9 in materials and labor to produce. There is only enough space in the stand to stock 200 total items. You want to know which combinations of hats and shirts will generate more income than expenses; that is, will create a profit.

1. Use a table like **Figure 3.10** to identify possible combinations of hats and shirts that satisfy the requirement to have no more than 200 items in stock.

Number of Hats	Number of Shirts	Total Number of Items

FIGURE 3.10.
Stadium sales table.

2. Neglecting the stadium stand rent, what is the net profit (difference between income and expenses) generated by the sale of one hat?

3. Neglecting the stadium stand rent, what is the net profit generated by the sale of one shirt?

4. Use your combinations of hats and T-shirts and a table like **Figure 3.11** to identify the total income and the total expenses for each combination.

Income Generated by Hats	Income Generated by Shirts	Total Income

FIGURE 3.11. Income and expenses table.

Expenses Generated by Hats	Expenses Generated by Shirts	Stand Rent	Total Expenses

5. How many possible combinations of hats and shirts can you bring to sell at the stadium that will satisfy the restrictions of the situation?

6. Which combination of hats and shirts is best? Justify your choice.

Not Everything is Created Equal

In the previous section we looked at the following problem.

Your sporting goods company plans to sell merchandise at a local baseball stadium. At the stadium souvenir stand, you will sell hats with the home team's logo for $12 and T-shirts with the home team's logo for $20. The stadium charges $500 to rent the space to sell items during a home game, and the team charges $1.50 per item with their logo in royalties. Each hat costs $7 in materials and labor to produce, and each T-shirt costs $9 in materials and labor to produce. There is only enough space in the stand to stock 200 total items. What possible combinations of hats and shirts will generate more income than expenses; that is, will create a profit?

You created a table of possible combinations of numbers of hats and T-shirts that satisfy this situation. Use your table and the context of the problem to answer these questions.

1. Let h represent the number of hats and s represent the number of T-shirts. Write an expression to represent the amount of income that the sale of hats (h) and T-shirts (s) will generate.

2. Write an expression to represent the amount of expenses that the sale of a number of hats (h) and a number of T-shirts (s) will generate.

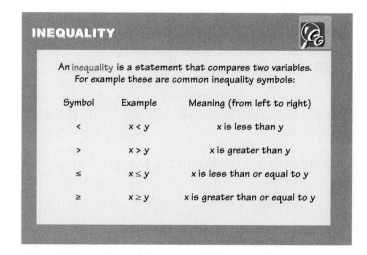

INEQUALITY

An inequality is a statement that compares two variables. For example these are common inequality symbols:

Symbol	Example	Meaning (from left to right)
$<$	$x < y$	x is less than y
$>$	$x > y$	x is greater than y
$\leq$	$x \leq y$	x is less than or equal to y
$\geq$	$x \geq y$	x is greater than or equal to y

3. Use the words **income** and **expenses** to write an inequality that describes the conditions under which a profit will be generated (income will exceed expenses).

4. Substitute your expressions from Questions 1 and 2 into your inequality from Question 3.

5. Solve this inequality for s in terms of h.

6. For this situation and ordered pairs (h, s), which quadrant of the coordinate plane should we consider? Why?

7. Use your graphing calculator to graph this inequality. Describe your window, and sketch your results.

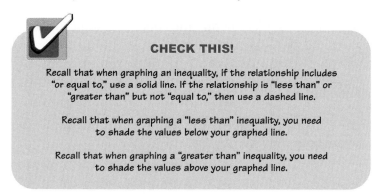

CHECK THIS!

Recall that when graphing an inequality, if the relationship includes "or equal to," use a solid line. If the relationship is "less than" or "greater than" but not "equal to," then use a dashed line.

Recall that when graphing a "less than" inequality, you need to shade the values below your graphed line.

Recall that when graphing a "greater than" inequality, you need to shade the values above your graphed line.

8. Write an inequality representing the possible combinations of hats (h) and T-shirts (s) that you can store in your souvenir stand.

Just like systems of equations, you can work with two inequalities at the same time.

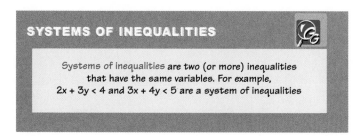

SYSTEMS OF INEQUALITIES

Systems of inequalities are two (or more) inequalities that have the same variables. For example, $2x + 3y < 4$ and $3x + 4y < 5$ are a system of inequalities

9. Use your graphing calculator to graph the number of T-shirts vs. the number of hats for the inequality from Question 8 in the same window as the inequality from Questions 4 and 5. Record your window and sketch your results.

10. Describe the graphs of both inequalities.

11. In this situation, what do the x-coordinate (h-coordinate) and y-coordinate (s-coordinate) represent?

12. Choose a point that lies above and to the right of both lines. Substitute the h-value and s-value for this point into both inequalities. Which inequalities does the point satisfy?

13. Choose a point that lies in the region between both lines. Substitute the h-value and s-value for this point into both inequalities. Which inequalities does the point satisfy?

14. Choose a point that lies below and to the left of both lines. Substitute the h-value and s-value for this point into both inequalities. Which inequalities does the point satisfy?

15. Choose two more points from the region where one point satisfies both inequalities. Do these points also satisfy both inequalities? Justify your answer.

16. Make a conjecture about the region of the coordinate plane where both inequalities are true.

Assignment

1. Graph the following system of inequalities.

$$\begin{cases} y \le 2x - 4 \\ 2x + 3y < 12 \end{cases}$$

a) Is the point (4, –3) a part of the solution to the system of inequalities? Why or why not?

b) Is the point (7, 5) a part of the solution to the system of inequalities? Why or why not?

c) Is the point (3, 2) a part of the solution to the system of inequalities? Why or why not?

d) Is the origin a part of the solution to the system of inequalities? Why or why not?

2. Graph the following system of inequalities.

$$\begin{cases} y \le 2x - 1 \\ x - 3y \ge 18 \end{cases}$$

a) At what point do the lines intersect? Is this point a part of the solution to the system of inequalities? Why or why not?

b) Describe the solution set to the system of inequalities in terms of x and y.

3. To meet shipping requirements at the local U Pack It We Ship It store, the perimeter of the base of a rectangular box must be less than 30 inches. The length must be at least the width of the base of the box.

a) Write two inequalities that describe this situation.

b) What are a reasonable domain and range? Assume width is the independent variable and length is the dependent variable.

c) What are some possible values for length and width that satisfy the requirements of the shipping store? Use a table like **Figure 3.12** to organize your data.

Length	Width	Perimeter

FIGURE 3.12.
Box measurement table.

d) Graph the inequalities relating length and width. Use width on the *x*-axis and length on the *y*-axis.

e) Are the lengths and widths from your table in the solution set according to your graph? How do you know?

4. The local petting zoo charges $1 for children's admission and $3 for adults. An elementary school class is going on a field trip to the zoo and has $50 budgeted for admission. The small bus they will take holds up to 30 people. What possible combinations of children and adults could attend the field trip? To find out, answer these questions.

a) Define your variables.

Let *x* = _____

Let *y* = _____

b) Write two inequalities representing this situation.

c) What are a reasonable domain and range?

d) Graph the two inequalities.

5. Use your graph to fill in each blank with a value so that the combination can attend.

a) 15 children, _____ adults

b) 3 children, _____ adults

c) ___ children, 2 adults

d) _____ children, 5 adults

Solutions to Systems of Inequalities

In the previous section you solved a system of inequalities graphically by identifying a region of the coordinate plane where the points describe pairs that make both of the inequalities true.

Now let's look at some important ideas about systems of inequalities and compare them to what we know about solving systems of equations.

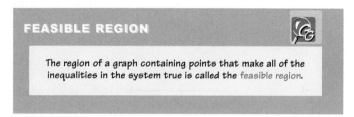

FEASIBLE REGION

The region of a graph containing points that make all of the inequalities in the system true is called the feasible region.

1. When you made a table of possible data points that satisfied all of the conditions of your problem, how did you decide which points to use?

2. How did you develop your expressions for income and expenses?

3. When you wrote your inequalities, how did you decide which relation to use: less than, greater than, or equal to?

4. When you graphed your inequalities, how did you decide which region to shade?

5. How did you decide which region satisfied both inequalities?

6. Are the lines in your graph part of the feasible region? Explain.

7. What does the point of intersection of the lines in the graph represent? Is it a part of the feasible region?

8. How does the solution of a system of inequalities compare to the solution of a system of equations?

9. Suppose a customer orders hats and T-shirts. They want no more than 60 items and no more than twice as many T-shirts as hats.

a) What are a reasonable domain and range for this situation? Justify your answer.

b) Write an inequality in terms of h, the number of hats, and s, the number of T-shirts, to describe the condition "they want no more than 60 items."

c) Write an inequality in terms of h and s to describe the condition "no more than twice as many T-shirts as hats."

d) Graph both of these inequalities together on your graphing calculator. Choose an appropriate window and sketch your results. Identify the solution to the system.

SUMMARY

Solving Systems of Inequalities

Systems of inequalities have more than one solution. So a good way to represent the solution is with a graph. To create a graph for the solution to a system of inequalities,

❖ identify an appropriate domain and range for the situation. Use these to set up your independent and dependent variable axes;

❖ graph each inequality. Use a solid line if the inequality uses the symbol ≥, "greater than or equal to," or the symbol ≤, "less than or equal to." Use a broken line if the inequality uses the symbol >, "greater than," or <, "less than";

❖ shade the appropriate region for each inequality. Shade the y-values that are greater than (above) the line if the inequality uses "greater than." Shade the y-values that are less than (below) the line if the inequality uses "less than"; and

❖ identify the feasible region. The feasible region is the part of the graph where the shaded regions of the individual inequalities overlap.

In this section you examined systems of linear inequalities.

1. You looked at tabular and graphical representations of the solution to systems.

2. You compared the solution for a system of equations to the solution for a system of inequalities.

Assignment

1. A men's medium baseball jersey requires $2\frac{1}{4}$ yards of fabric. A men's large baseball jersey requires $3\frac{3}{4}$ yards of fabric. You have 75 yards of fabric and want to make no more than 30 jerseys. How many of each type of baseball jersey can you make?

   a) Define your variables. Identify the independent and dependent variables.

   b) What are a reasonable domain and range for this situation? Justify your answer.

   c) Write two inequalities to describe the situation.

   d) Solve each inequality for your dependent variable in terms of your independent variable.

   e) Graph both of these inequalities together. Choose an appropriate window and sketch your results. Identify the solution to the system.

2. A loaf of rye bread requires 3 cups of flour and $\frac{1}{2}$ cup of sugar. A loaf of pumpernickel bread requires $2\frac{1}{2}$ cups of flour and 1 cup of sugar. You have 40 cups of flour and 10 cups of sugar. How many of each kind of loaf can you bake?

   a) Define your variables. Identify the independent and dependent variables.

   b) What are a reasonable domain and range for this situation? Justify your answer.

   c) Write two inequalities to describe the situation.

   d) Solve each inequality for your dependent variable in terms of your independent variable.

   e) Graph both of these inequalities together. Choose an appropriate window and sketch your results. Identify the solution to the system.

3. A ballpark offers two packages for birthday party favors. Package A includes 5 tickets for a ball toss game and 6 pennants for the home team. Package B includes 15 tickets for a ball toss game and 3 pennants for the home team. The ballpark management want to have at least 30 packages available. They also want to include at least 300 tickets but no more than 180 pennants. How many of each package can they assemble?

a) Define your variables. Identify the independent and dependent variables.

b) What are a reasonable domain and range for this situation? Justify your answer.

c) Write three inequalities to describe the situation.

d) Solve each inequality for your dependent variable in terms of your independent variable.

e) Graph both of these inequalities together. Choose an appropriate window and sketch your results. Identify the solution to the system.

Make the Most of It

In Sections 3.12 and 3.13, you used a system of inequalities to represent a problem about your sports apparel business. A local baseball stadium has invited you to sell hats and T-shirts at home games. Thus far, you have used linear inequalities to represent constraints on the situation. The system of inequalities yielded a feasible region with possible combinations of hats and T-shirts that satisfy all of the constraints.

Which one of those combinations can you use to generate the most income for your business? In this section you will explore a way to use the graphs of linear inequalities to answer this question.

Earlier in this chapter we have explored the following problem.

Your sporting goods company plans to sell merchandise at a local baseball stadium. At the stadium souvenir stand, you will sell hats with the home team's logo for $12, and T-shirts with the home team's logo for $20. The stadium charges $500 to rent the space to sell items during a home game, and the team charges $1.50 per item with their logo in royalties. Each hat costs $7 in materials and labor to produce and each T-shirt costs $9 in materials and labor to produce. There is only enough space in the stand to stock 200 total items. What possible combinations of hats and shirts will generate more income than expenses; i.e., what combinations will create a profit?

For now, let's ignore the limit of 200 items, since we are thinking about production at the factory. Consider that the cost for hats is $2 in material and $5 in labor. Also, the cost for T-shirts is $4 in material and $5 in labor. There is still a licensing fee of $1.50 per item for the use of the team's logo.

Upon further analysis of your business accounts, you decide that you can spend no more than $1000 in material and $1500 in labor for one week. In order to maximize your income, how many hats and how many T-shirts should you make?

In order to solve this problem, answer these questions.

1. First, create a table like **Figure 3.13** to organize the information:

	Cost of Materials per Item	Cost of Labor per Item	Expected Income per Item
Hats			
T-shirts			
Maximum Allowed			

FIGURE 3.13.
Table of cost data.

2. Let h represent the number of hats sold and s represent the number of T-shirts sold. Write a function rule that describes the amount of income (I) in terms of the number of hats (h) and the number of T-shirts (s) sold.

3. Write a system of inequalities to represent each of these costs in terms of h and s:

   a) Cost of Materials

   b) Cost of Labor

4. What domain and range restrictions do we need to consider in the context of this problem? How do you know?

5. Solve the inequalities from Question 3 for s in terms of h.

6. Graph the two inequalities from Question 5. Consider your answer to Question 4 to set an appropriate window for your graph. Describe your window and sketch your results.

7. What is the feasible region for this system?

8. What are the vertices of the feasible region? Are these points included in the solution to the system of inequalities?

9. Use your income function to find the income that is generated by these four combinations of hats and T-shirts. Use a table like **Figure 3.14** to organize your data.

Points (h, s)	Income Function $I = 12h + 20s$

FIGURE 3.14.
Income possibilities.

10. According to our table, how many hats and T-shirts should we produce in order to maximize our income?

11. Is it possible, within the constraints of this problem, to earn an income of $7000? Justify your answer.

12. Is it possible, within the constraints of this problem, to earn an income of $3000? Justify your answer.

13. Are there other points from the feasible region that generate more income than one of the vertices? Expand your table to record your findings.

If you want to minimize or maximize a quantity when you have two constraints that can be represented by linear inequalities, you can use a method called **linear programming**. Here are the steps:

❖ *Define a system of inequalities.* Use the information in the problem to write a system of inequalities that describe the constraints. A table, such as the one in Figure 3.14, will help you organize the data and write your inequalities.

❖ *Write an equation describing the quantity you wish to minimize or maximize.* In the example used in this section, you tried to maximize income, so you wrote an income function.

❖ *Graph both inequalities on the same coordinate plane.*

❖ *Identify a feasible region.* The feasible region is the area of overlapped shading between the inequalities. The domain and range of the situation will also help define the feasible region. In the example used in this section, you can only have positive numbers of hats and T-shirts, so the feasible region is restricted to Quadrant I.

❖ *Find the coordinates of the vertices of the feasible region.* Using technology such as a graphing calculator can help you to find the intersection point of two lines.

❖ *Substitute the coordinates of each of the vertices into the function you are trying to minimize or maximize.* You will need to substitute each ordered pair into your function and calculate the desired quantity.

❖ *Identify the coordinates that yield the minimum or maximum value of the function.* One of the vertices of the feasible region will yield a minimum or maximum for the quantity. This ordered pair is the solution.

Assignment

1. Two machines, Machine A and Machine B, produce two types of chili: beef and vegetarian. One machine does the processing of the raw ingredients and mixes them together. The other machine cooks the chili and packages it. There is a profit of $150 per case of vegetarian chili and $100 per case of beef chili. To make a case of vegetarian chili, Machine A must run 2 hours and Machine B must run 9 hours. To make a case of beef chili, Machine A must run 4 hours and Machine B must run 2 hours. Each machine runs 24 hours a day. What combination of cases of vegetarian chili and beef chili will result in a maximum profit?

   Let x = the number of cases of vegetarian chili and y = the number of cases of beef chili.

   a) What domain and range make sense for this situation?

   b) Write an income function in terms of x and y.

   c) Write four inequalities, in terms of x and y, that describe the constraints.

   d) Graph the system of inequalities. Identify the feasible region. If you use a graphing calculator, also record your viewing window.

   e) Identify the vertices of your feasible region. Use your income function to calculate the income for each combination of cases of vegetarian chili and cases of beef chili.

   f) What combination of cases of vegetarian chili and beef chili will result in a maximum profit?

2. A trucking company can ship the hats and T-shirts produced by your sporting goods company. Their trucks can hold a maximum of 250 cubic feet in volume and 2030 pounds in weight. One box of T-shirts has a volume of 5 cubic feet, weighs 35 pounds, and will generate $114 in profit. One box of hats has a volume of 3 cubic feet, weighs 35 pounds, and will generate $70 in profit. What combination of boxes of hats and T-shirts can you ship to maximize your profit?

Let x = the number of boxes of hats and y = the number of boxes of T-shirts.

a) What domain and range make sense for this situation?

b) Write four inequalities, in terms of x and y, that describe the constraints.

c) Write a profit function in terms of x and y.

d) Graph the system of inequalities. Identify the feasible region. If you use a graphing calculator, also describe your viewing window.

e) Identify the vertices of your feasible region. Use your income function to calculate the profit for each combination of boxes of hats and boxes of T-shirts.

f) What combination of boxes of hats and boxes of T-shirts will result in a maximum profit?

SECTION 3.15

Count the Trees

Let's apply what you have learned thus far about building and using systems of linear inequalities to a new situation.

1. Your friend, Judy, has started a tree farm. She grows oak and pine seedlings and then ships them to customers. Because your business has become so successful, she comes to you for advice.

   A customer wants to order a combination of oak and pine seedlings. The customer wants at least 8 seedlings to include at least 5 pine seedlings. The box your friend usually uses for shipping can hold no more than 18 pounds. One oak seedling weighs 1 pound and costs $3 to ship. One pine seedling weighs 2 pounds but because of favorable shipping regulations only costs $2 to ship. What combination of oak and pine seedlings should Judy advise that the customer order to minimize shipping costs? Justify your answer.

Modeling Project Growing a Business

Titangrow is an amazing new fertilizer developed by Newton Farm Products. Demand is expected to be high, but there are many issues to think about besides sales.

First of all, the company must think about making the product. A key ingredient they use in Titangrow is salmon bone meal. This ingredient is expensive: Each increase of 5% in the quantity of salmon bone meal adds 20% to the manufacturing costs.

In testing the product, the company found that when the product has 25% bone meal it is most effective. At 15% bone meal it is very effective. And at 10% bone meal it is somewhat effective. Below 10% bone meal, the product is not effective. The company has decided to create 3 products:

Titangrow Super (25%)

Titangrow Advanced (15%)

Titangrow Standard (10%)

Each 10-lb bag of Titangrow Standard costs the company $3 to make.

Market research makes the company think that demand for Titangrow Super will be equal to Titangrow Advanced and Standard combined.

The company must also keep track of inventory at three warehouses.

Create a model for manufacturing, pricing (and profit), and keeping track of the inventory for these three products. Then create a summary report that addresses these issues for the entire product line. When you develop your model, remember that systems of equations, matrices, and linear programming are powerful business tools. Use them wisely.

Practice Problems

1. Suppose that one music subscription service, Dozster, charges $11 per month plus $0.85 per song; and a second service, Melody, charges $8 per month plus $1.00 per song. Let c be the monthly cost in dollars and n be the number of songs downloaded in a month.

   a) Write a linear equation that represents the monthly subscription cost for Dozster.

   b) Write a linear equation that represents the monthly subscription cost for Melody.

   c) Compare the monthly subscription cost for each company if you download 10 songs. Which is cheaper?

   d) Compare the monthly subscription cost for each company if you download 30 songs.

   e) How many songs could you download from each subscription service for $50?

   f) Use a system of equations to find the number of downloads and the cost at which the two services are the same.

   g) Graph this system of equations and record your window.

   h) For what number of songs is Melody a better deal? For what number of songs is Dozster a better deal?

2. A coffee shop sells several different kinds of coffee. The shop also uses some of its coffees to make its own custom blends. Coffee A sells for $6.00 a pound. Coffee B sells for $10.00 a pound. The shop's manager wants to create a blend of the two types A and B that sells for $7.00 a pound. The manager wants to make 10 pounds of this blend.

   Use a for the number of pounds of coffee A in the blend. Use b for the number of pounds of coffee B.

   a) Write an equation that describes the total number of pounds of coffees A and B in the blend.

b) Write an equation that describes the total dollar value of the blend.

c) What is the number of pounds of each coffee in 10 pounds of the blend?

3. Joel is saving his money to buy a used car. The price of the car is $5525, but it will be reduced by $150 for each month that the car remains unsold. Joel currently has $3250 in his savings account and will be able to save an additional $175 each month.

a) Write an algebraic expression to represent each of the following:

the price of the car in n months

the amount of money Joel will have saved after n months

b) Determine the number of months until Joel will be able to buy the car. Show your work.

4. Using only 34-cent stamps and 20-cent stamps, Peggy put $3.52 postage on a package. She used twice as many 34-cent stamps as 20-cent stamps. Determine how many of each type of stamp she used.

5. Mr. Parson sells nuts at a corner stand. He sells peanuts for $1.00 per pound and walnuts for $2.00 per pound. He wants to make 50 pounds of peanut-walnut mix. He will maintain the cost per pound of each type of nut and sell the mix for $1.60 per pound. How many pounds of each nut should he put in the mix? Show how you arrive at your answers.

6. A florist is offering two different package deals of roses and carnations. One package contains 20 roses and 34 carnations for $50.40. The other package contains 15 roses and 17 carnations for $32.70. This information can be represented by the system of equations below, where r is the cost of one rose and c is the cost of one carnation.

$20r + 34c = 50.40$

$15r + 17c = 32.70$

Solve the system of equations to find the cost of one rose.

7. Sketch a graph of this system of equations.

$$y = -x - 3$$
$$y = x - 3$$

8. In the following system of equations, what would be the first step in eliminating the variable y?

$$x + y = 7$$
$$2x - y = 5$$

9. This graph was made to compare the costs of renting copy machines from Company A and from Company B. What information is given by the point of intersection of the two lines?

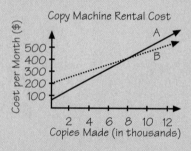

10. A clothing company receives orders from three shops. The first shop orders 25 jackets, 75 shirts, and 75 pairs of pants. The second shop orders 30 jackets, 40 shirts, and 35 pairs of pants. The third shop orders 20 jackets, 40 shirts, and 35 pairs of pants. Display this information in a matrix with rows representing the shops and columns representing the type of clothing ordered. Label the rows and columns of your matrix.

11. Through July 20, 1997, the three baseball players with the highest batting average in the National League had these batting statistics.

	AB	R	H	HR	RBI	Avg.
L. Walker (Colorado)	343	88	138	27	79	.402
Gwynn (San Diego)	372	64	147	15	84	.395
Piazza (Los Angeles)	332	56	118	19	62	.355

These are the statistics for the same players through September 30, 1997.

	AB	R	H	HR	RBI	Avg.
L. Walker (Colorado)	568	143	208	49	130	.366
Gwynn (San Diego)	592	97	220	17	119	.372
Piazza (Los Angeles)	556	104	201	40	124	.355

Find and label a matrix that displays the changes in these statistics. Notice that the batting averages for two of the three players decreased. How is a decrease shown in your matrix?

12. A state university announced a 7% raise in tuition. The current rates per semester hour are shown in the following table.

	Undergraduate	Graduate
Resident	$75.00	$99.25
Nonresident	$204.00	245.25

a) Write and label a matrix that represents this information.

b) Find a new matrix that represents the tuition rates per semester hour after the 7% raise goes into effect. Label your matrix.

c) Find a matrix that represents the dollar increase for each of the categories. Label your matrix.

d) Which matrix operation did you use in b? Which matrix operation did you use in c?

13. Nancy has jewelry shops in Westmarket, Eastmarket, and Oldmarket plazas. Her sales of cultured pearls for July are shown in the following table.

	Old	West	East
Earrings	10	8	12
Pins	6	5	4
Necklaces	3	2	2
Bracelets	4	3	2

Earrings sell for $40 a pair, pins for $35 each, necklaces for $80 each, and bracelets for $45. Use matrix multiplication to find Nancy's total sales at each location.

14. Use matrices to find (x, y) if

$$5x + 3y = 2$$
$$7x - 2y = 3$$

15. A small company makes unfinished tables and chairs. Each table uses 40 board feet of wood, and each chair uses 20 board feet. It takes 6 hours of labor to make a table and 8 hours to make a chair. There are 2000 board feet of wood and 600 labor hours available for the next week.

   a) Let T represents the number of tables made in the next week and C the number of chairs. Write inequalities that relate T and C to the total available amount of wood, and to the total available labor.

   b) The inequalities $T \geq 0$ and $C \geq 0$ also describe this situation. Why?

   c) Draw a graph that represents this situation.

   d) Can the company produce 30 tables and 35 chairs in the next week? Defend you answer.

   e) Can the company produce 50 tables and 10 chairs in the next week? Defend you answer.

16. Eric wants to buy chips and soda for the guests at his party. Each large bag of chips costs $2.40 and each large bottle of soda costs $2.00. He has $48.00 to spend.

   a) Write a system of inequalities that describes the limits on Eric's choices for number of bags of chips C and number of bottles of soda S that he can buy.

   b) Draw a graph that represents the possible numbers of bags of chips and bottles of soda that Eric can buy.

   c) If Eric buys 10 bags of chips, what is the largest number of bottles of soda that he can buy?

17. Write a system of inequalities that describes the graph in **Figure 3.15.**

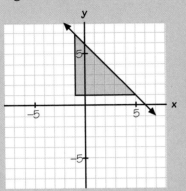

FIGURE 3.15.
Graph for Question 17.

18. A to Z Auto Service claims that their car repair rates are the lowest in town. They charge an initial fee of $50 plus $30 per hour. Assuming their claim is true, draw a graph that describes the rates charged by A to Z's competitors.

19. Julie does not want to spend more than $300 on ice skating. Her skates will cost $42, her lessons will cost a total of $56, and the practice time will cost $7.50 per hour. Write an inequality Julie could use to determine the maximum number of hours, h, she can practice without spending more than $300.

20. Principal Greene has received a $1500 grant to buy new printers at his school. He has a choice between $50 color printers and $130 high-resolution laser printers. He wants at least 20 new printers. If C represents the number of color printers and L represents the number of laser printers, write a set of inequalities that models his choice.

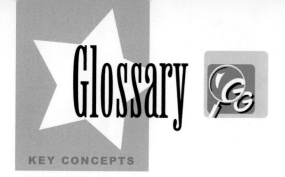

Glossary

Additive Inverse: The additive inverse of a number a is the number b, such that $a + b = 0$. So the additive inverse of 2 is –2.

Coefficient Matrix: A matrix that contains the coefficients from a system of equations.

Constant Matrix: A matrix that contains the constant from a system of equations.

Corresponding Elements: Elements in matrices that are in the same position (row and column) of each matrix.

Equal Matrices: Two matrices are equal matrices if and only if they have the same dimensions and their corresponding elements are equal.

Expense: An amount paid for a good or service. In business, expenses must be deducted from income to find profit.

Feasible Region: The area of a graph containing all the points that make all of the inequalities in the system true.

Frequency: In this chapter, frequency is the number of times a value occurs. If it occurs often the frequency is high. If it does not occur often the frequency is low.

Identity Matrix: A square matrix (the same number or rows and colums) that contains ones running diagonally from the upper left corner to the lower right corner and has zeroes in all of the other entries. Multiplying a square matrix by an identity matrix does not change the matrix.

Income: In most cases the amount earned from work. In business, income minus expenses equals profit.

Inequality: A type of statement that compares two values. For example these are common inequality symbols:

Symbol	Example	Meaning (from left to right)
$<$	$x < y$	x is less than y
$>$	$x > y$	x is greater than y
$\leq$	$x \leq y$	x is less than or equal to y
$\geq$	$x \geq y$	x is greater than or equal to y

Intersect or Intersection: In this chapter, the point (x, y) in a graph where two lines cross.

Inverse Matrix: The product of a square matrix and its inverse matrix is an identity matrix. Not every square matrix has an inverse matrix.

Linear Combination Method: A way to solve systems of equations in which one of the variables is eliminated by adding equations.

Linear Programming: The study and processes for maximizing or minimizing a function based on linear constraints. Linear programming is a tool used in business to make financial decisions.

Matrix (Matrices): An arrangement of numbers written between brackets. The numbers are arranged in rows and columns and make a rectangular shape. A row is a horizontal group of numbers. A column is a vertical group of numbers. The plural of matrix is matrices.

Matrix Addition: A process of adding two matrices. Matrix addition can only be performed on matrices with the same dimensions.

Matrix Dimensions: The number of rows and columns in a matrix. A matrix with 3 rows and 2 columns is a 3 × 2 matrix (read "3 by 2").

Matrix Element or Component: A single entry in a matrix.

Matrix Multiplication: A process of multiplying two matrices.

Matrix Operation: A process, such as addition or scalar multiplication, carried out on one or more matrices.

Matrix Subtraction: A process of subtracting two matrices. Matrix subtraction can only be performed on matrices with the same dimensions.

Multiplicative Inverse: The multiplicative inverse of a number a is the number b, such that $a \times b = 1$. So the multiplicative inverse of 2 is $\frac{1}{2}$.

Profit: The amount left over after expenses have been deducted from income. This can be a negative number (often called "loss").

Scalar Multiplication: A process where all of the elements in matrix are multiplied by a number. The number is called a scalar.

Solution to a System of Equations: A set of values that are solutions to every individual equation in a system.

Substitution Method: A way to solve systems of equations by isolating a variable in one equation then substituting into the other equation.

System of Equations: Two or more equations. A system of linear equations is a group of two or more linear equations.

Systems of Inequalities: Two (or more) inequalities that have the same variables. For example, $2x + 3y < 4$ and $3x + 4y < 5$ are a system of inequalities.

Variable Matrix: A matrix that contains the variables from a system of equations.

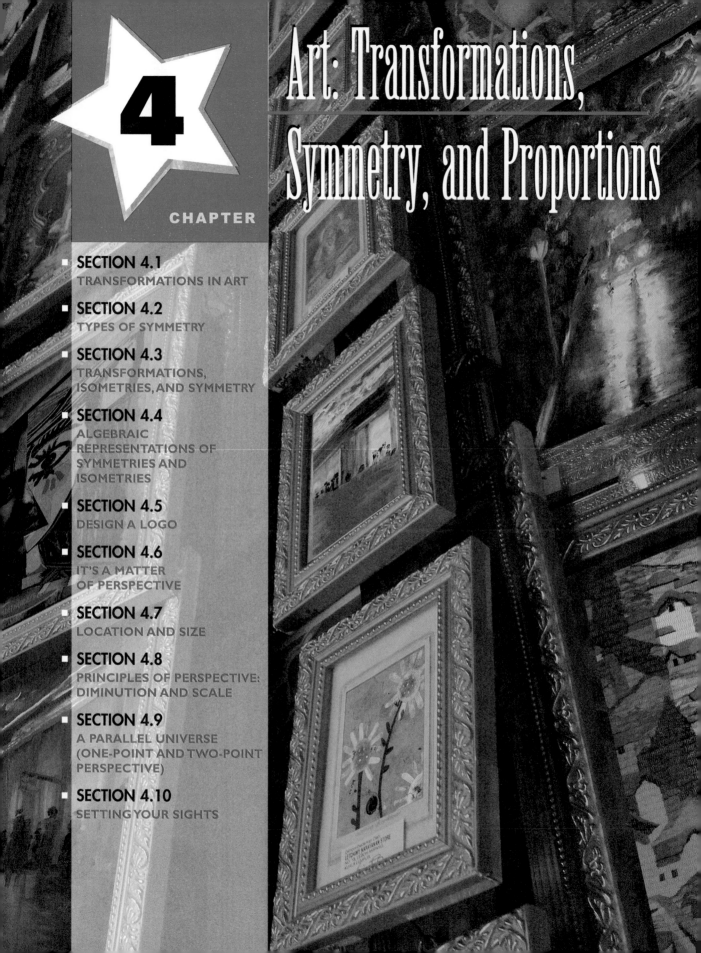

4

CHAPTER

Art: Transformations, Symmetry, and Proportions

Picture Perfect

Visual Art takes many forms. A pencil drawing and a graphic design are examples of art. A computer-generated graphic, a quilt, and a painting are also forms of art. Many occupations make use of art as well. For example, architects use drawings to represent building designs.

Artists and architects use flat surfaces to create pictures that appear to be three-dimensional. In using a flat surface, such as a canvas or paper, to represent three-dimensional space, artists and architects use mathematical ideas and geometric principles to make a flat image look like the real object.

What does mathematics have to do with creating art? Have you noticed patterns that repeat in paintings, logos, and even wallpaper? Sometimes the images that make up the pattern are always the same size, sometimes they are made to look 3-D, or three-dimensional, by drawing some objects over others and changing their size.

An architect uses the geometry of one-point or multi-point perspective to help a client visualize what a proposed building will look like. A theater designer uses geometry to create the illusion of depth and distance on a small stage. An animator guides you into and around three-dimensional objects using a two-dimensional screen. A painter uses perspective and shading to add depth to drawings.

Before you begin, take a look around you and notice the lines and shapes that make up your world. Think about how you might sketch the room you are in or the front of your school.

Small children view the world differently than you do. Their sense of depth is not well developed. Just look at a picture drawn by a young child, such as **Figure 4.1.**

FIGURE 4.1.
House by Jackson Barber, age 8.

Notice that the sun is too large and the building appears flat. Now compare Figure 4.1 with an architect's drawing for a new school (**Figure 4.2**).

FIGURE 4.2 Tantasqua Regional High School.

The drawing helped community members imagine what the completed project might look like before they voted on whether or not to build the new school. A realistic drawing is an important tool in their decision.

In this chapter we will explore three questions:

❖ How do artists create patterns by moving or transforming an object?

❖ What geometric principles guide an artist's creation of an accurate drawing?

❖ What principles give a picture depth?

This chapter explores how the answers to these questions help artists, architects, and others develop realistic drawings.

Transformations in Art

Repetition is a technique used often by artists. By repeating a basic element an artist can create a pleasing painting, tapestry, or other work. There are several ways to repeat a basic design element.

Consider the tapestry in **Figure 4.3.** The artist has repeated a basic condor element in two ways.

Figure 4.4 shows how the condor in the upper left corner (condor 1) can slide to its right to produce another condor. A **slide** is one type of repetition used by artists.

FIGURE 4.3.
Condor by Cerapio Vallejo.

FIGURE 4.4.
A slide produces another condor.

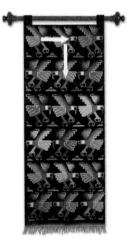

FIGURE 4.5. Slide condor 1 to the right, then slide it down, and then flip it to the left.

CHECK THIS!

In mathematics a slide is called a translation.

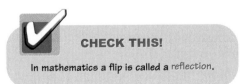

CHECK THIS!

In mathematics a flip is called a reflection.

But not all of the condors can be produced by sliding one of them. For example, the condor directly below condor 1 cannot be obtained by sliding condor 1. It can be obtained from condor 1 by sliding condor 1 to the right, then down, and then flipping it to the left (see **Figure 4.5**). A **flip** is another kind of repetition used by artists.

All of the condors in this tapestry can be obtained from condor 1 by translating or reflecting or a combination of the two.

The mirror in **Figure 4.6** demonstrates a third way artists use repetition.

FIGURE 4.6.
Art Nouveau mirror by Cidinha.

The crescent shape on the right edge of the mirror can be obtained from the one on the left by spinning the left one 180° about a central point. **Figure 4.7** shows how one crescent tip can be rotated to get the corresponding tip of the other crescent. A **spin** is another kind of repetition used by artists.

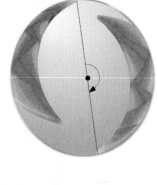

FIGURE 4.7.
Spinning one crescent tip 180° produces the other.

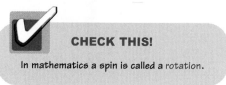

CHECK THIS!

In mathematics a spin is called a rotation.

Translations, reflections, and rotations are types of **transformations**. That is, each is a process that uses a basic image to create new ones. In this lesson you will learn more about transformations and how they are used in art and in mathematics.

In each of the following figures, identify a basic element and describe ways to get the other sections of the figure by translating, reflecting, and/or rotating the basic element. Your basic element should be as small a portion of the entire figure as possible.

1.

FIGURE 4.8. Image for Question 1.

2.

FIGURE 4.9. Image for Question 2.

3.

FIGURE 4.10. Image for Question 3.

4.

FIGURE 4.11. Image for Question 4.

5.

FIGURE 4.12. Image for Question 5.

6.

FIGURE 4.13. Image for Question 6.

7.

FIGURE 4.14. Image for Question 7.

8.

FIGURE 4.15. Image for Question 8.

9.

FIGURE 4.16. Image for Question 9.

10.

FIGURE 4.17. Image for Question 10.

Types of Symmetry

Many works of art have one or more kinds of symmetry. Symmetry is often easy to recognize, but can be hard to define. In Section 4.1 you learned about translations, reflections, and rotations. One way to describe a symmetric image is that a copy of the image can be translated, reflected, or rotated to match the original.

In this section you will create symmetric images. The basic instructions for Questions 1–4 are:

❖ Use two circular coffee filters. Place one on top of the other.

❖ Fold the double-filter as described.

❖ Make a variety of cuts along each straight edge of the folded filters.

❖ Unfold them.

❖ Describe how one filter (the copy) can be translated, rotated, or reflected to obtain the other. If there is more than one way to obtain one from the other, describe all of the ways that you can find.

1. Fold the filters in half once as shown in **Figure 4.18.** Make various cuts along the edge as shown in **Figure 4.19** (but not exactly the same as in the figure).

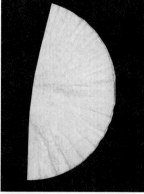

FIGURE 4.18.
Folded filters.

FIGURE 4.19.
Folded and cut filters.

2. Fold the filters in half and then in half again. (After the two folds, you should have quarter-filters). Make various cuts along the edge.

3. Fold the filters in half, then in half again, and then in half again. (After the three folds, you should have an eighth-filters). Make various cuts along the edge.

4. Fold the filters in half, and then fold into thirds. Make various cuts along the edge.

An image has **reflection symmetry** (also called line symmetry) when a copy of it can be reflected through a line to match the original image. The line is called a **line of symmetry**. For example, **Figure 4.20** shows the line of symmetry for a butterfly image.

FIGURE 4.20.
Reflection symmetry.

An image has **rotation symmetry** when a copy of it can be rotated less than 360° about a central point to match the original image. When you describe rotation symmetry, try to identify the central point and to state the size of the smallest possible rotation for which the copy and original match. For example, the flower in **Figure 4.21** has 72° rotation symmetry.

FIGURE 4.21.
72° rotation symmetry.

72°

5. For each of the objects you created in Questions 1–4, identify all lines of symmetry and the size of any rotation symmetry.

6. Does the flower in Figure 4.21 have any symmetry other than rotation symmetry? Explain.

Transformations, Isometries, and Symmetry

Many computer software programs have drawing features that allow you to create and edit images. For example, you can copy an image and paste it elsewhere. Many programs let you reflect or rotate an image. All of these operations are mathematical transformations. In this section you will take a closer look at how some of these operations work.

When a geometric object is transformed into another one, the original is called the **pre-image**. The new object is called the **image**. The vertices of the pre-image are labeled with capital letters, such as ABC for a triangle. The vertices of the image are often labeled with the same letters, but with an apostrophe after each. The apostrophe is read as **prime**. The transformation is often indicated with an arrow.

CHECK THIS!

The notation △ABC→△A'B'C' says that triangle ABC is transformed into triangle A-prime B-prime C-prime. △ABC is the pre-image. △A'B'C' is the image.

Draw a triangle on a sheet of paper and label its vertices A, B, and C. Be sure the triangle is not special; that is, don't draw an equilateral triangle, an isosceles triangle, or a right triangle. Draw the triangle so that one vertex is pointing upward; use A for the label of this vertex.

1. Place a sheet of patty paper over the triangle and trace it. Slide the patty paper a few inches to the right. On the original paper, mark the locations of the new vertices and connect them. Label the new triangle's vertices A', B', and C'. Discuss the type of transformation that A'B'C' is of ABC. Also discuss the properties of the original that changed and those that are the same.

2. On the paper with the original triangle, draw a vertical line to the right or the left of the triangle. Place the patty paper triangle back on the original triangle. Fold the patty paper along the line. On the original paper, mark the locations of the new vertices and connect them. Label the new triangle's vertices A', B', and C'. Discuss the type of transformation that A'B'C' is of ABC. Also discuss the properties of the original that have changed and those that are the same.

3. On the paper with the original triangle, mark a point somewhere outside of the triangle. Place the patty paper triangle back on the original triangle. Place the point of your pencil on the point that you marked and spin the patty paper about 90°. On the original paper, mark the locations of the new vertices and connect them. Label the new triangle's vertices A′, B′, and C′. Discuss the type of transformation that A′B′C′ is of ABC. Also discuss the properties of the original that have changed and those that are the same.

4. Does your original triangle have any lines of symmetry? That is, does it have reflection symmetry? If not, what type of triangle does?

5. Does your original triangle have rotation symmetry? If not, what type of triangle does?

Translations, reflections, and rotations are all special types of transformations called isometries. An **isometry** is a transformation that does not change size or shape. (Later in this chapter you will examine a transformation that is not an isometry.)

Isometries change the location of an object. Some of them change an object's orientation. You can orient a simple geometric figure by labeling the vertices A, B, C, and so on as you move from vertex to vertex in a clockwise direction. When an isometry changes the orientation, as you move from A′ to B′ to C′, and so on, you move in a counterclockwise direction.

6. Which transformations change orientation: translation, reflection, or rotation?

Each of these three isometries has specific characteristics that are used to identify it.

❖ A translation has a distance and a direction. For example, you might slide △ABC two inches to the right. Translations change location, but do not change size, shape, or orientation.

❖ A reflection has a line (sometimes called a mirror). For example, you might reflect △ABC about line $\overleftrightarrow{CD}$. Reflections change location and orientation, but do not change size or shape.

❖ A rotation requires a point and an angle. For example, you might rotate △ABC 30° counterclockwise about point D. Rotations change location, but do not change size, shape, or orientation.

Sometimes two or more isometries are combined. For example, in **Figure 4.22**, △ABC is translated to the right to get △A′B′C′.

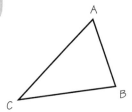
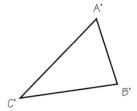

FIGURE 4.22.
A translation.

In **Figure 4.23**, △A′B′C′ is reflected across the line shown to obtain △A″B″C″.

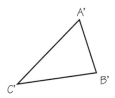
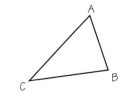

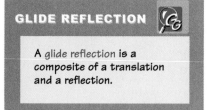

GLIDE REFLECTION

A *glide reflection* is a composite of a translation and a reflection.

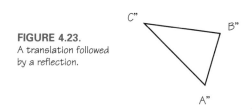

FIGURE 4.23.
A translation followed by a reflection.

△A″B″C″ is a called a **glide reflection** of △ABC.

7. What properties of a figure are changed by a glide reflection?

8. Use patty paper to create a composite of two reflections through a pair of parallel lines. That is, draw a line to the right of △ABC and reflect the triangle through it. Then draw a second line parallel to the first and to the right of the image. Reflect the image through this second line. How is the final image related to △ABC?

9. Use patty paper to create a composite of two reflections through a pair of intersecting lines. That is, draw a line to the right of △ABC and reflect the triangle through it. Then draw a second line that intersects the first and that is to the right of the image and below it. Reflect the image through this second line. How is the final image related to △ABC?

Assignment

1. **Figure 4.24** is a design element. Identify the smallest basic portion of it that can be used to obtain the rest and describe isometries that can be used to build up the design.

FIGURE 4.24.
A design element.

FIGURE 4.25.
Fabric design by Debra L. Hayden.

2. **Figure 4.25** shows how artist Debra Hayden used a basic element similar to the one in Figure 4.24 to create a larger work. Describe at least two ways that she could have done this.

3. Describe the symmetries of the basic element in Figure 4.24.

4. Discuss how an artist could use transformations to create **Figure 4.26** from a basic element of the figure.

FIGURE 4.26.
Image for Question 4.

5. **Figure 4.27** is a capital letter A in the Arial font. Some capital letters are symmetric. Identify those that have symmetry and describe the symmetry of each.

FIGURE 4.27.
Image for Question 5.

6. You may hear people talk about point symmetry. The plant in **Figure 4.28** demonstrates this type of symmetry. **Point symmetry** occurs when every point of a figure has an image directly across the figure's center, as shown in **Figure 4.29**.

FIGURE 4.28.
Image for Question 6.

FIGURE 4.29.
Image for Question 6.

a) Do any letters of the alphabet demonstrate point symmetry? If so, which ones?

b) Point symmetry is the same as another type of symmetry that you have studied in this lesson. Explain.

7. **Figures 4.30, 4.31, and 4.32** are oil company logos. Describe the symmetry of each.

FIGURE 4.30.
Shell Oil logo.

FIGURE 4.31.
Gulf Oil logo with letters.

FIGURE 4.32.
Gulf Oil logo without letters.

Algebraic Representations of Symmetries and Isometries

All of the isometries that you have examined change an object's location. People who use isometries in their work often need to describe locations precisely. When precise location is important, people use coordinates. For example, each pixel on a computer screen has coordinates that identify its location and that are used to transform the pixel or an object composed of many pixels in various ways.

In this section you will use coordinates to describe isometries exactly.

PART A:
TRANSLATIONS ON A COORDINATE PLANE

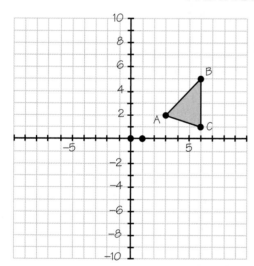

FIGURE 4.33. Triangle ABC.

A **translation** is a transformation that slides an object a given distance and in a given direction. Thus, every translation has a distance and a direction.

1. On a sheet of grid paper, plot △ABC as shown in **Figure 4.33.** Record the coordinates of the vertices of △ABC, the pre-image, in a table like **Figure 4.34.**

2. Trace △ABC and the coordinate axes onto a sheet of patty paper. Label the copy, the image, A′B′C′.

Pre-Image			Image		
A	B	C	A′	B′	C′

FIGURE 4.34. Table for Question 1.

3. Place the copy on top of the original so that the axes are aligned. Slide the copy 3 units left and 2 units up. Record the coordinates of the image in your table.

4. Did the triangle change size or shape?

5. Return the image to its original position and repeat 3 and 4 two more times using different values for the horizontal and the vertical translation.

6. Write equations that describe a translation of (x, y) horizontally h units and vertically k units. Use x' and y' for the coordinates of the image.

7. How does one represent a vertical or horizontal direction and a distance of a translation on a coordinate plane?

A **reflection** is a transformation that flips an object across a line.

PART B: REFLECTION ACROSS THE Y-AXIS

8. Refer back to your original △ABC. Record the coordinates of the vertices of △ABC, the pre-image, in a table like **Figure 4.35**.

Pre-Image			Image		
A	**B**	**C**	**A′**	**B′**	**C′**

FIGURE 4.35.
Table for Question 8.

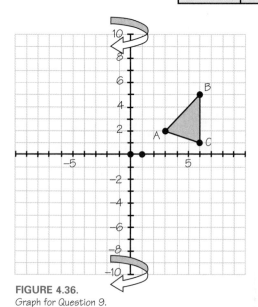

FIGURE 4.36.
Graph for Question 9.

9. Place the copy of △ABC from Part A on top of the original so that the axes are aligned. Reflect the triangle across the y-axis, the line of reflection, by flipping the paper and realigning the axes (**Figure 4.36**). Record the coordinates of the image in your table.

10. Did the triangle change size or shape?

11. Describe the relationship between the line of reflection and vertices A and A′. Are these relationships true for the other vertices of the triangle?

12. Repeat 8–11 two times drawing the pre-image △ABC in a different position, the fourth quadrant for example, each time.

13. Write equations that describe a reflection of (x, y) across the y-axis.

14. Do the y-coordinates change? If so, how?

15. Why are x-coordinates of the image opposites of those of the pre-image?

PART C: REFLECTION ACROSS THE X-AXIS

16. Refer back to your original $\triangle ABC$. Record the coordinates of the vertices of $\triangle ABC$, the pre-image, in a table like **Figure 4.37.**

Pre-Image			Image		
A	B	C	A′	B′	C′

FIGURE 4.37.
Table for Question 16.

17. Place the copy of $\triangle ABC$ from Part A on top of the original so that the axes are aligned. Reflect the triangle across the x-axis, the line of reflection, by flipping the copy of $\triangle ABC$ and realigning the axes (**Figure 4.38**). Record the coordinates of the image in your table.

18. Did the triangle change size or shape?

19. Describe the relationship between the line of reflection and vertices A and A′. Are these relationships true for the other vertices of the triangle?

20. Repeat 16–19 two times drawing the pre-image $\triangle ABC$ in a different position (the fourth quadrant for example) each time.

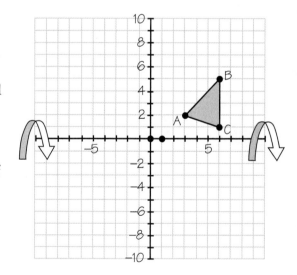

FIGURE 4.38.
Graph for Question 17.

21. Write equations that describe a reflection of (x, y) across the x-axis.

22. Do the x-coordinates change? If so, how?

23. Why are the y-coordinates of the image the opposite of those of the pre-image?

PART D: 90° ROTATIONS ON A COORDINATE PLANE

A **rotation** is a transformation that spins an object about a given center a given number of degrees.

24. Draw triangle ΔABC in the first quadrant of a new sheet of grid paper. Record the coordinates of the vertices of ΔABC, the pre-image, in a table like **Figure 4.39**.

Angle of Rotation	Pre-Image			Image		
	A	B	C	A′	B′	C′

FIGURE 4.39.
Table for Question 24.

25. Trace ΔABC and the coordinate axes onto another sheet of patty paper. Label the image A′B′C′.

26. Place the image on top of the original so that the coordinate axes are aligned. Rotate the copy 90° about the origin by turning the copy counterclockwise (**Figure 4.40**). Record the coordinates of the image in your table.

CHECK THIS!

In geometry, a rotation is counterclockwise if the angle is positive and clockwise if the angle is negative.

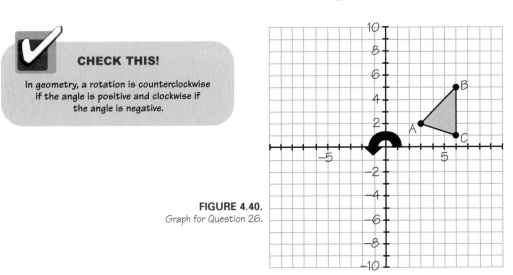

FIGURE 4.40.
Graph for Question 26.

27. Did the triangle change size or shape?

28. Repeat 26 and 27 for rotations of 180°, 270°, and 360°. Record the results in your table.

29. Describe a rotation by multiples of 90° in words.

Coordinate descriptions of rotations that are not multiples of 90° use trigonometry, so you will not do them now. Trigonometry is discussed in Chapter 8.

PART E:
GLIDE REFLECTIONS USING THE X-AXIS

Since glide reflections are a composite of a translation and a reflection they require a distance, a direction, and a line of reflection.

Conduct an investigation into glide reflections using the x-axis as the line of reflection. Proceed as you did in Parts A–D. Begin with a triangle drawn in one of the quadrants. Select a distance to translate it horizontally and a distance to translate it vertically. After you have translated it, reflect the image across the x-axis and record the results. Do the same for more triangles until you think you can answer Question 30.

30. Write equations that describe a glide reflection of the point (x, y) h units horizontally, k units vertically, and across the x-axis.

 Assignment

1. What are four types of isometries?

2. What are the basic attributes of translations?

3. What are the basic attributes of reflections?

4. What are the basic attributes of rotations?

5. Draw △ABC on your paper. If you reflect the triangle across any one of its sides, what shape is formed by combining the original triangle and the new triangle?

6. In **Figure 4.41**, which of these do not produce an image of the rectangle with two of its vertices lying on the *y*-axis?

   A. A reflection across the *x*-axis

   B. A translation right 3 units

   C. A translation up 2 units

   D. A reflection across the *y*-axis

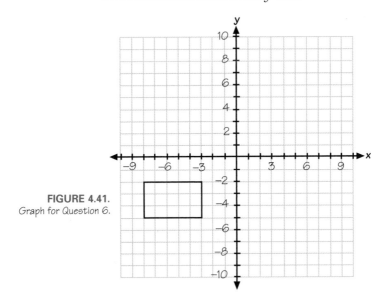

FIGURE 4.41.
Graph for Question 6.

7. In **Figure 4.42**, if triangle ΔABC is reflected across the *x*-axis, what are the coordinates of A'?

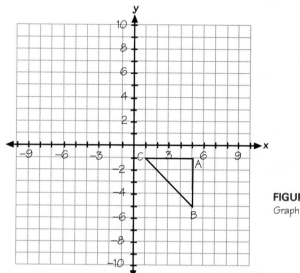

FIGURE 4.42.
Graph for Question 7.

8. In **Figure 4.43**, the vertices of a pre-image are at (−2, −2), (−1, −2), (−1, 0), and (−2, 0).

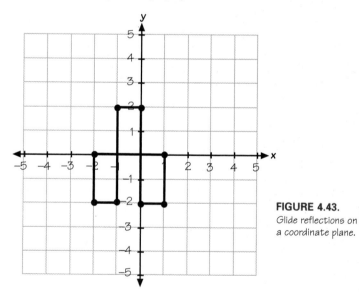

FIGURE 4.43.
Glide reflections on a coordinate plane.

a) Write equations that describe the use of a glide reflection to obtain another part of the figure.

b) Write equations that describe the use of a translation to obtain the remaining part of the figure.

Design a Logo

Create a graphic design for a corporate logo that incorporates translations, reflections, rotations, or glide reflections. The design should include elements of translation, rotation, and reflection symmetry.

Transfer your logo to a coordinate plane. Label points on the pre-image. Use algebraic notation to verify the accuracy of your use of symmetry to create your logo.

Write a short paragraph describing how and why each element of symmetry is incorporated into the design.

It's a Matter of Perspective

Artists, architects, illustrators, and animators are trained to draw objects and scenes. Their drawings need to be accurate and realistic. Small children have not received training to draw objects and scenes. A child's drawing may appear to be less accurate and realistic than the drawing of a trained artist.

Examine the picture assigned to your group by your teacher. Use **Figures 4.44 to 4.47** to answer the following questions:

1. What do you notice about this picture?

2. What do you notice about the sizes of the different objects in the picture?

3. What do you notice about the sizes of the different objects and their placement in the picture?

FIGURE 4.44.
Cave drawings similar to those found at Hamangala.

FIGURE 4.45.
Architectural rendering of a building.

Chapter 4 Art: Transformations, Symmetry, and Proportions

FIGURE 4.46.
Perspective Absurdities by William Hogarth.

FIGURE 4.47. Ancient Egyptian art.

4. Which pictures most accurately depict a real-life scene? Why?

5. Which pictures least accurately depict a real-life scene? Why?

The term perspective has several different meanings:

a) A view: "From what perspective are you looking down into the parking lot?"

b) A mental outlook: "What is your perspective on standardized dress codes for high school students?"

c) The relationship of parts to the whole: "What is the perspective on the soccer team's success this year? What role did the players play? What role did their training play? What role did the coach play?"

d) The technique of representing objects in three-dimensional space with a two-dimensional plane: "How does the artist use perspective to make a painting that looks like real life?"

6. Which paintings seem to make use of perspective?

Sometimes an artist may use perspective to get your attention. The painting shown in Figure 4.46 contains several intentional mistakes.

7. Work together with your group to identify the real-world inaccuracies in the painting by William Hogarth (Figure 4.46). Describe each error in detail.

8. Describe what the artist needs to do to correct each item you identified in Question 7.

Question 9 will help you identify elements or principles involved in perspective drawing.

9. Look at *The Bathers* by George Seurat (**Figure 4.48**). The artist has tried to represent a three-dimensional subject on a two-dimensional plane. The two-dimensional plane is the surface of the canvas or paper.

FIGURE 4.48.
The Bathers at Asnieres by George Seurat.

a) Imagine that your group is in a hot-air balloon floating over the subjects in this picture. Draw a bird's-eye view of what you would see. You don't have to sketch every detail. Just draw simple outlines of some of the objects in each picture and label them. (For example, you might use ovals labeled as dog, man lying down, man wearing hat, or sailboat to indicate objects.)

b) Explain what clues in the original picture helped you decide where to place particular objects in your drawing.

c) Discuss how the artist tried to convey depth.

SECTION 4.7

Location and Size

PART 1: WHAT'S IN THE FRONT?

In Section 4.6 you identified several factors that are important to the proper use of perspective in art. One of these is the location of objects with respect to each other: objects close to the viewer should overlap those that are behind them. Another factor is the relative size of objects. In this part of this section you will take a closer look at overlapping. In the second part you will take a closer look at size.

Within your group, use centimeter grid paper to create 4 cubes as described in the table in **Figure 4.49.**

Cube	Side Length (cm)
A	2
B	4
C	6
D	8

FIGURE 4.49.
Measurements of cubes.

Use masking tape or string to mark a 35 centimeter by 35 centimeter square region on a flat surface. Label the sides of the square north, south, east, and west.

Position the cubes according to the diagram shown in **Figure 4.50.**

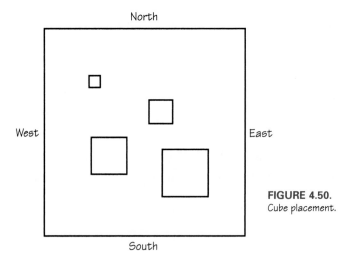

FIGURE 4.50.
Cube placement.

1. Lower yourself so that you are eye level with the cubes. Draw a two-dimensional sketch of what you see from the north, the south, the east, and the west.

2. How are the sketches alike?

3. How are the sketches different?

4. How does overlapping reveal which cube is in front of another cube?

5. **Figure 4.51** shows the top view of a table on which three cubes are sitting. Draw four eye level views of what you would see if you were sitting at positions A, B, C, and D.

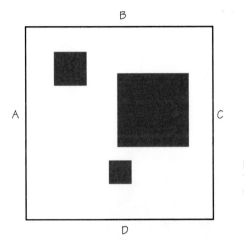

FIGURE 4.51.
Top view of three cubes on a table.

6. What statements can you make about how to draw images of objects so that the person looking at the image knows which objects are closer than other objects?

PART 2: THE RULER METHOD

In Part 1 you investigated the principle of overlapping: objects close to the viewer should overlap those that are behind them. You have also seen that objects far away from the viewer should be drawn smaller than objects close to the viewer. In this part you will take measurements of the size an object appears to be to a viewer.

❖ Hold a cube directly in front of you so all you see is a square.

❖ Move the cube toward you. What happens?

❖ Move the cube away from you. What happens?

❖ What general statement might we make about objects as they move farther away?

You will work with your group to take some measurements that illustrate numerically why objects appear to grow smaller as they move farther away.

Decide which member of your group will do each of the following:

❖ hold the ruler (holder)

❖ stand at a distance (stander)

❖ take measurements (measurer)

❖ record measurements (recorder)

The instructions that follow are written from the holder's point of view.

7. Hold a ruler in your hand, and extend your arm in front of you at eye level so that the ruler is vertical and your arm is extended fully (see **Figure 4.52**).

FIGURE 4.52.
Photograph showing how to hold the ruler.

8. The measurer should carefully measure the distance from your eye to the ruler.

9. Instruct a member of your group (the stander) to stand several meters away from you. The measurer should use a meter stick or tape measure to measure the distance between your eye and the other person.

10. Use the ruler in your extended hand to measure the apparent height of the other person (the height you would draw the person if the paper or canvas coincided with the ruler). See **Figure 4.53**.

FIGURE 4.53.
Measuring the apparent height of a person.

11. Record the measurements in a table like **Figure 4.54.**

Measure	Distance (eye to ruler)	Distance (eye to person)	Apparent Height of Person	Actual Height of Person
1				
2				
3				
4				

FIGURE 4.54.
Table for Question 11.

12. Complete the ratios in the table in **Figure 4.55.**

Measure	Distance Eye to Ruler / Apparent Height	Distance Eye to Person / Actual Height
1		
2		
3		
4		

FIGURE 4.55.
Table for Question 12.

13. What do you notice about the ratios of the measures?

14. **Figure 4.56** shows a viewer looking at a person. The picture plane represents the canvas or paper on which an artist draws or paints. Use the figure to explain your conclusion about ratios in Question 13.

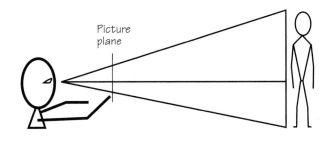

Picture plane

FIGURE 4.56. Image for Question 14.

Assignment

1. Look at Figure 4.45 on p. 215. Describe at least one object that overlaps another. Which of the two objects is closer to the viewer?

2. Refer to Hogarth's painting (see Figure 4.46 on p. 216). Describe where Hogarth violates the principle of overlapping.

3. **Figures 4.57 and 4.58** show the top view of two different tables on which three cubes are sitting.

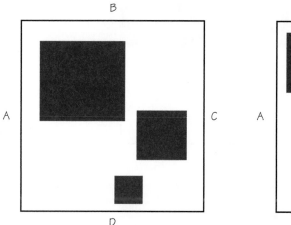

FIGURE 4.57.
Top view of three cubes on Table 1.

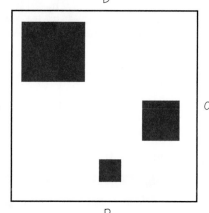

FIGURE 4.58.
Top view of three cubes on Table 2.

a) Look at the top view presented in Figure 4.57. Draw what you would see if you were sitting at position D.

b) Look at the top view presented in Figure 4.58. Draw what you would see if you were sitting at position D.

4. Martin built a cityscape using rectangular prisms. He made the following statements about his cityscape as viewed from eye level.

a) From the southern view, I see a model building that is 2 inches tall. Behind it is a model building that is 6 inches tall. To the right of the 2-inch model, I see a 4-inch tall model building.

b) From the eastern view, I see a model building that is 4 inches tall. To its right, I see a model building that is 3 inches tall. A 6-inch tall building stands behind this building.

c) From the northern view, I see a model building that is 4 inches tall that stands behind a 3-inch tall building. I also see a 6-inch tall building.

d) From the western view, I see a 6-inch tall building. I also see a 2-inch tall building with a 4-inch tall building behind it.

Sketch the four side views to scale and the top view that match Martin's description. Explain your thinking.

5. Tommy used cubes to build five models of buildings that are each 1 cube wide. The models are described in **Figures 4.59 and 4.60.**

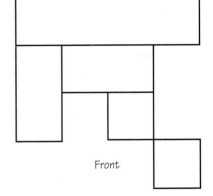

Building	Height (cubes)	Length (cubes)
A	1	4
B	2	2
C	4	1
D	3	1
E	1	2

FIGURE 4.59. Table for Question 5.

FIGURE 4.60. Top view.

How many possible arrangements of these five models match the top view? Sketch the front, right, and back views of each arrangement.

6. **Figure 4.61** is a sketch of your hand held up 2 feet in front of your eye.

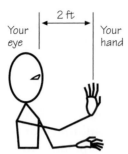

FIGURE 4.61. *Figure for Question 6.*

Suppose your hand is 7 inches long and just blocks out a friend who is 5′ 6″ tall.

a) Make a sketch showing your eye, your hand, and your friend. Show all of the given measurements in your figure.

b) How far from your eye is your friend standing? Explain how you got your answer.

Principles of Perspective: Diminution and Scale

In the last section you probably noticed that the farther an object is away from you the smaller it appears. This basic principle is called **diminution**.

Diminution

Look at the Seurat painting (Figure 4.48) and think about how he used diminution. For example, Seurat used the principle of diminution when he made people in the boat smaller than the people on the land. But he had to decide how much smaller to make them. The key to this decision lies in a technique called **scaling**. To help you see how scaling works you first need to know what is meant by **lines of sight**. You also need to recall a few facts about **similar triangles**.

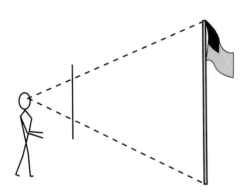

FIGURE 4.62.
Lines of sight to top and bottom of a flagpole.

Suppose a person is viewing a flagpole as shown in **Figure 4.62.** The dashed lines represent the lines of sight from the viewer's eye to the top and bottom of the flagpole. The vertical line in front of the viewer represents a canvas (the picture plane). The lines of sight intersect the picture plane to indicate where the top and bottom of the flagpole should be in a sketch made on the canvas.

Figure 4.62 shows two triangles. One of them is the small triangle with portions of the two lines of sight and the picture plane as sides. Another is the large triangle with the lines of sight and the flagpole as sides. These two triangles appear to be similar. That is, they appear to be the same shape, but of different sizes.

Mathematicians use the following conventions when discussing triangles:

❖ Vertices of triangles are labeled with capital letters.

❖ A side of a triangle is labeled with the same letter (but in lower case) as its opposite angle. For example, in **Figure 4.63**, side *a* is opposite angle A. A side can be named with the letters of its endpoints. Thus, side *a* is also referred to as $\overline{BC}$.

❖ An angle is named with the letter of its vertex. If two or more angles shared a vertex, three letters are used to name an angle. For example, ∠A can also be called ∠BAC.

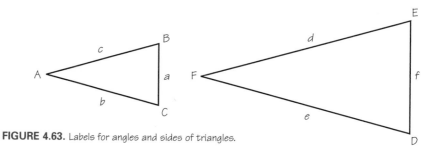

FIGURE 4.63. Labels for angles and sides of triangles.

In Figure 4.63, triangle ABC appears to be similar to triangle FED. Mathematicians write this statement with symbols: △ABC~△FED. When two triangles are similar, corresponding angles are congruent and ratios of corresponding sides are equal. For example, in Figure 4.63, if △ABC~△FED, then

❖ ∠A ≅ ∠F; ∠B ≅ ∠E; ∠C ≅ ∠D

❖ $\dfrac{AB}{FE} = \dfrac{BC}{ED} = \dfrac{AC}{FD}$.

Mathematicians have proved a theorem that is helpful in deciding whether two triangles are similar. It says that if two triangles have two pairs of congruent angles, then the triangles must be similar. The proof is based on the fact that the sum of the measure of any triangle's angles is always 180°.

CHECK THIS!

Although having all pairs of angles congruent makes triangles similar, the same is not true of other polygons. For example, a square and a rectangle have four pairs of congruent angles, but they are not similar.

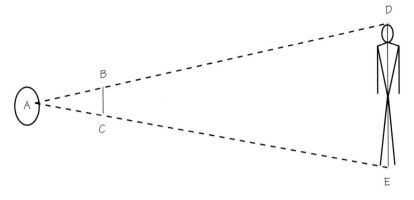

FIGURE 4.64.
Image for Question 1.

1. **Figure 4.64** shows a viewer's eye at A, lines of sight to the top (D) and bottom (E) of a person, and the points where the lines of sight cross the picture plane (B and C). What triangles are similar? Why?

2. In Question 1, what ratios must be equal?

The **scale** of an object in a picture is the ratio of the image height in the picture (the apparent height) to the actual height of the object. That is, the scale is the fraction $\frac{\text{apparent height}}{\text{actual height}}$.

3. In Figure 4.64, what ratio represents the scale?

In **Figure 4.65**, a line representing the distance from the viewer to the person being viewed has been added to Figure 4.64. This line creates an altitude in each triangle.

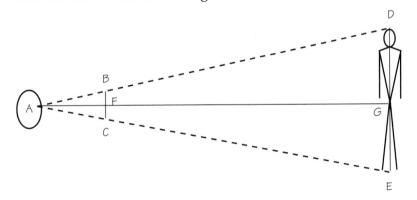

FIGURE 4.65.
Figure for Question 4.

 CHECK THIS!

An altitude of a triangle connects a vertex to the opposite side and is perpendicular to the opposite side.

Mathematicians have proved that corresponding altitudes of similar triangles have the same ratio as corresponding sides.

4. In Figure 4.65, what ratio of altitudes must equal the ratio $\frac{BC}{DE}$?

5. Suppose you are drawing on a canvas that is 2 feet in front of you. You use proper perspective to sketch an image 6 inches tall of an object that is really 3 feet tall.

   a) What is your drawing's scale?

   b) How far away are you from the object?

6. Suppose an object is 6 feet tall. You are 18 feet away from it, and you are sketching it on a canvas that is 2 feet in front of you. How tall should the object be in your picture?

In scaling an object to its proper size, an artist uses a mathematical transformation called **dilation**. A dilation uses a fixed point to project every point of a geometric figure. To an artist, the fixed point is the artist's eye. To a mathematician, the fixed point is the dilation's center.

Figure 4.66 shows a dilation of △ABC from point E that doubles the distance between E and each point of △ABC. △A′B′C′ is the image that results. For example, the distance from E to A′ is twice the distance from E to A. Since the distance from E to △ABC is doubled, the sides of △ABC are scaled by a factor of 2.

In a dilation, a segment's **scale factor** is the ratio $\frac{\text{length in image}}{\text{length in pre-image}}$.

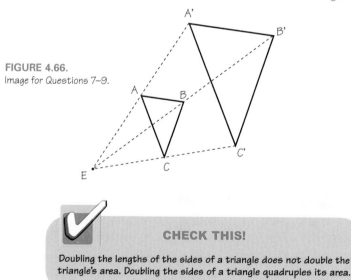

FIGURE 4.66.
Image for Questions 7–9.

CHECK THIS!

Doubling the lengths of the sides of a triangle does not double the triangle's area. Doubling the sides of a triangle quadruples its area.

7. Use rulers and protractors to confirm that ΔABC and ΔA′B′C′ are similar and that dilation doubles the lengths of ΔABC's sides.

8. Describe a dilation using point E that triples the lengths of ΔABC's sides. Trace ΔABC and point E onto a sheet of paper and perform the dilation.

9. Describe a dilation using point E that halves the lengths of ΔABC's sides. Trace ΔABC and point E onto a sheet of paper and perform the dilation.

Assignment

1. The Washington Monument is 169 meters high. How far should you stand from it to block it out with your hand? Assume your hand is 18 cm in length and the picture plane is 50 cm from your eye. Sketch the situation first. (Be careful with the units.)

2. Suppose you are sketching a tree on a piece of paper taped to an easel (see **Figure 4.67**). The paper is 2 feet from your eye. The tree is 10 feet high and 40 feet from your eye. How tall should you make the image of the tree on the paper?

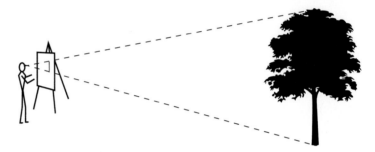

FIGURE 4.67.
Lines of sight for drawing a tree.

3. At many amusement parks and beaches, there are stores that take a photo, enlarge it, and give you a larger-than-life portrait suitable for framing. They also give you a small wallet-sized copy. **Figure 4.68** shows examples using stick pictures (not to the same scales).

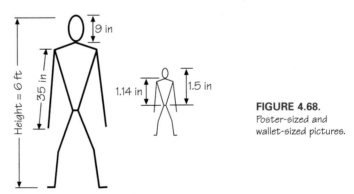

FIGURE 4.68.
Poster-sized and wallet-sized pictures.

a) Is enough information given to find the height of the smaller figure? If not, make up a reasonable value for the information you need.

b) Assume the leg length of the large portrait is 35 inches (so the torso length is 28 inches). Find the leg length and head height for the smaller figure.

c) What fraction of the large figure's height is in its legs? What fraction of the small figure's height is in its legs?

4. Trace **Figure 4.69** onto your paper. Sketch a side-doubling dilation of ΔABC using E as the center.

FIGURE 4.69.
Image for Question 4.

5. In Question 4, does the dilation produce a larger similar triangle if E is inside ΔABC? Does it matter where point E is located? Explain.

6. a) Since two triangles are similar if they have two pairs of congruent angles, two right triangles are similar if they have just one pair of congruent acute angles. Explain.

b) **Figure 4.70** shows a right triangle ABC with right angle at A and an altitude drawn from vertex A to the hypotenuse $\overline{BC}$. List all of the similar triangles. Be sure you have the vertices in proper correspondence.

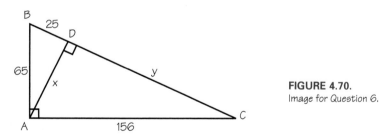

FIGURE 4.70.
Image for Question 6.

c) Use the fact that corresponding sides of similar triangles are proportional to find lengths x and y in Figure 4.70.

d) In Figure 4.70, ∠B measures approximately 67.4°. Find the measures of all the angles of the triangles.

A Parallel Universe (One-Point and Two-Point Perspective)

When you hold a cube at eye level so one face is parallel to your plane of vision, the cube looks like a square. If the cube is transparent, then you see the otherwise invisible sides and edges of the cube (see **Figure 4.71**).

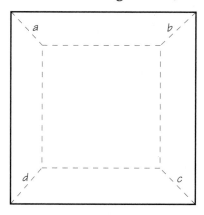

FIGURE 4.71.
Transparent cube.

1. The dotted lines represent the edges of the hidden faces. The edges labeled *a*, *b*, *c*, and *d* are perpendicular to the plane of vision.

   a) What do you notice about the vertical edges?

   b) How do the front and back faces compare?

   c) Why does the back face appear smaller than the front face of the cube?

   d) What do you notice about the top, bottom, and side faces?

   e) What do you notice about the edges labeled *a*, *b*, *c*, and *d*, which are perpendicular to the plane of vision?

FIGURE 4.72.
The inside of a hallway.

2. Refer to the picture of a hallway in **Figure 4.72.**

    a) There are several lines that run the length of the hallway. Select two of these lines. Place a ruler or edge of a paper along each of them. Describe where the two lines intersect.

    b) Repeat a using two lines that run the length of the ceiling. How does their intersection point compare to the intersection point of the floor lines?

In reality, the walls of the hallway in Figure 4.72 are parallel. Yet, in the picture the distance between the walls appears to narrow. If you imagine the walls were extended, they would converge to a single point. This is an example of the artistic principle of **convergence**: The apparent distance between parallel horizontal lines narrows. The single point to which the lines converge is called a **vanishing point**.

The vanishing point for horizontal lines is at the eye level of the viewer (see **Figure 4.73**). This eye level is called the **horizon line**—the line on which the earth and the sky appear to meet. The vanishing point for the railroad ties in Figure 4.73 is a point on the horizon.

FIGURE 4.73. The vanishing point is on the horizon at the eye level of the viewer.

A similar effect is visible when you look down the parallel rails of a railroad track. They also appear to converge in the distance (see **Figure 4.74**).

FIGURE 4.74.
Railroad tracks illustrate convergence.

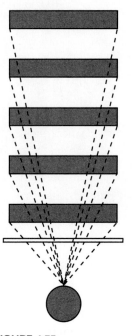

FIGURE 4.75.
Top view of person viewing
a series of railroad ties.

3. **Figure 4.75** is a top view of a person observing a railroad track and a series of equally spaced railroad ties. The lines of sight are drawn from the viewer to the ends of the first five ties.

a) To simplify the picture, the rails connecting the ties are not shown. Describe the relationship between the two rails in real life.

b) The **projection** of the first tie in the picture plane is almost as wide as the picture (see Figure 4.74). Compare the length of the projection of the fourth tie to the length of the projection of the first tie. How do they differ?

c) Describe the projection of the railroad tie that is as far as the eye can see from the viewer. (What does it look like? Where is it located in the picture plane?)

d) Each tie connects the parallel rails. What does your answer to c tell you about the images of the rails in the picture?

CHECK THIS!

In this chapter the projection of a
real object is its image on the
picture plane. The image is formed
by lines of sight from the viewer
to points on the object.

4. **Figure 4.76** is a side view of the same person viewing the first four railroad ties.

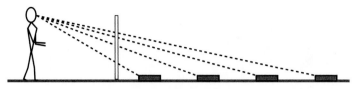

FIGURE 4.76.
Side view observing a series of equally spaced railroad ties.

a) The projection of the first tie appears near the bottom of the picture plane (see Figure 4.74). How is the location of the projection of the fourth tie different from the location of the projection of the first tie?

b) Describe the location in the picture plane of the tie (not shown) that is farthest from the viewer. Assume the ground is level.

Lines of sight may be drawn from a viewer to one or more objects in a scene. A line of sight that is parallel to the ground (assuming the ground is level) is said to be at the eye level of the viewer (see **Figure 4.77**).

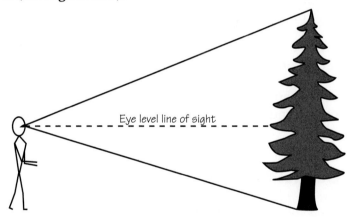

Eye level line of sight

FIGURE 4.77.
Sketch illustrating line of sight at the eye level of the viewer.

5. **Figure 4.78** shows an incomplete picture. The artist has drawn in the **horizon**, the horizontal line at the viewer's eye level where the earth and sky appear to meet. She has added two dots at the bottom of her picture to mark the edges of a roadway that she plans to sketch.

a) Where in the picture do you expect to find the portion of roadway that is as far as the eye can see: above the horizon, below the horizon, or on the horizon? How large will it appear?

Horizon

FIGURE 4.78.
Incomplete picture of roadway.

Roadway

b) Trace a copy of Figure 4.78. Sketch the roadway for the artist. What assumptions did you make about the viewer's location in relation to your roadway?

FIGURE 4.79.
Print Shop Interior by Jan van der Straet.

6. a) On Handout 4.1, which is the same as **Figure 4.79**, draw lines along all edges that represent lines parallel to the center aisle. Extend the lines to identify the locations of any corresponding vanishing points.

b) What is true of the vanishing points for sets of parallel lines from various objects in Figure 4.79? Explain.

Next, you will apply what you have learned about the principles of diminution and convergence to drawings with two vanishing points.

THE CORNER STONE

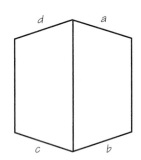

FIGURE 4.80.
View of cube looking directly at a vertical edge.

7. Hold a cube so that the top and bottom are parallel to the ground and one face is parallel to your plane of vision. Keeping the bottom of the cube parallel to the ground, rotate the cube so that no face is parallel to your plane of vision.

a) Trace a copy of **Figure 4.80** onto paper.

b) Which pairs of edges in Figure 4.80 are, in reality, parallel? How is the principle of convergence apparent in the sketch of the rotated cube?

c) For the cube in Figure 4.80, there are two vanishing points. Draw them on your copy of Figure 4.80.

d) The vanishing point is on the horizon for horizontal lines that increase in distance from the viewer. You have drawn two vanishing points in c. Are there two horizons? Explain.

8. a) Locate the vanishing points and horizon in **Figures 4.81 and 4.82.** Draw the vanishing points and horizon on Handout 4.2 provided by your teacher.

FIGURE 4.81.
Photograph for Question 8.

FIGURE 4.82.
Painting for Question 8.

b) How many vanishing points are there? How do you know?

9. Practice drawing a rectangular box using two vanishing points. Use pencil and paper or a geometric drawing utility. Begin with a drawing that looks similar to **Figure 4.83.** Notice the box is drawn entirely below the horizon.

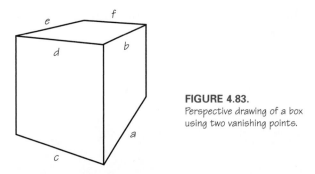

FIGURE 4.83.
Perspective drawing of a box using two vanishing points.

a) Why does edge *e* appear to converge to the same vanishing point as edges *a* and *b*?

b) Why does edge *f* appear to converge to the same vanishing point as edges *c* and *d*?

c) In Figure 4.83, you see two sides and the top of the box. Why is the artist able to see the top of the box in Figure 4.83 but not in Figure 4.80?

d) Describe what happens to the drawing of the box when you bring the two vanishing points closer together.

e) Describe what happens to the drawing of the box when you move the two vanishing points farther apart.

10. Revisit the painting by William Hogarth (Figure 4.46 on p. 216). How many vanishing points do you observe? Describe where they are located and explain how you found them.

1. Draw lines of convergence and identify the vanishing points for **Figure 4.84.**

FIGURE 4.84.
*Le Pont de l'Europe 1876
by Gustave Caillebotte.*

2. a) Find the vanishing point for **Figure 4.85.** Use Handout 4.3 provided by your teacher.

   b) Is the vanishing point in the center of the picture, to the right of center, or to the left of center? Is the vanishing point inside or outside of the bounds of the picture?

3. Revisit Figure 4.79 on p. 236. Draw the horizon line using a different color pen from the one used to draw the lines of convergence.

4. Revisit Figure 4.85. Draw the horizon line using a different color pen from the one you used in Question 2.

FIGURE 4.85.
The Flatiron Building.

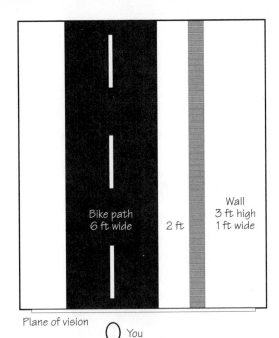

FIGURE 4.86. Aerial view.

Bike path
6 ft wide

2 ft

Wall
3 ft high
1 ft wide

Plane of vision

You

5. **Figure 4.86** shows an aerial view of a scene.

 a) Draw a perspective view of the same scene with one vanishing point.

 b) Suppose power poles are in line with the viewer's line of sight to the vanishing point on the horizon. Describe what the viewer sees. What principle(s) of perspective is (are) responsible for this phenomenon?

6. Optical illusions can be created when the principle of diminution or the principle of convergence is violated.

 a) Describe the effect of not reducing the height of a series of objects and not reducing the spacing between the objects as other objects converge to the vanishing point or points (see **Figure 4.87**).

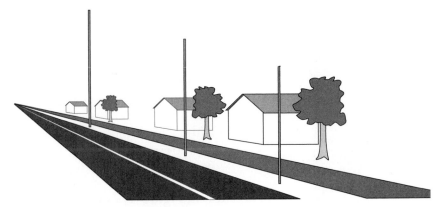

FIGURE 4.87.
Drawing for 6a.

 b) Describe the effect of not reducing the height but allowing the spacing between the objects to agree with principles of perspective (see **Figure 4.88**).

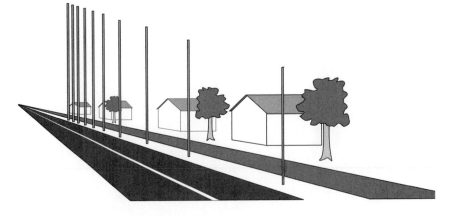

FIGURE 4.88.
Drawing for 6b.

c) Explain how the B.C. cartoon in **Figure 4.89** violates a principle of perspective drawing.

FIGURE 4.89.
B.C. cartoon.

7. **Figure 4.90** shows a sketch of a room containing three rectangles representing a chest, a large wardrobe, and an air purification unit. The drawings of the objects are incomplete. Only the sides facing the viewer are sketched.

a) Trace Figure 4.90 onto paper. Complete the perspective drawings of the chest, wardrobe, and air purification unit so that they appear to have depth. What principles of perspective did you use to guide your drawing?

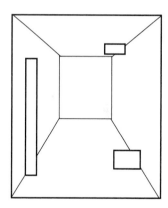

FIGURE 4.90. Incomplete drawing of room containing three objects.

b) In your completed drawing, you should be able to see the top of one of the rectangles and the bottom of another. For the third object, you should be able to see neither its top nor its bottom. What determines whether the viewer can see the top or the bottom of an object in a perspective drawing? Under what conditions are both the top and the bottom of an object not visible to the viewer?

8. **Figure 4.91** shows the front view of a cottage. Draw the cottage in perspective with two vanishing points.

FIGURE 4.91.
Front view of cottage.

9. Eight-year old Jackson Barber drew the picture in **Figure 4.92.** It does not adhere to the principles of perspective. Draw the same scene on your own paper using principles of perspective and two vanishing points.

FIGURE 4.92.
Child's drawing that does not conform to principles of perspective.

Setting Your Sights

FIGURE 4.93.
Trees lining a roadway.

1. In **Figure 4.93** you see a photograph of a roadway.

   a) What do you notice about the lines that form the sides of the road in the picture?

   b) Next, focus on the trees on the right side of the road. Suppose you draw a line connecting the treetops (assume the trees are approximately the same height) and another line connecting the tree bottoms. What would you notice about these lines?

   c) Use the rulers that surround the picture to identify the location of the vanishing point for the lines joining the tops of the trees and the bottoms of the trees. Then imagine drawing a horizontal line through that vanishing point. What does this horizontal line represent?

   d) The shoulders of the road extend beyond the white lines on both edges of the road. Pretend a ladder is placed from the edge of the shoulder to the top of each tree, forming a triangle. Describe the triangles that result from doing this with each tree.

e) Sketch a top view of the road. (Use circles to indicate the trees.) What should be true of the lines that form the sides of the road? What about the lines connecting the treetops and tree bottoms?

FIGURE 4.94.
Chemin de la Machine, Louveciennes by Alfred Sisley.

2. a) On Handout 4.4, which is the same as **Figure 4.94**, draw lines marking the sides of the road and along the treetops on either side of the road. Draw lines along the roofs of buildings on the right side of the road.

   b) What is true of these lines? Explain.

3. **Figure 4.95** shows two roads meeting at an intersection. You are an architect, and your client wants to build an office at the corner opposite where the viewer is standing. Draw Figure 4.95 on your own paper, or use Handout 4.5 provided by your teacher.

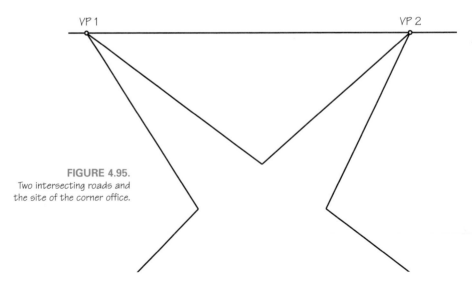

FIGURE 4.95.
Two intersecting roads and the site of the corner office.

a) Make a detailed drawing showing what the office will look like when it is constructed. Include windows, doors, and a sign on the building. (For an extra challenge, try drawing a sloped roof rather than a flat roof.)

b) What is the effect if the vanishing points are brought closer together or moved farther apart? Draw sketches to illustrate your answer.

c) What would have to change in the context to increase the apparent distance between the vanishing points?

Modeling Project It's a Masterpiece!

In this chapter you have seen a number of ways artists use mathematics to create art. Now it is *your* turn. Use tools you have developed in this chapter to create an original piece of art. This drawing or painting should use the principles of symmetry, overlapping, and diminution. While the subjects of the art can be anything you would like to draw, including an architectural drawing of a building or objects around your home and school, your drawing should include notes that describe how you used mathematics to transform your objects in order to create patterns and give the drawing depth. These notes should include the types of transformations you used to create your work and details like the scale factors you chose and why.

For a twist on this project, revisit the Hogarth painting (Figure 4.46 on p. 216) and create your own impossible drawing. Instead of your notes explaining how you used mathematics to create the image, your notes should explain how you could use mathematics to "fix" your drawing.

Finally, be creative and have fun. Be ready to share your drawing with the class and answer questions about your work.

Practice Problems

1. In each of these figures, identify a basic element and describe ways to get the other sections of the figure by applying one or more of the transformations you studied in this chapter. Your basic element should be as small a portion of the entire figure as possible.

a)

b)

c)

d)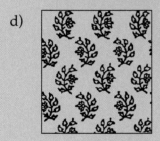

e)

f)

2. The natural world has many examples of symmetry (although it is usually not perfect). Describe the lines of symmetry and the types of symmetry in each of these photos of living things.

3. Three spheres are arranged on a table.

   a) **Figure 4.97** shows the top view. Draw the views from A and B. What principle of perspective did you use in your drawing?

Table

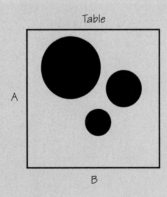

A

B

FIGURE 4.97.
Three spheres arranged on a table.

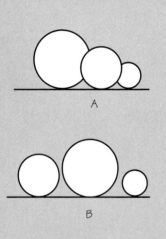

A

B

FIGURE 4.98.
Side views of the rearranged spheres.

   b) Suppose the spheres are rearranged. Views from sides A and B are shown in **Figure 4.98**. Draw an overhead view of the table. Explain how you arrived at your answer.

4. In each of these questions, suppose a ruler is held at arm's length so the plane of vision is 27 inches from the eye of the viewer.

a) You are 100 yards away from the goalpost on a football field. The image height of the goalpost is 1.6 inches. How high are the goalposts?

b) Close to shore on the opposite side of a lake is a tower that is 50 feet tall. The image height of the tower is 1 inch. How wide is the lake?

c) A certain basketball player stands 86 inches tall. You are standing under the basket and he is attempting a free throw, which means he is about 18 feet from you. How tall is his image?

5. **Figure 4.99** shows the top view of a person looking at five railroad ties.

a) Measure the length of each projection in the picture plane. Then measure the distance between each tie and the viewer's eye. Record your measurements in a table like **Figure 4.100**.

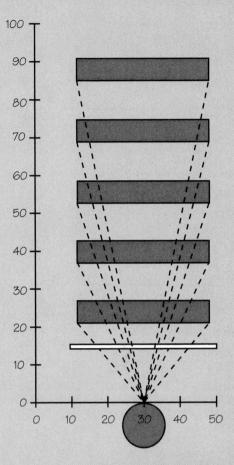

FIGURE 4.99.
Top view of person looking at railroad ties.

Tie Number	1	2	3	4	5
Distance to Viewer's Eye					
Projection Length					

FIGURE 4.100. Table for recording railroad tie lengths and distances.

b) Based on your measurements, describe the relationship between the length of the projection of each tie and its distance from the viewer's eye.

c) Graph your data. Label the horizontal axis distance to eye and label the vertical axis projection length. Describe the shape of your plot.

6. a) Copy **Figure 4.101** on your own paper and label the unlabeled sides and vertices according to mathematical convention.

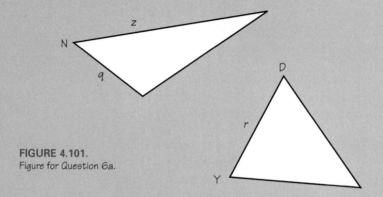

FIGURE 4.101.
Figure for Question 6a.

b) For each of the triangles in **Figure 4.102**, how long is the side opposite angle V?

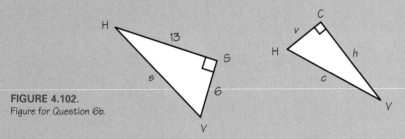

FIGURE 4.102.
Figure for Question 6b.

7. Three equal-height poles are to be placed 100 feet apart, increasing in distance from the viewer. Which drawing (see **Figure 4.103**) seems to be the best representation? Explain your answer.

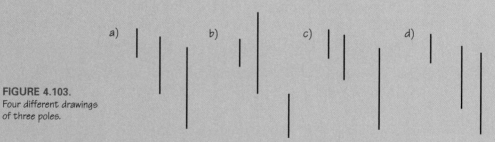

FIGURE 4.103.
Four different drawings of three poles.

8. **Figure 4.104** is a perspective view of a hallway.

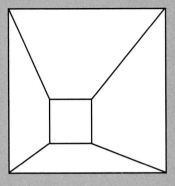

FIGURE 4.104.
Perspective view of hallway.

a) Trace a copy of Figure 4.104 on your own paper. Determine the vanishing point and the horizon line.

b) Raise the vanishing point and move it to the right. Redraw the hallway using the new vanishing point.

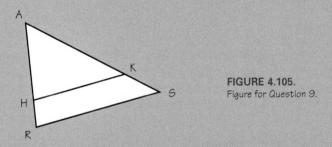

FIGURE 4.105.
Figure for Question 9.

9. In **Figure 4.105**, RS is parallel to HK.

a) Which angles have equal measure?

b) What is the relationship between triangles ARS and AHK? Explain.

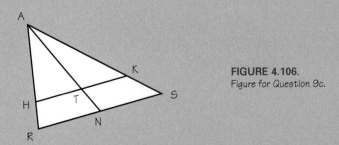

FIGURE 4.106.
Figure for Question 9c.

c) **Figure 4.106** was created by adding the line segment AN to Figure 4.105. Segment AN bisects segment HK. Explain why it must also bisect RS.

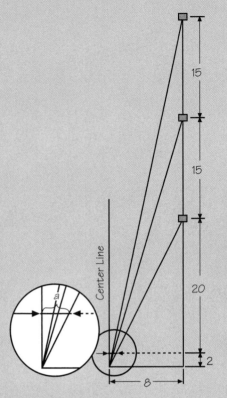

10. Suppose you want to draw accurately a series of poles that support a cover above a walkway. **Figure 4.107** shows a top view of the poles in relation to the artist and the plane of vision. The artist chooses a viewing position 8 feet to the left of the line of poles and 22 feet from the first pole that is to be drawn in the picture. The 9-foot poles are 15 feet apart. The distance between the artist's eye and the picture plane is 2 feet.

a) The center line is an imaginary line from the artist's eye to the vanishing point. In a top view, this line is parallel to the line of poles. Describe the relationship in a perspective drawing between (1) the center line and (2) a line drawn through the poles at the artist's eye height. If drawn, how would the center line appear in the picture?

b) In the drawing, what is the scale at the first pole? At the second pole? At the third pole?

c) What is the image size of Pole 1? What are the image sizes of Pole 2 and Pole 3?

d) Determine the horizontal distance *a*, the distance between the image of Pole 1 and the center line. How can you use the scale at Pole 1 to determine this distance?

e) Determine the horizontal distance *b*, the distance between the image of Pole 2 and the imaginary center line.

f) Determine the horizontal distance *c*, the distance between the image of Pole 3 and the imaginary center line.

Glossary

KEY CONCEPTS

Convergence: Artistic principle asserting that lines or edges of objects that in reality are parallel appear to come together as they recede from the observer.

Corresponding angles: Angles in corresponding positions within similar figures. Corresponding angles are equal in measure.

Dilation: A transformation in which the distance to every point's image is exactly k times its original distance from some specified, fixed point. The fixed point is called the center of the dilation; k is the scale factor for the dilation.

Diminution: The phenomenon by which an object appears smaller as its distance from the observer increases.

Glide reflection: A composite of translation and reflection. A glide reflection reverses a figure's orientation.

Horizon Line: The imaginary line on the plane of vision (or picture plane) containing the vanishing points of all horizontal (in reality, parallel to the ground) converging lines. It is always on the same level as the viewer's eyes (the eye level).

Hypotenuse: The side opposite the right angle of a right triangle. It is the longest side in the right triangle.

Image: In transformations, a new object created by transforming a pre-image.

Isometry: A transformation that preserves size and shape.

Line of Sight: An imaginary line between the viewer's eye and a point on a three-dimensional object being observed.

Line of Symmetry: A line that divides a figure into two identical mirror images.

One-Point Perspective: Occurs with only one family of horizontal parallel lines not parallel to the plane of vision; all the lines converge to a single vanishing point located on the horizon line.

Overlapping: A technique to achieve a sense of depth and space in drawings by showing which objects are in front and which are in back.

Perspective: A technique of representing objects from three-dimensional space in a two-dimensional plane, like a picture. Through the use of perspective, an artist's two-dimensional drawing or painting imitates the appearance of a three-dimensional object or scene.

Plane of Vision (or Picture Plane): An imaginary plane between the observer and the three-dimensional object(s) being viewed. The image of the object is projected onto the plane. In this chapter the picture plane is always vertical.

Point Symmetry: A figure has point symmetry when it fits exactly on itself after a rotation of 180°.

Pre-image: When a geometric object is transformed into another one, the original is called a pre-image.

Projection: The projection of a real object is its image on the picture plane. The image is formed by lines of sight from the viewer to points on the object.

Pythagorean Formula: A formula relating the lengths of three sides of a right triangle: $a^2 + b^2 = c^2$, where c is the length of the hypotenuse and a and b are the lengths of the other two sides (legs).

Reflection: A transformation that flips a figure across a line. A reflection reverses a figure's orientation.

Reflection (line) Symmetry: When a figure fits exactly on itself after reflection through a line. The line divides the figure into two identical halves.

Rotation: A transformation that spins a figure about a given center a given number of degrees.

Rotation Symmetry: When a figure fits exactly on itself after it spins less than 360° about a center.

Scale: The ratio of an image size (height or width) in a picture to the actual size of the object.

Scale Factor: In a dilation, the ratio of the new lengths to the old lengths.

Similar Triangles: Two triangles are similar when they have equal corresponding angles and equal ratios of corresponding sides.

Transformation: A process that creates a new figure from an original. The original is called the pre-image; the new figure is called the image.

Translation: A transformation that slides a figure a given distance in a given direction.

Two-Point Perspective: Occurs with exactly two families of horizontal parallel lines not parallel to the plane of vision; all the lines converge to one of two vanishing points located on the horizon line.

Vanishing Point: The imaginary point to which parallel lines not in the plane of vision appear to converge.

5
CHAPTER

Motion: Quadratic Functions

It's Show Time

You may have watched scenes like these in the movies:

The star jumps off a roof and lands in the back of a passing truck.

During a chase the star speeds down the street on a motorcycle, through a cross street and just misses a truck.

Auto thrill shows also do stunts using cars and trucks. Jeff Lattimore's stunt in Chittwood's Thrill Show is "The Leap for Life." Jeff has performed it for years. In his stunt Jeff climbs a ladder and stands on an eight-foot stool. Then the ladder is removed leaving Jeff in the air just as a car comes speeding at him. Jeff jumps right before the car hits the stool and knocks it out from under him. Jeff lands safely on the ground.

Since this stunt is complicated, trial-and-error would be a poor method. A mistake could result in loss of life. Using mathematics and understanding the laws of physics are key to planning stunts.

In this chapter you'll see functions that model motion. You'll use mathematical models to predict where an object will be at a specific time. Then you'll use the models to plan and test a small-scale stunt in your class.

Walking the Walk

In this section you will look at distance-versus-time graphs. For these graphs, you will consider time as the independent variable and distance as the dependent variable.

A motion detector can track a student walking toward or away from it. The motion detector along with a graphing calculator can be used to create a distance-versus-time graph of a student walk.

Imagine a student walking away from a motion detector.

1. As time increases, what happens to the student's distance from the motion detector?

2. Imagine a distance-versus-time graph of the walk. Would you expect the graph to be a straight line or a curved line? Why?

3. Would you expect the graph to increase or decrease from left to right? Why?

Use a motion detector and a graphing calculator to collect data and create a distance-versus-time graph for a classmate who walks away from the motion detector.

Sketch your graph.

4. How can you tell from the graph that the student was walking away from the motion detector?

5. Was the student walking at a constant rate? How can you tell from the graph?

Again use a motion detector and a graphing calculator to collect data and create a distance-versus-time graph for a second classmate who walks away from the motion detector.

Sketch your graph.

A sample graph is shown in **Figure 5.1.**

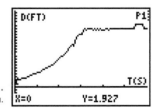

FIGURE 5.1.
A sample distance-versus-time graph.

6. How can you tell from the graph that the second student was walking away from the motion detector?

7. Was the second student walking at a constant rate? How can you tell from the graph?

Now you will analyze data taken from student walks in front of a motion detector. When you track the walk of another student, you can see how you would have to walk to produce the same distance-versus-time graph.

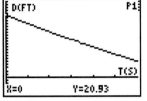

Cara walked in a straight line in front of a motion detector. The motion detector recorded her distance from it every 0.1 second for 6 seconds. Cara's distance-versus-time graph appears in **Figure 5.2.**

FIGURE 5.2.
Cara's distance-versus-time graph.

8. Based on Figure 5.2, did Cara walk toward or away from the motion detector? How can you tell from her graph?

9. Did she begin moving as soon as the motion detector began collecting data or did she pause first? How can you tell from her graph?

10. After she began moving, did she walk at a constant rate, or did she speed up or slow down? Explain how you decided.

11. What plan could you give to a walker so that he or she could walk a graph that is the same as Cara's?

12. Using your group's plans, have one group member walk in front of a motion detector. Is the graph of the walk close to the graph of Cara's walk?

13. How can you modify your plans so that the walk will more closely model Cara's walk?

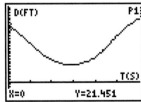

Paul walked in a straight line in front of a motion detector. The motion detector recorded his distance from it every 0.1 second for 6 seconds. Paul's distance-versus-time graph appears in **Figure 5.3.**

FIGURE 5.3.
Paul's distance-versus-time graph.

14. Based on Figure 5.3, did Paul walk toward or away from the motion detector? How can you tell from his graph?

15. After he began moving, did he walk at a constant rate, or did he speed up or slow down? Explain how you decided.

16. What rules could you give to a walker so he or she could walk a graph like Paul's?

17. Using your group's rules, have one group member walk in front of a motion detector. Is the graph of the walk like the graph of Paul's walk?

18. How can you modify your rules so that the walk will more closely model Paul's walk?

19. What differences in Cara's and Paul's walks caused the differences in the two graphs?

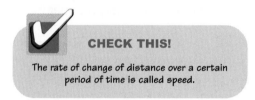

CHECK THIS!

The rate of change of distance over a certain period of time is called speed.

Linear versus Non-Linear

In the last section you saw graphs created by students walking in a straight line in front of a motion detector. Cara's graph was close to a straight line while Paul's graph was curved.

In this section you will compare data that create a straight line (a linear relationship) with data that create a curved graph (a quadratic relationship).

CHECK THIS!

A linear relationship has a constant rate of change and is represented by a function of the form $f(x) = mx + b$.

CHECK THIS!

A quadratic relationship has a variable rate of change and is represented by a function of the form $f(x) = ax^2 + bx + c$.

Victoria walked in front of a motion detector. Some of the data are shown in **Figure 5.4.**

Time, t (seconds)	Distance, d (feet)
0	2
1	5
2	8
3	11
4	14
5	17

FIGURE 5.4.
Data from Victoria's walk.

Ricardo also walked in front of a motion detector. Some of the data recorded by the motion detector for his walk are shown in **Figure 5.5.**

Time, t (seconds)	Distance, d (feet)
0	25
1	15
2	9
3	7
4	9
5	15

FIGURE 5.5.
Data from Ricardo's walk.

1. What do you see in the data for Victoria's and Ricardo's walks?

2. Use your graphing calculator to create a distance-versus-time scatterplot of Victoria's data. Record your window and sketch your graph.

3. Use your graphing calculator to create a distance-versus-time scatterplot of Ricardo's data. Record your window and sketch your graph.

4. What do you see in the graphs for Victoria's and Ricardo's walks?

5. What do you think might be a cause of the differences in the graphs?

One tool to help develop representation of a function is differences in consecutive table values.

Let's look at the first and second differences in the two tables.

CHECK THIS!

First difference is the change from one table value to the next.

CHECK THIS!

Second difference is the change from one first difference to the next.

6. Find the first and second differences in the table values for Victoria's walk. Record them in a table like the one in **Figure 5.6.**

Time (seconds)	Distance (feet)	First Difference	Second Difference
0	2		
+1		—	
1	5		—
+1		—	
2	8		—
+1		—	
3	11		—
+1		—	
4	14		—
+1		—	
5	17		

FIGURE 5.6.
Differences for Victoria's walk.

7. What patterns do you see?

The function that models Victoria's walk where d is distance and t is time is $d = 3t + 2$. Recall that an equation in this form ($y = mx + b$) has a linear graph where m is the slope of the line and b is the y-intercept.

8. Look at the table with differences for Victoria's walk. Where do you see the number 3? What does 3 represent here?

9. Look at the table with differences for Victoria's walk. Where do you see the number 2? What does 2 represent here?

10. How do you think the first and second differences in a table of data can be represented by a linear function?

11. Explain how you think first differences relate to the function rule.

12. Find the first and second differences in the table values for Ricardo's walk. Record them in a table like the one in **Figure 5.7.**

13. What patterns do you see?

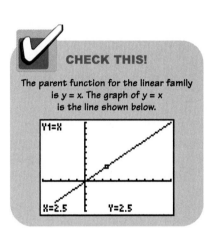

Time (seconds)	Distance (feet)	First Difference	Second Difference
0	25		
+1		—	
1	15		—
+1		—	
2	9		—
+1		—	
3	7		—
+1		—	
4	9		—
+1		—	
5	15		

FIGURE 5.7.
Differences for Ricardo's walk.

The equation for the function that models Ricardo's walk where d is distance and t is time is $d = 2t^2 - 12t + 25$. Recall that $y = ax^2 + bx + c$ where $a \neq 0$ is a **quadratic function**. Quadratic functions are often used to model relationships in the real world such as distance versus time and area versus length. The graph of a quadratic function is U-shaped and is called a **parabola**. The point at which the graph changes between increasing and decreasing is called the **vertex**.

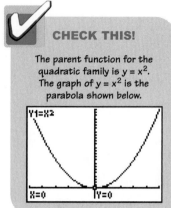
14. Look at the table for Ricardo's walk. What is the relationship between the second differences and the number 2, the coefficient of t^2, in $d = 2t^2 - 12t + 25$?

15. Look at the table for Ricardo's walk. Where do you see the number 25? What does 25 represent here?

16. Look at the table for Ricardo's walk. How does the first, first difference compare to the coefficients of t^2 and t in $d = 2t^2 - 12t + 25$?

17. How can the first and second differences in a table of data be represented by a quadratic function?

18. How do the first and second differences relate to the function rule that models the data in a quadratic relationship?

19. In **Figure 5.8,** one of the tables represents a linear function while the other one shows a quadratic function. Without graphing, find which one is linear and which one is quadratic. How did you decide?

FIGURE 5.8.
Two tables of x- and y-values.

Table 1

x	y
0	0
1	2
2	4
3	6
4	8

Table 2

x	y
0	0
1	2
2	8
3	18
4	32

20. Use the first and second differences in Table 1 to write a function rule.

21. Use the first and second differences in Table 2 to write a function rule.

Assignment

INTERPRETING MOTION GRAPHS

The first graph in **Figure 5.9** was recorded when Jasmyne walked in front of a motion detector. The program recorded time in seconds and distance in feet. The TRACE feature of her calculator was used to find the distance for 0.9, 2.9, and 4.9 seconds (the other three graphs).

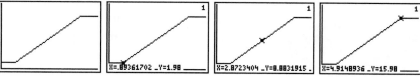

FIGURE 5.9. *Graph of Jasmyne's walk.*

1. How far was Jasmyne from the motion detector when the program began running?

2. How many seconds did Jasmyne stand still before moving?

3. How much time did Jasmyne spend walking?

4. How far did she walk?

5. During the time that Jasmyne was walking, did she walk at a constant rate, increase her speed, or decrease her speed?

6. During the time that Jasmyne was walking, at what rate did she walk?

7. The two graphs in **Figure 5.10** were recorded by a motion detector when a student walked in front of it. Assuming the scales are the same for both graphs, in which case was the student walking faster? Explain your answer.

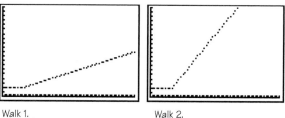

Walk 1. Walk 2.

FIGURE 5.10.
Two walks recorded by a motion detector.

A motion detector can be used to create a distance-versus-time graph for a toy car.

8. Imagine a toy car moving along a straight line in front of a motion detector. The motion produces a distance-versus-time graph that is a straight line. What does this tell you about the toy car's rate?

9. How could you determine the toy car's rate?

10. Suppose that the distance-versus-time graph has a negative slope. What does that tell you about the car's motion?

11. Suppose that a toy car is traveling along a straight line in front of a motion detector. The motion produces a distance-versus-time graph that is curved. What does this tell you about the car's rate? Explain.

Suppose a movie stunt calls for a person to step off a roof as soon as a truck reaches a white line painted across a road. To design such a stunt, you need to calculate details about the person's fall. For example, you need to know how long it would take for the person to land on the ground.

12. Imagine that a stunt person steps off a roof 25 feet above the ground and falls vertically to the ground. Sketch a possible height-versus-time graph for the falling body. Add scales and labels to your axes.

13. Explain why the stunt person will fall as you have shown in your graph.

14. How might you collect data that would help you decide whether your graph does a good job of describing the stunt person's fall?

Jackie and Jermaine drew the graphs in **Figure 5.11** as part of their answers to Question 12.

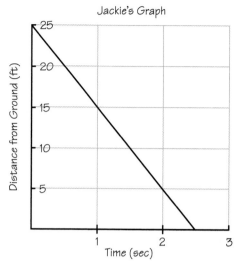

Jackie's Graph

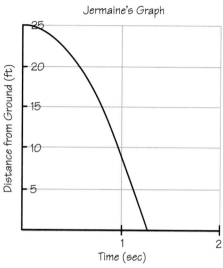

Jermaine's Graph

FIGURE 5.11.
Jackie's and
Jermaine's graphs.

15. Suppose these graphs show the motion of a walker in front of a motion detector. Write a plan for a walker so that the graph would look like Jackie's.

16. Write rules for a walker so that the graph would look like Jermaine's.

A motion detector tracked Rashida as she jogged. Some of the data are shown in **Figure 5.12.** Create a scatterplot of the distance-versus-time data. Be sure to add labels and scales to your axes.

17. Sketch and describe the shape of Rashida's graph.

18. Did Rashida jog at a steady pace, speed up, or slow down? How can you tell from the graph?

19. Use first and second differences to find a rule. Test your rule over your scatterplot. Write your rule and sketch the graph.

Time (seconds)	Distance from Sensor (feet)
0	2
1	3.15
2	6.8
3	12.95
4	21.6
5	32.75
6	46.4
7	62.55
8	81.2

FIGURE 5.12.
Distance-versus-time
data for Rashida's walk.

Characteristics of Quadratic Functions

In the last section you explored linear and quadratic relationships. In this section you will formalize how and why those relationships work the way they do.

Recall the student walks in front of a motion detector.

1. Describe a walk that creates a linear relationship.

2. Describe a walk that creates a non-linear relationship.

3. Describe a walk that creates a linear relationship with a positive slope.

4. Describe a walk that creates a linear relationship with a negative slope.

5. Describe a walk that has a graph similar in shape to a parabola.

As you discovered in the last section, the use of first and second differences is a good tool to develop a function rule.

Let's take a closer look at linear and quadratic relationships.

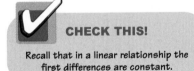

CHECK THIS!

Recall that in a linear relationship the first differences are constant.

6. In a linear relationship, how are the first differences related to the function rule?

7. In a linear relationship, how are the first differences related to the graph of the function rule?

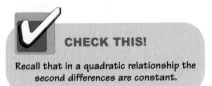

CHECK THIS!

Recall that in a quadratic relationship the second differences are constant.

8. In a quadratic relationship, how are the first differences related to the graph of the function rule?

9. In a quadratic relationship, how are the second differences related to the function rule?

x	$y = ax^2 + bx + c$	First Differences	Second Differences
0	$a \cdot 0^2 + b \cdot 0 + c = c$		
		$a + b + c - c = \quad a + b$	
1	$a \cdot 1^2 + b \cdot 1 + c = a + b + c$		$2a$
		$4a + 2b + c - (a + b + c) = \quad 3a + b$	
2	$a \cdot 2^2 + b \cdot 2 + c = 4a + 2b + c$		$2a$
		$9a + 3b + c - (4a + 2b + c) = \quad 5a + b$	
3	$a \cdot 3^2 + b \cdot 3 + c = 9a + 3b + c$		$2a$
		$16a + 4b + c - (9a + 3b + c) = \quad 7a + b$	
4	$a \cdot 4^2 + b \cdot 4 + c = 16a + 4b + c$		

FIGURE 5.13.
Quadratic differences table.

10. Notice that the first of the first differences in **Figure 5.13** is equal to $a + b$ and the second difference is equal to $2a$. How can you use these facts to develop a quadratic model?

11. Use these facts to justify the quadratic model, $d = 2t^2 - 12t + 25$, for Ricardo's walk in Section 5.2.

12. Use first and second differences to find a function rule for each data set.

a)

x	y
0	2
1	10
2	24
3	44
4	70

b)

x	y
0	4
1	6
2	8
3	10
4	12

SUMMARY

Using differences can help write a function rule for linear or quadratic data. Assume that the difference between consecutive x-values in the table is constant. If the relationship is **linear**, then the first differences in the y-values will be constant, indicating a constant rate of change. Linear relationships can be expressed in the form $y = mx + b$ where m and b are real numbers.

If the first differences in the y-values are not constant, then there is not a constant rate of change and the relationship is non-linear. If the second differences, or the differences between the first differences, are constant then the relationship is **quadratic**. Quadratic relationships can be expressed in the form $y = ax^2 + bx + c$ where a, b, and c are real numbers.

Using Finite Differences to Write Linear Functions:

Time (seconds)	Distance (feet)
0	2
1	5
2	8
3	11
4	14
5	17

+1 ... +3 (between each row)

Δx ... Δy

FIGURE 5.14.
Finite differences for linear functions.

$y = mx + b$ where

❖ b is the y-value when $x = 0$

❖ m is the ratio of $\frac{\Delta y}{\Delta x}$.

Using Finite Differences to Write Quadratic Functions:

❖ Use the polynomial form $y = ax^2 + bx + c$.

❖ If the x-interval is equal to 1, the value for a is half of the constant second difference ($2a$ = second difference).

❖ If the first x-value is 0, the first, first difference is equal to $a + b$.

❖ The y-value when $x = 0$ is the value of c.

CHECK THIS!

A quadratic is a type of polynomial, a mathematical expression of the form $a_n x^n + a_{n-1} + a_{n-2}x^{n-2} + \ldots + a_1 x^1 + a_0$. Polynomials of one, two, or three terms are called monomial, binomial, or trinomial, respectively. The polynomial form of a quadratic function is the same as the general form, $y = ax^2 + bx + c.$

1. Use first and second differences to find a quadratic function for **Figure 5.15.**

2. Make a quadratic function and create a table.

    a) First choose values for *a*, *b*, and *c*.

    b) Next substitute them into $y = ax^2 + bx + c$. Write the results in a table like the one shown in **Figure 5.16.**

    c) Use first and second differences to check your work.

x	y
0	6
1	5
2	10
3	21
4	38

FIGURE 5.15.
Table of x- and y-values.

The table in **Figure 5.17** shows the distance a car travels from the time the driver decides to stop to the time the car comes to a complete stop. These data are for an alert driver, a well-maintained car, and dry road conditions.

3. Find a function rule to model the relationship between each distance and speed.

    a) Reaction distance: _____

    b) Braking distance: _____

    c) Stopping distance: _____

4. Complete Figure 5.17.

x	y
0	
1	
2	
3	
4	

FIGURE 5.16.
Table for Question 2.

Speed	Reaction Distance	Braking Distance	Stopping Distance
0	0	0	0
10	10	5	15
20	20	20	40
30	30	45	75
40	40	80	120
50			
60			
70			

FIGURE 5.17.
Car stopping distance data.

5. According to Figure 5.17, a driver should allow 120 feet to stop safely when driving 40 mph. About how many car lengths is this? In your experience, how much space do most drivers allow?

6. How might an advocate for reducing highway speeds from 70 mph to 55 mph use stopping distances to support his or her case?

7. The Figure 5.17 data are for an alert driver. How might tuning the radio or talking on a cell phone or to other passengers affect these data?

8. Use your knowledge of quadratic models to complete the table in **Figure 5.18.**

Speed	Stopping Distance for Large Trucks	Stopping Distance for Trains
0	0	0
10	21	900
20	54	2020
30	99	3360
40	156	4920
50		
60		
70		

FIGURE 5.18.
Stopping distance data for large trucks and trains.

9. Find a function rule to model the relationship between each distance and speed.

a) Stopping distance for large trucks: _____

b) Stopping distance for trains: _____

10. The average speed of trains traveling through town is about 40 mph. What is the stopping distance for that speed in feet? What is the stopping distance in miles?

11. If the train comes around a bend and the conductor sees a car stalled on the tracks about half a mile ahead, what is the fastest speed the train can travel and be able to stop to avoid a collision?

Quadratics on the Move

In Chapter 4 you explored translations, reflections, and dilations. These transformations can be applied to the graphs of functions. Since graphs of functions are done on a coordinate plane, you can use algebraic rules for these transformations.

Knowing about function transformations will help you later in this chapter. If you know how to translate, reflect, and dilate a parabola then you can quickly fit a quadratic function to a set of data.

TRANSLATIONS OF QUADRATIC GRAPHS

1. Use grid paper to sketch the graph of $y = x^2$. Then complete a table like **Figure 5.19.**

The effect of changing $y = x^2$ to $y = x^2 + k$.

2. Complete the table in **Figure 5.20** for $y = x^2$ and $y = x^2 + 3$, then graph both functions on your graphing calculator. Make a sketch of both graphs.

x	$y = x^2$
−3	
−2	
−1	
0	
1	
2	
3	

FIGURE 5.19.
Table for Question 1.

x	Pre-Image $y = x^2$	Image $y = x^2 + 3$
−3		
−2		
−1		
0		
1		
2		
3		

FIGURE 5.20.
Table for Question 2.

3. Write a sentence that describes the transformation.

4. Complete the table in **Figure 5.21** for $y = x^2$ and $y = x^2 - 2$, then graph both functions on your graphing calculator. Make a sketch of both graphs.

x	Pre-Image	Image
	$y = x^2$	$y = x^2 - 2$
−3		
−2		
−1		
0		
1		
2		
3		

FIGURE 5.21.
Table for Question 4.

5. Write a sentence that describes the transformation.

6. Describe what you think the effect will be on the graph of a quadratic function when a positive or negative number is added to the function after squaring the x-value.

The effect of changing $y = x^2$ to $y = (x + h)^2$.

7. Complete the tables in **Figure 5.22** for $y = x^2$ and $y = (x - 3)^2$, then graph both functions on your graphing calculator. Make a sketch of both graphs.

x	Pre-Image
	$y = x^2$
−3	
−2	
−1	
0	
1	
2	
3	

x	Image
	$y = (x - 3)^2$
0	
1	
2	
3	
4	
5	
6	

FIGURE 5.22.
Tables for Question 7.

8. Write a sentence that describes the transformation.

9. Describe the effect on the graph of a quadratic function when a positive number is subtracted from the x-value before squaring.

10. Describe the effect on the graph of a quadratic function when a negative number is subtracted from the x-value before squaring.

The effect of changing $y = x^2$ to $y = -x^2$.

11. Complete the table in **Figure 5.23** for $y = x^2$ and $y = -x^2$, then graph both functions on your graphing calculator. Make a sketch of both graphs.

x	Pre-Image $y = x^2$	Image $y = -x^2$
-3		
-2		
-1		
0		
1		
2		
3		

FIGURE 5.23. Table for Question 11.

12. Write a sentence that describes the transformation.

The effect of changing $y = (x + 2)^2$ to $y = -(x + 2)^2$.

13. Complete the table in **Figure 5.24** for $y = (x + 2)^2$ and $y = -(x + 2)^2$, then graph both functions on your graphing calculator. Make a sketch of both graphs.

x	Pre-Image $y = (x + 2)^2$	Image $y = -(x + 2)^2$
-5		
-4		
-3		
-2		
-1		
0		
1		

FIGURE 5.24. Table for Question 13.

14. Write a sentence that describes the transformation.

15. Describe the effect on the graph of a quadratic function when the opposite sign is applied to the function values.

The effect of changing $y = x^2$ to $y = ax^2$.

16. Complete the table in **Figure 5.25** for $y = x^2$ and $y = 2x^2$, then graph both functions on your graphing calculator. Make a sketch of both graphs.

17. Write a sentence that describes the transformation.

x	Pre-Image $y = x^2$	Image $y = 2x^2$
-3		
-2		
-1		
0		
1		
2		
3		

FIGURE 5.25. Table for Question 16.

x	Pre-Image $y = x^2$	Image $y = \frac{1}{2}x^2$
−3		
−2		
−1		
0		
1		
2		
3		

FIGURE 5.26.
Table for Question 18.

18. Complete the table in **Figure 5.26** for $y = x^2$ and $y = \frac{1}{2}x^2$, then graph both functions on your graphing calculator. Make a sketch of both graphs.

19. Write a sentence that describes the transformation.

20. Describe the effect on the graph of a quadratic function when a scale factor greater than 1 is applied to the function values.

21. Describe the effect on the graph of a quadratic function when a scale factor less than 1, but greater than 0, is applied to the function values.

$y = a(x - h)^2 + k$		
	Verbal Description	Visual
$|a| > 1$	Vertical stretch of the graph of the function	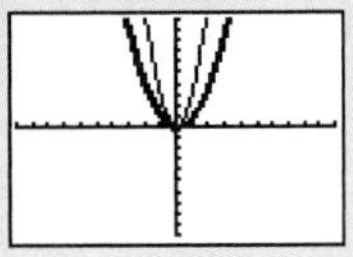
$|a| < 1$	Vertical compression of the graph of the function	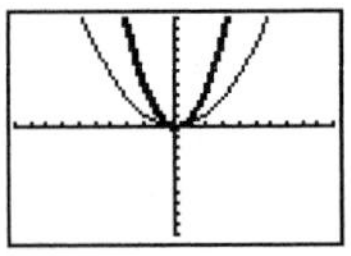
$-a$	Reflection of the graph of the function across the x-axis	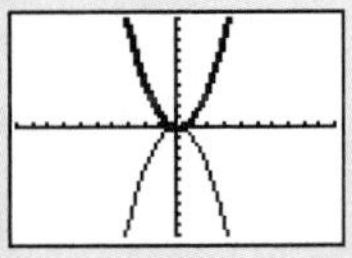
h	Horizontal translation of the graph of the function	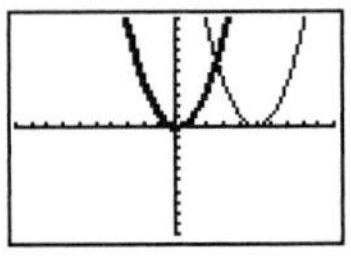
k	Vertical translation of the graph of the function	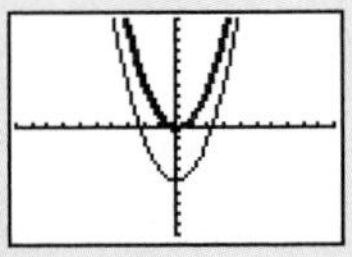

FIGURE 5.27.
Transformation summary.

Transforming functions is a useful tool when you want to fit a function to data. For example, recall Paul's parabola-shaped walk from Section 5.1 shown in **Figure 5.28.**

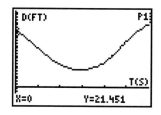

FIGURE 5.28.
Paul's walk.

To fit a function to these data, first compare the graph of the parent function for quadratics, $y = x^2$, to the scatterplot of Paul's walk shown in **Figure 5.29.**

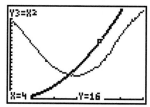

FIGURE 5.29.
Parent function and Paul's walk.

22. The graph of $y = x^2$ must be translated to the right to resemble the walk more closely. Write a function rule that translates the parabola to the right.

23. Now the graph of $y = (x - 3)^2$ must be shifted vertically to more closely resemble the walk. Write a function rule that has the necessary vertical shift.

24. Next the graph of $y = (x - 3)^2 + 7$ must be stretched vertically to resemble the walk more closely. Write a function rule that has the necessary vertical stretch.

The graph of the parent function $y = x^2$ is graphed in the window shown in **Figure 5.30**.

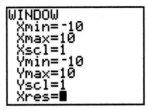

FIGURE 5.30.
The parent function $y = x^2$.

Each graph below was graphed using the window above, and is a transformation on $y = x^2$. The vertex of the parabola is labeled in each case. For each graph, write a function rule **and** a verbal description of the transformation.

1.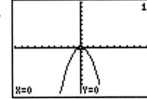

2.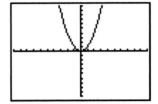

3.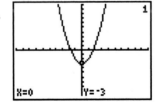

4.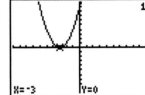

5.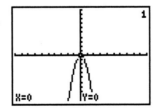

6.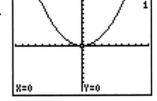

Questions 7–11 each represent a transformation of $y = x^2$. For each, sketch a graph **and** a write a verbal description of the transformation.

7. $y = x^2 - 4$

8. $y = (x - 4)^2$

9. $y = 2(x - 3)^2$

10. $y = \frac{1}{3}x^2$

11. $y = (x - 5)^2 + 3$

12. The scatterplot in **Figure 5.31** was made with the window shown.

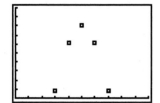
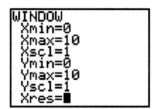

FIGURE 5.31.
Figure for Question 12.

13. Use transformations to develop a function that fits the data in the scatterplot. Explain your process.

Oh, That Traffic!

Let's apply to a new situation what you have learned about quadratic functions.

Sometimes motion isn't as speedy as at other times.

A mass transit organization in a large city is measuring the speed at which vehicles travel on the freeways. By measuring the speed at specific times of day over a long period of time, they can calculate average speeds during the day. This information can be put into a graph (see **Figure 5.32**) that helps commuters decide how much time they should allow to get to work.

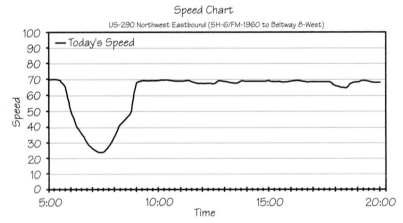

FIGURE 5.32.
Travel times for
a local freeway.

For one part of a freeway in this city, the speeds at half-hour intervals during the morning rush hour have been recorded (see **Figure 5.33**). The start of rush hour, 5:00 a.m., is time interval 0. The time interval increases by 1 for each successive half hour; i.e., 5:30 a.m. is time interval 1, 6:00 a.m. is time interval 2, etc.

Time	Time Interval	Average Speed (mph)
5:00 a.m.	0	70
5:30 a.m.	1	50
6:00 a.m.	2	35
6:30 a.m.	3	25
7:00 a.m.	4	20
7:30 a.m.	5	20
8:00 a.m.	6	25
8:30 a.m.	7	35
9:00 a.m.	8	50
9:30 a.m.	9	70

FIGURE 5.33.
Morning rush hour data.

1. Use Figure 5.33 to make a scatterplot of speed versus time interval. Then build a model to predict the speed in terms of the time interval and graph your model over the scatterplot.

2. Ms. Sanchez and Mr. Williams travel this part of the freeway on their way to work in the morning. Ms. Sanchez reaches this part of the freeway at 6:10 a.m., and Mr. Williams reaches this part of the freeway at 8:10 a.m. If the traffic moves at average speed, who will travel faster? Justify your answer.

SECTION 5.6

3...2...1... Blast Off!

On Earth, gravity pulls objects toward the ground. This force, as you may have learned in your science class, changes an object's speed. If the object is moving away from Earth, gravity slows it down. If the object is moving toward Earth, gravity speeds it up. This change in speed is called acceleration.

CHECK THIS!

Acceleration **is the change in an object's speed per unit of time.**

When astronauts try to escape Earth's gravity and travel into space, they must overcome this force. One way they do that is to use a rocket. In this section you will observe a model rocket launch. While your rocket won't fly into space, you will observe changes in its speed as a result of the force of gravity.

MODEL ROCKET LAUNCH SIMULATION

Begin by setting the MODE and the WINDOW on your graphing calculator as shown in **Figure 5.34.**

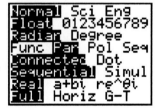

FIGURE 5.34.
Settings for
graphing calculator.

You've now changed your calculator setting from FUNCTION mode (what we normally use to graph, in terms of x and y) to PARAMETRIC mode. In parametric mode, we graph two functions, x_T and y_T, both in terms of *time*.

1. Press the Y= key on your graphing calculator. Enter each of these into your calculator.

   $X_{1T} = 2.5$

   $Y_{1T} = 1.6T^2 + 80T$

2. Press the GRAPH key on your calculator. Sketch the graph produced on the axes.

3. Is this graph what you expected? Why or why not?

4. In Section 5.1 you examined distance-versus-time walking graphs. One of the graphs had a parabolic shape. How does the flight of the rocket compare to the walk that produced a parabolic graph?

 Assignment

1. Based on the information provided, graph a parabola.

   ❖ Line of symmetry is $x = 2$.

   ❖ The vertex has a y-coordinate of -1.

   ❖ $(3, 0)$ is an x-intercept.

   ❖ $(0, 3)$ is the y-intercept.

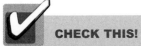

CHECK THIS!

A line of symmetry in a parabola is a line that passes through the vertex as shown in Figure 5.35.

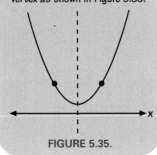

FIGURE 5.35.

Each point on the parabola can be reflected across the line of symmetry to match a point on the other side of the parabola.

2. What are the coordinates of the vertex?

3. What are the coordinates of the other x-intercept?

4. Name one other point that is on the parabola and explain how you found this point.

5. Write an equation of this parabola.

In Chapter 1 equations of the form $y - y_1 = m(x - x_1)$ are introduced as a way of describing linear models. This form is called point-slope form.

The **vertex form** of a quadratic function is $y = a(x - h)^2 + k$. This form can be modified by subtracting k from both sides to get $y - k = a(x - h)^2$.

6. Compare the point-slope form for linear functions with the modified vertex form for quadratics. How are they similar? How are they different?

There Could Be Several Factors

Quadratic functions can be used to model many things that occur in the real world. In Section 5.6 you used a graphing calculator to simulate a rocket launch.

Aerospace engineers use quadratic functions to model the motion of a rocket, much like you did in Section 5.6. Then they use these quadratic functions to get quadratic equations to help solve problems.

Recall that we used $Y_{1T} = -16T^2 + 80T$, where T represents time and Y represents the height of a rocket, to describe the motion of the rocket (see **Figure 5.36**).

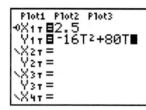
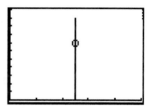

FIGURE 5.36.
Modeling a rocket's height.

$Y_{1T} = -16T^2 + 80T$ can be rewritten as $y = -16x^2 + 80x$ if we let x be time and y be the height of the rocket.

1. Write an equation that can be solved to find the times when the rocket was 64 feet above the ground.

2. Rewrite this equation in $ax^2 + bx + c = 0$ form, and completely factor the polynomial.

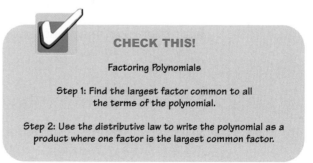

CHECK THIS!

Factoring Polynomials

Step 1: Find the largest factor common to all the terms of the polynomial.

Step 2: Use the distributive law to write the polynomial as a product where one factor is the largest common factor.

EXAMPLE:

Factor $18x^5 - 9x^3 + 27x^2$.

Although there are other factors common to the three terms (18, 9, and 27), such as $3x$, the largest common factor is $9x^2$.

So you factor the polynomial using $9x^2$.

$$18x^5 - 9x^3 + 27x^2$$
$$= (9x^2)(2x^3) + (9x^2)(3)$$
$$= 9x^2(2x^3 - x + 3)$$

3. Use your graphing calculator to graph $y = ax^2(2x^3 - x + 3)$. Sketch the graph and record your viewing window.

4. At which x-values does the graph cross the x-axis?

5. Use your graphing calculator to make a table of values for $y = -16x^2 + 80x - 64$. At what x-values is $y = 0$? How do these values relate to the x-values where the graph crosses the x-axis?

6. How do the x-values from Questions 4 and 5 relate to the factors in the factored form from Question 2?

7. What happens when you substitute each x-value into the factored form?

8. What is the meaning of $y = 0$ in this situation?

9. Write an equation that can be solved to find the times when the rocket was on the ground.

10. Completely factor the polynomial you wrote in Question 9.

11. Use your graphing calculator to graph the function in factored form. Sketch the graph and record your viewing window.

12. At which x-values does the graph cross the x-axis?

13. Use your graphing calculator to make a table of values for $y = -16x^2 + 80x$. At what x-values is $y = 0$? How do these values relate to the x-values where the graph crosses the x-axis?

14. How do the x-values from Questions 11 and 12 relate to the factors in the factored form from Question 9?

15. Substitute the x-values from Question 13 into the factored form and simplify. Describe your results.

16. Write a sentence that describes the relationship between the solutions to a quadratic equation of the form $ax^2 = bx + c = 0$ and the factors of $ax^2 + bx + c$.

Solving Quadratic Equations by Factoring

$y = ax^2 + bx + c$ is called the **general form** of a quadratic function. This form does not provide a lot of information about the graph of the function. Other forms are more useful because they display some important features of the graph. One form of a quadratic function is called the **factored form** and is written $y = a(x - r_1)(x - r_2)$, where r_1 and r_2 are integers.

1. Consider $y = -0.5(x - 1)(x - 5)$, which is written in factored form.

   a) Use a graphing calculator to graph the function. Sketch the graph and record your viewing window.

   b) Where does the graph cross the x-axis?

   c) Substitute the x-values where the graph crosses the x-axis into the function. What y-values do they yield?

Factored form $y = a(x - r_1)(x - r_2)$ is a useful way to write a quadratic function. The numbers r_1 and r_2 are the x-coordinates of the points where the graph crosses the x-axis. These x-coordinates are called the **roots** of the quadratic equation $-0.5x(x - 1)(x - 5) = 0$. They are also known as **x-intercepts** of the graph or **zeros** of the function $y = -0.5x(x - 1)(x - 5)$.

   d) Why is an x-intercept also called a zero?

   e) How can you tell if a point is an x-intercept from just the coordinates of the point?

In the factored form of a quadratic, the only things that change are the numbers. In general, it can be written like this:

$y = \underline{\quad} (x - \underline{\quad})(x - \underline{\quad})$

The challenge is to fill in the blanks with the correct numbers.

2. Write a quadratic function in factored form that has x-intercepts at -4 and $+2$. Use your graphing calculator to graph the function, sketch the graph, and record your window.

3. Adjust your answer so that the vertex is located at the point (–1, –3.6). Explain how you determined this answer.

4. a) Change your answer into polynomial form
       $(y = ax^2 + bx + c)$.

   b) Use your graphing calculator to display the graph of both the factored form and the polynomial form. Compare the two graphs and explain any similarities or differences.

   c) If you are graphing two functions, but only one graph appears, what does this mean?

You can use factored form to solve quadratic equations. You may have noticed that substituting a zero of a function causes one of the factors to be 0. Multiplying any number or factor by 0 yields a value of 0. So, if you have a quadratic in polynomial form that equals 0, such as $x^2 - 6x + 5 = 0$, you can use factoring to solve the equation.

Here are the steps to use factored form to solve quadratic equations.

❖ Factor the polynomial completely.

$$x^2 - 6x + 5 = 0$$

$$(x - 5)(x - 1) = 0$$

❖ Set each factor equal to 0.

$$x - 5 = 0 \qquad x - 1 = 0$$

❖ Solve each equation for x.

$$x - 5 = 0 \qquad x - 1 = 0$$

$$x = 5 \qquad x = 1$$

This method of solving a quadratic equation uses the **Zero-Product Property**. This property states that if the product of two real numbers is zero, then one or both of the numbers must be equal to zero. In other words, if $ab = 0$, then either $a = 0$ or $b = 0$.

If a polynomial is factored and the polynomial is equal to zero, then at least one of its factors must also be equal to zero. In other words, if $(x - 5)(x - 1) = 0$, then $x - 5 = 0$ or $x - 1 = 0$. As long as one of these two factors is equal to 0, then that value of x will solve the equation.

Let's take another look at our rocketry example from Section 5.7.

Recall that the function describing our rocket launch simulation from Section 5.6 was $y = -16x^2 + 80x$. We wrote an equation that could be solved to find the times when the rocket was 64 feet above the ground, $-16x^2 + 80x = 64$.

5. Rewrite this equation in $ax^2 + bx + c = 0$ form, and completely factor the polynomial.

6. Use the Zero-Product Property to solve the equation.

7. The height (in feet) of a rocket, y, after x seconds of flight can be found using $y = -16x^2 + 80x$. At what time(s) will the rocket be 84 feet above the ground?

8. What types of problems are best solved with the Zero-Product Property?

SUMMARY

If a quadratic that can be factored equals 0, then the equation can be solved using the Zero-Product Property.

❖ The Zero-Product Property states that for all real numbers a and b, if $ab = 0$, then $a = 0$ or $b = 0$.

To solve an equation by factoring:

❖ First, write the quadratic equation in polynomial form, $ax^2 + bx + c = 0$.

❖ Second, completely factor the polynomial.

❖ Third, set each factor equal to zero.

❖ Fourth, solve each of these equations for x.

❖ Since each of these x-values makes at least one factor equal to zero, by the Zero-Product Property, each of these x-values solves the equation.

Assignment

1. One way to see factored form is with an area model that represents the various parts of a quadratic expression. The pieces needed to represent $2x^2 + 7x + 3$ are shown in **Figure 5.37**.

FIGURE 5.37.
Area model for a quadratic.

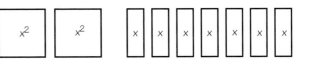

a) What are the dimensions for each type of piece?

b) $2x^2 + 7x + 3$ can be in factored form by arranging the pieces to form a rectangle. On a piece of paper, trace the pieces in Figure 5.37, and then arrange them to form a rectangle. Sketch the results.

c) The length and width of the rectangle represent the factors. What are the factors of $2x^2 + 7x + 3$?

d) Write $y = 2x^2 + 7x + 3$ in factored form.

e) Solve $2x^2 + 7x + 3 = 0$ using the Zero-Product Property.

f) Write $y = 4x^2 + 12x + 9$ in factored form.

g) Solve $4x^2 + 12x + 9 = 0$ using the Zero-Product Property.

2. A flare is launched from a life raft. The relationship between height and time is modeled by $h = 192t - 16t^2$ where h is height in feet and t is time in seconds. When is the flare 512 feet above the raft?

3. A toy rocket is fired in the middle of a field. The relationship between height and time is modeled by $h = -16t^2 + 256t$ where h is height in feet and t is time in seconds. When does the rocket's height equal 540 feet?

4. A rectangle has a length, l, and a width, w. The area of a rectangle can be found using $A = lw$. The perimeter of a rectangle can be found using $P = 2l + 2w$. The perimeter of a certain rectangle is 48 centimeters.

a) Use the perimeter formula to write a function rule for the length of the rectangle in terms of its width.

b) Write a function for the area of the rectangle in terms of its width.

c) If the rectangle has an area of 143 square centimeters, what are its length and width?

So What's Your Point?

Quadratic functions can be used to model many things that occur in the real world. In Section 5.6 you used a graphing calculator to simulate a rocket launch.

Suppose that a rocket launch can be simulated with $y = -16x^2 + 128x$, where x represents the time since launch in seconds and y represents the height of the rocket in feet.

1. Use your graphing calculator to graph the function. Sketch your graph and record your window.

2. Use the TRACE feature to estimate the coordinates of the vertex.

3. Use your graphing calculator to find the location of the vertex. How did you find your answer?

4. Recall that the vertex form of a quadratic function is $y = a(x - h)^2 + k$. Use the vertex you found in Question 3 to write a vertex form for this function.

5. Use transformations to fit an appropriate function, in vertex form, to the parabola. Use your graphing calculator to confirm your answer.

6. Use algebra to show that your function from Question 5 is equivalent to $y = -16x^2 + 128x$.

7. Here is a quadratic expression: $2(x + 3)^2 + 2$.

   a) List the operations you would use, in order, to evaluate this expression. Then evaluate the expression for $x = 4$.

   b) Knowing the order of operations can help in solving equations. Use your answer from a to list the opposite operations (i.e., opposite of multiplication is division).

c) If you want to solve $2(x + 3)^2 + 2 = 20$ you can start with 20 and apply the operations that you listed in b in reverse order. What numbers do you get? (Hint: there are two answers!)

d) To formalize your work, apply the same steps to both sides of $2(x + 3)^2 + 2 = 20$, one at a time, in the same order you used in c. Write down what the equation becomes after each of the steps.

8. a) A ball is shot straight up from a cannon. After 6 seconds, it reaches a height of 576 feet. Using $a = -16$, write a function in vertex form that can be used to model this rocket's flight.

b) Use this function to find the height of the ball 4 seconds after launch.

c) At what time will the ball be 320 feet above the ground?

Solving Quadratic Equations Using Inverse Operations

There are many ways to solve a quadratic equation. The best method depends on the form of the equation. Section 5.9 uses vertex form.

The Tower of the Americas in San Antonio, Texas, was built for the 1968 World's Fair. At 750 feet it is taller than both the Washington Monument in Washington, DC and the Space Needle in Seattle, Washington.

1. A penny is dropped from the top of the Tower of the Americas. The height of the penny, h, after t seconds can be described by $h = -16t^2 + 750$. At about what time will the penny be 100 feet from the ground?

One way to look at the vertex form, $y = a(x - h)^2 + k$, is by transformations from Section 5.4. Vertex form is the result of starting with the parent function, $y = x^2$, stretching or compressing it by a factor of a, reflecting it if $a < 0$, and then translating it horizontally h units and vertically k units. In each translation the only point that needs to be tracked is the vertex. The dilation (compression or stretch) affects how quickly or slowly the graph grows as the values for x increase or decrease.

Another way to look at the vertex form is through order of operations. They are shown as an arrow diagram in **Figure 5.38.**

FIGURE 5.38.
Arrow diagram.

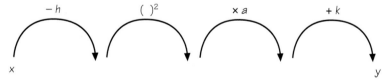

Because the operations can be done in sequence, one at a time, vertex form can be useful for solving equations using inverse operations.

2. $y = a(x - h)^2 + k$, if you know the values of y, a, h, and k, describe how to solve the equation for x. (Hint: Look back at work in Question 1.)

Every year for New Year's Eve, a fireworks display is launched from the Tower of the Americas. Suppose that a firework is launched from the top of the tower. Its height, h, above the ground can be found from the time, t, since launch using $h(t) = -16t^2 + 64t + 750$.

Planners need to know how high the firework will go before it begins to descend. Also, they must know how long the firework will take to reach this height. One way that we can answer these questions is to rewrite the function in vertex form using a method called **completing the square**.

Before using completing the square to answer these questions, let's consider a simpler problem.

Algebra	Tiles
a) Represent the function using tiles. $f(x) = x^2 + 4x + 1$	
b) Group the x-terms using parentheses. $f(x) = (x^2 + 4x) + 1$	
c) Find $\frac{1}{2}$ of the coefficient of x. Square this value, then add it to your x-terms inside the parentheses. $f(x) = (x^2 + 4x + \_\_\_) + 1$ $\frac{4}{2} = 2$ $2^2 = 4$	
d) You want to manipulate the equation, not change its value. So, take the value from step c) that you added and subtract it outside the parentheses. Factor your trinomial, and combine like terms to write the vertex form. To add 4, then, we also need to subtract 4. $f(x) = (x^2 + 2x + 4) + 1$ $f(x) = (x + 2)^2 \,(-4 + 1)$ Combine like terms. $f(x) = (x + 2)^2 - 3$	

FIGURE 5.39.
Table for Question 3.

3. Write $f(x) = x^2 + 4x + 1$ in vertex form. To do this, use algebra tiles to represent the polynomial. In your notebook, make a table like **Figure 5.39** to record the steps and sketch the tiles.

4. Write $g(x) = 2x^2 + 4x + 3$ in vertex form. To do this, use algebra tiles to represent the polynomial. In your notebook, make a table like **Figure 5.40** to record the steps and sketch the tiles.

Algebra	Tiles
a) Group the x-terms: $g(x) = (2x^2 + 4x) + 3$	
b) We just followed a procedure for completing the square when $a = 1$, so let's factor 2 out of both of the x-terms. $g(x) = 2(x^2 + 2x) + 3$	
c) Find $\frac{1}{2}$ of the coefficient of x. Square this value, then add it to your x-terms inside the parentheses. $g(x) = 2(x^2 + 2x + \underline{\quad}) + 3$ $\frac{2}{2} = 1$ $1^2 = 1$	
d) You want to manipulate the equation, not change its value. So, take the value from step c) that you added and subtract it outside the parentheses. Factor your trinomial, and combine like terms to write the vertex form. To add 1, we need to subtract 1. Don't forget, however. We are adding TWO groups of 1, or 2, and need to subtract 2 to compensate. $g(x) = 2(x + 1)^2 - 2 + 3$ $g(x) = 2(x + 1)^2 + 1$	

FIGURE 5.40.
Table for Question 4.

Completing the square can be thought of in two ways.

Geometrically, you are physically completing a square. The tiles reveal this process. In Question 3 we were completing the square for $x^2 + 4x$. We built what we could out of algebra tiles then asked ourselves, "What number of unit tiles do I need to complete the square?" The answer is 4 tiles (see **Figure 5.41**). The factors of the resulting polynomial are $(x + 2)$ and $(x + 2)$.

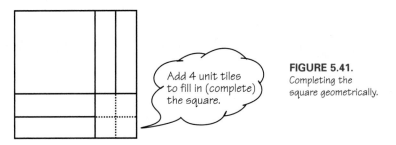

Add 4 unit tiles to fill in (complete) the square.

FIGURE 5.41.
Completing the square geometrically.

Algebraically, you are completing a binomial perfect square. In Question 3, we were completing the square for $x^2 + 4x$. We want to write this expression as a binomial squared; that is, a polynomial of the form $(x + \#)^2$.

$x^2 + 4x + \underline{\hspace{1cm}}$

$x^2 + 4x + \left(\dfrac{4}{2}\right)^2$

$x^2 + 4x + 4$

$(x + 2)(x + 2)$

$(x + 2)^2$

Solving a quadratic equation by completing the square has two parts.

Part 1. Rewrite the polynomial in vertex form using completing the square.

Part 2. Use inverse operations to isolate the variable.

EXAMPLE:

Solve $x^2 - 3x = 10$ by completing the square.

Step 1: The left-hand side needs to be written in vertex form. Since $-3 \div 2 = -1.5$, and $(-1.5)^2 = 2.25$, add 2.25 to both sides of the equation.

$$x^2 - 3x + 2.25 = 10 + 2.25$$

Step 2: Rewrite the left-hand side as a binomial squared.

$$(x^2 - 3x + 2.25) = 12.25$$
$$(x - 1.5)^2 = 12.25$$

Step 3: Use inverse operations to solve for x.

Take the square root of each side:

$$\sqrt{(x - 1.5)^2} = \sqrt{12.25}$$
$$x - 1.5 = \pm 3.5$$

Add 1.5 to each side of the equation.

$$x - 1.5 = \pm 3.5$$
$$x - 1.5 + 1.5 = \pm 3.5 + 1.5$$

Simplify.

$$x = \pm 3.5 + 1.5$$
$$x = 3.5 + 1.5 \qquad x = -3.5 + 1.5$$
$$x = 5 \qquad\qquad x = 2$$

SUMMARY

If a quadratic equation is in vertex form, $y = a(x - h)^2 + k$, then it can be solved by using inverse operations.

❖ Start with y.

❖ Subtract k.

❖ Divide by a.

❖ Take the square root.

❖ Add h.

Sometimes a quadratic equation can be solved by a method called **completing the square**. To solve $x^2 + bx + c = 0$ using this method:

❖ Write the equation in the form $x^2 + bx = -c$.

❖ Add $\left(\frac{b}{2}\right)^2$ to both sides:

$$x^2 + bx + \left(\frac{b}{2}\right)^2 = -c + \left(\frac{b}{2}\right)^2$$

❖ Rewrite the left side as a perfect square:

$$\left(x + \frac{b}{2}\right)^2 = -c + \left(\frac{b}{2}\right)^2$$

❖ Take the square root of each side and solve for x.

Assignment

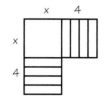

FIGURE 5.42.
An incomplete area model.

1. **Figure 5.42** is an incomplete area model. Complete the square.

   a) What algebraic expression does Figure 5.42 represent?

   b) How many small squares (area of each = 1) do you need to add to complete the square?

   c) What algebraic expression does the model then represent?

   d) What algebraic expression represents the sum of the pieces being used to complete the square?

2. Complete each square, then write the polynomial as a binomial squared.

   a) $x^2 - 16x +$ _____

   b) $x^2 + 7x +$ _____

3. Write $h(x) = 3x^2 - 12x - 1$ in vertex form. Show your work in a table like **Figure 5.43**.

Algebra	Sketch of Tiles
a) Group the x-terms using parentheses.	
b) Factor out a 3 from both the x^2 and x-terms.	
c) Find $\frac{1}{2}$ of the coefficient of x. Square this value, then add it to your x-terms inside the parentheses.	
d) You want to convert the equation, not change its value. So, take the value from step c) that you added, multiply it by the 3 that you factored out (distribute, distribute!), and subtract it outside the parentheses. Factor your trinomial, and combine like terms to write the vertex form.	

FIGURE 5.43.
Table for Question 3.

4. Use completing the square to write $f(x) = \frac{1}{2}x^2 + 2x + 3$ in vertex form.

For Questions 5–7, solve by completing the square and inverse operations.

5. $x^2 + 4x = 12$

6. $x^2 + 8x - 11 = 0$

7. $5x^2 - 10x - 30 = 0$

8. A football is kicked into the air. It hits the ground 60 yards downfield. At its highest point, the ball is 7 yards above the ground. Assume the relationship between height and distance is quadratic.

a) Sketch a graph of the relationship between height and distance.

b) Label the vertex with its coordinates. What does this point mean here?

c) Label the x-intercepts with their coordinates. What do these points mean here?

d) Substitute the coordinates of the vertex into the vertex form $y = a(x - h)^2 + k$.

e) To find the value of a, choose a known point on the parabola and substitute the values for x and y. Solve for a.

f) Write a function rule to model the relationship between the height of the ball and the distance downfield.

g) Assume the ball is being kicked for a 51-yard field goal. The height of the field goal crossbar is 10 feet. Will the ball make it through the goal posts? Show how you found your answer.

The Quadratic Safety Net

You have seen three ways to write a quadratic function:

Polynomial Form: $y = ax^2 + bx + c$

Factored Form: $y = a(x - r_1)(x - r_2)$

Vertex Form: $y = a(x - h)^2 + k$

You have also seen two ways to solve quadratic equations. The first method, factoring, involves applying the Zero-Product Property to solve each factor for x. If the quadratic is in polynomial form, it must first be factored in order to use this method. The second method, using inverse operations, involves applying the inverse operations to the equation to isolate x, which includes taking the square root to "undo" the quadratic nature of the equation. If the quadratic is in polynomial form, it must first be expressed as a binomial squared, which usually involves completing the square.

1. Consider $y = x^2 + 4x + 3.75$.

   a) Does the polynomial $x^2 + 4x + 3.75$ factor? How can you tell? If so, what are the factors?

   b) Use your graphing calculator to graph the function $y = x^2 + 4x + 3.75$. Sketch your graph and record your window.

   c) What are the zeros of the function? How do you know?

   d) Based on your answers so far, what is the solution to $x^2 + 4x + 3.75 = 0$?

   e) Now, consider $y = x^2 + 5x - 3$. Can the function be written in factored form? If so, write it in factored form. If not, why not?

   f) Graph $y = x^2 + 5x - 3$ on your graphing calculator. Sketch your graph and record your window.

g) Find the zeros of $y = x^2 + 5x - 3$. Explain your process.

h) Based on your answers, what is the solution to $x^2 + 5x - 3 = 0$? Are these exact or approximate? How do you know?

i) Solve $x^2 + 5x - 3 = 0$ without using a graphing calculator. Leave your answer in exact form.

Solving Quadratic Equations Using the Quadratic Formula

The method of completing the square, followed by applying inverse operations, can be used to solve any quadratic equation. However, the arithmetic and algebra are time comsuming. So, mathematicians have developed a formula to solve any quadratic equation.

Instead of solving quadratic equations one at a time by completing the square, you can solve $ax^2 + bx + c = 0$ for x. This will give you a formula that can be used every time. You can complete the square once and for all!

Begin with $ax^2 + bx + c = 0$. Your goal is to solve this equation for x using completing the square, followed by inverse operations to isolate x.

Step 1: Factor out the a from the x-terms:

$$a\left(x^2 + \frac{b}{a}x\right) + c = 0$$

Step 2: Complete the square:

Take half of the coefficient of x. Square this value.

$$\left(\frac{1}{2} \cdot \frac{b}{a}\right)^2 = \frac{b^2}{4a^2}$$

Add this to the left side of the equation.

$$a\left(x^2 + \frac{b}{a}x + \frac{b^2}{4a^2}\right) + c = 0 + \boxed{???}$$

But wait! You cannot add something to one side of an equation without adding it to the other! To balance this equation, we have to add the same thing to the right side.

Look closely at the left side of the equation. We added $\frac{b^2}{4a^2}$ to the left side but we placed it inside the parentheses. When the a is distributed to each term in the parentheses, we actually added $\frac{b^2}{4a^2}$ to the left side. So we need to add this term to the right side: $a\left(x^2 + \frac{b}{a}x + \frac{b^2}{4a^2}\right) + c = 0 + \frac{a}{1} \cdot \frac{b^2}{4a^2}$.

Simplify the right side.

$$a\left(x^2 + \frac{b}{a}x + \frac{b^2}{4a^2}\right) + c = 0 + \frac{\cancel{a}}{1} \cdot \frac{b^2}{4a \cdot \cancel{a}}$$

$$a\left(x^2 + \frac{b}{a}x + \frac{b^2}{4a^2}\right) + c = \frac{b^2}{4a}$$

Factor the left side.

$$a\left(x + \frac{b}{2a}\right)^2 + c = \frac{b^2}{4a}$$

Step 3: Subtract c from both sides.

$$a\left(x + \frac{b}{2a}\right)^2 = \frac{b^2}{4a} - c$$

Step 4: Divide by a (or, multiply by the reciprocal of a).

$$\frac{1}{\cancel{a}} \cdot \cancel{a}\left(x + \frac{b}{2a}\right)^2 = \frac{1}{a}\left(\frac{b^2}{4a} - c\right)$$

$$\left(x + \frac{b}{2a}\right)^2 = \frac{b^2}{4a^2} - \frac{c}{a}$$

Step 5: Find a common denominator on the right side:

The common denominator can be found by identifying the least common multiple of $\frac{b^2}{4a^2}$ and $\frac{c}{a}$. In other words, we need to multiply the second fraction by $\frac{4a}{4a}$ in order to have a common denominator of $4a^2$.

$$\left(x + \frac{b}{2a}\right)^2 = \frac{b^2}{4a^2} - \frac{4a}{4a} \cdot \frac{c}{a}$$

$$\left(x + \frac{b}{2a}\right)^2 = \frac{b^2}{4a} - \frac{4ac}{4a^2}$$

$$\left(x + \frac{b}{2a}\right)^2 = \frac{b^2 - 4ac}{4a^2}$$

Step 6: Take the square root of both sides. (Don't forget that there are a positive and a negative square root!)

$$\sqrt{\left(x + \frac{b}{2a}\right)^2} = \sqrt{\frac{b^2 - 4ac}{4a^2}}$$

$$x + \frac{b}{2a} = \pm\sqrt{\frac{b^2 - 4ac}{4a^2}}$$

$$x + \frac{b}{2a} = \pm\frac{\sqrt{b^2 - 4ac}}{\sqrt{4a^2}}$$

$$x + \frac{b}{2a} = \pm\frac{\sqrt{b^2 - 4ac}}{2a}$$

Step 7: Solve for x.

Subtract $\frac{b}{2a}$ from both sides.

$$x = -\frac{b}{2a} \pm \frac{\sqrt{b^2 - 4ac}}{2a}$$

$$x = \frac{-b \pm \sqrt{b^2 - 4ac}}{2a}$$

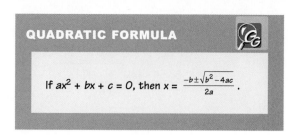

QUADRATIC FORMULA

If $ax^2 + bx + c = 0$, then $x = \frac{-b \pm \sqrt{b^2 - 4ac}}{2a}$.

Now we can use the Quadratic Formula to solve any quadratic equation.

EXAMPLE 1:

Use the Quadratic Formula to solve $3x^2 + 4x + 1 = 0$ for x.

Step 1: Define a, b, and c.

Let $a = 3$, $b = 4$, and $c = 1$.

Step 2: Substitute the values for a, b, and c into the Quadratic Formula.

$$x = \frac{-b \pm \sqrt{b^2 - 4ac}}{2a} \qquad x = \frac{-4 \pm \sqrt{4^2 - 4(3)(1)}}{2(3)}$$

Step 3: Simplify using the order of operations (the square root sign acts as a grouping symbol).

$$x = \frac{-4 \pm \sqrt{4^2 - 4(3)(1)}}{2(3)} \qquad x = \frac{-4 \pm 2}{6}$$

$$x = \frac{-4 \pm \sqrt{16 - 12}}{6} \qquad x = \frac{-4 + 2}{6} \qquad x = \frac{-4 - 2}{6}$$

$$x = \frac{-4 \pm \sqrt{4}}{6} \qquad x = \frac{-2}{6} \qquad x = \frac{-6}{6}$$

$$x = -\frac{1}{3} \qquad x = -1$$

EXAMPLE 2:

Use the Quadratic Formula to solve $4x^2 - 6x - 9 = 0$ for x.

Step 1: Define a, b, and c.

Let $a = 4$, $b = -6$, and $c = -9$.

Step 2: Substitute the values for a, b, and c into the Quadratic Formula.

$$x = \frac{-b \pm \sqrt{b^2 - 4ac}}{2a}$$

$$x = \frac{-(-6) \pm \sqrt{(-6)^2 - 4(4)(-9)}}{2(4)}$$

Step 3: Simplify using the order of operations (the square root sign acts as a grouping symbol).

$$x = \frac{-(-6) \pm \sqrt{(-6)^2 - 4(4)(-9)}}{2(4)}$$

$$x = \frac{6 \pm \sqrt{36 + 144}}{8}$$

$$x = \frac{6 \pm \sqrt{180}}{8}$$

$$x = \frac{6 \pm 6\sqrt{5}}{8}$$

$$x = \frac{6 \pm 6\sqrt{5}}{8}$$

$$x = \frac{6\left(1 \pm \sqrt{5}\right)}{8}$$

$$x = \frac{3\left(1 \pm \sqrt{5}\right)}{4}$$

$$x = \frac{3}{4} \pm \frac{3\sqrt{5}}{4}$$

SUMMARY

A quadratic equation in the form $ax^2 + bx + c = 0$ can be solved with the Quadratic Formula.

❖ If $ax^2 + bx + c = 0$, then $x = \frac{-b \pm \sqrt{b^2 - 4ac}}{2a}$.

To solve an equation with this formula:

❖ First, identify the values of a, b, and c.

❖ Second, substitute the values for a, b, and c into the Quadratic Formula.

❖ Third, simplify using the order of operations.

   ✓ The square root sign acts as a grouping symbol.

   ✓ Simplify the square root completely.

   ✓ Reduce all fractions.

Assignment

1. Use the Quadratic Formula to solve each of these:

   a) $3x^2 + 10x + 7 = 0$

   b) $2x^2 + 5x - 9 = 0$

2. Solve each of these using the most appropriate method.

   a) $y = x^2 + 6x + 9$

   b) $y = x^2 - 2.5x - 6$

   c) $y = -2x^2 - x - 0.12$

   d) $y = x^2 - 21x + 14$

   e) $y = \frac{1}{2}x^2 - 2x + 2$

   f) $y = -3x^2 + 9x + 12$

3. A stone is thrown from a catapult. The function $h(x) = -16x^2 + 80x$ describes the height (h) of the stone as a function of time.

   a) How high is the stone at 3.5 seconds? Explain how you found your answer.

   b) When will the stone be 36 feet high? Explain how you found your answer.

It's a Wrap!

In this chapter you have explored three ways to write quadratic functions:

Polynomial form: $y = ax^2 + bx + c$

Factored form: $y = a(x - r_1)(x - r_2)$

Vertex form: $y = a(x - h)^2 + k$

You have used three methods to solve quadratic equations:

✓ Factor the polynomial, then apply the Zero-Product Property.

✓ Complete the square, then apply inverse operations.

✓ Use the Quadratic Formula.

Which method is best? It depends on the situation. In this section you will look at problems involving motion. You will consider why one form of a quadratic function is better than others and why one method of solution is quicker than others.

THREE WAYS TO REPRESENT QUADRATIC FUNCTIONS

1. Enter each of these into your graphing calculator:

   $p(x) = 2x^2 - 12x + 16$

   $f(x) = 2(x - 2)(x - 4)$

   $v(x) = 2(x - 3)^2 - 2$

   a) Graph the functions on your calculator. Sketch the graphs and record your window.

   b) What can you conclude about the three functions? On what evidence do you base your conclusion?

   c) Prove that $p(x)$ and $f(x)$ are equivalent.

d) Prove that $p(x)$ and $v(x)$ are equivalent.

e) What is the vertex of this parabola? Which function most closely reveals the vertex?

f) What are the x-intercepts of this parabola? Which function most closely reveals them?

g) What is the y-intercept of this parabola? Which function most closely reveals it?

2. For each function in **Figure 5.44,** fill in the missing representations.

Graph	Factored Form	Vertex Form	Polynomial Form
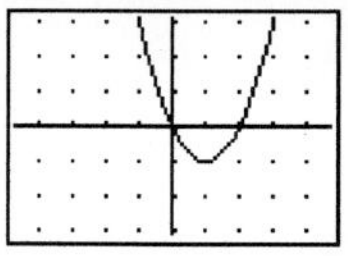	$y = x(x - 2)$	$y = (x - 1)^2 - 1$	$y = x^2 - 2x$
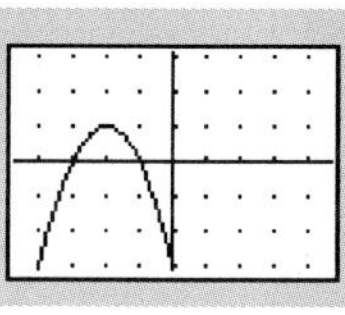			
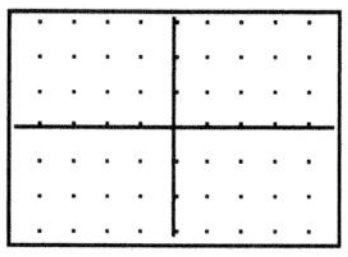	$y = (x - 2)(x + 1)$		
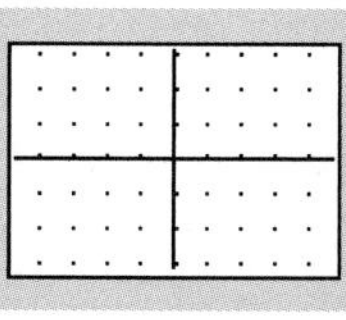		$y = 2(x - 2)^2 - 2$	
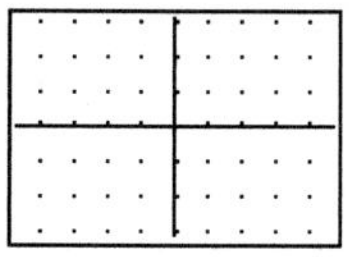			$y = -\frac{1}{2}x^2 + 2$

FIGURE 5.44.
Table for Question 2.

3. When is it best to solve equations with factoring and the Zero-Product Property?

4. When is it best to solve equations with inverse operations?

5. When is it best to solve equations with the Quadratic Formula?

6. Use the table in **Figure 5.45** to record your findings about the forms of quadratic functions and the methods to solve quadratic equations.

	General Form of Equation	Critical Attributes	Preferred Method of Solution
Factored Form			
Vertex Form			
Polynomial Form			

FIGURE 5.45.
Table for Question 6.

Assignment

1. In **Figure 5.46,** fill in the blank columns.

Graph	Factored Form	Algebra Tiles	Vertex Form	Polynomial Form
				$y = -3x^2 + 6x$

FIGURE 5.46.
Table for Question 1.

2. Change each of these into the specified form.

   a) $y - 5 = 0.5(x + 2)^2$ into polynomial form

   b) $y = 2x^2 - 7x + 6$ into factored form

   c) $y = -2(x + 2)(x - 1)$ into polynomial form

   d) $y = 1.4(x - 1)(x - 5)$ into vertex form

   e) $y - 8 = -2(x + 4)^2$ into factored form

   f) $y = x^2 - 2x - 15$ into vertex form

3. Sketch the graph of each function without using a graphing calculator. In each case explain how the form of the function helped you determine the shape of the graph.

   a) $y = -0.5(x + 1)(x - 3)$

   b) $y = 2(x + 2)^2 - 4$

   c) $y = x^2 + 3x - 2$

4. A toy rocket blasts off from the ground and peaks in 3 seconds at 144 feet. Assume the relationship between height and time is quadratic, and let the value of a be –16.

a) Write a function in vertex form for the height of the rocket at time t.

b) Write a function in factored form for the height of the rocket at time t.

c) Write a function in polynomial form for the height of the rocket at time t.

d) Sketch a graph of the relationship between height and time. If you use a graphing calculator, record your window.

e) When does the rocket hit the ground? Why?

f) Find the coordinates of the vertex and the x-intercepts. Label these on your graph.

g) How high was the rocket 2 seconds after launch? Show how you found this.

h) When will the rocket again be the same height as your answer in g? Explain how you found this.

5. The freshman class is deciding whether or not to raise the price of tickets to the spring dance. $p = 75 + 100d - 20d^2$ can be used to estimate profit, p, by raising the ticket price d dollars.

a) What profit is expected if they do not raise the price (i.e., if $d = 0$)?

b) What is the least amount they can raise the price if they want to make $155?

c) What method did you use to answer b? Why did you choose that method?

Build a Better Sandbox . . .

A company builds sandboxes as shown in **Figure 5.47.** The series number determines the surface area covered with sand.

Series Number	Sandbox & Seating Tiles	Written Description
1		A 3 x 3 sandbox has 1 square unit of its surface area covered with sand.
2		A 4 x 4 sandbox has 4 square units of its surface area covered with sand.
3		A 5 x 5 sandbox has 9 square units of its surface area covered with sand.
4		A 6 x 6 sandbox has 16 square units of its surface area covered with sand.

FIGURE 5.47.
A series of sandboxes.

1. Find a function rule that describes the total surface area of the sandbox, including the part that is covered with sand and the surrounding seating tiles, in terms of the series number. Justify your answer.

2. Find the series number of the sandbox with 196 square units of surface area. Justify your answer.

Motion with a Pendulum

A **pendulum** is a string with a mass (called a "bob") attached at the end.

Galileo

One of the first people to investigate the motion of a pendulum was Galileo, a famous astronomer. He noticed a chandelier moving in a cathedral in Pisa, Italy. He explored the relationships among the length of a pendulum, the weight on the end of the pendulum, the angle of release, and the time it takes for one swing. Galileo's work led to the invention of the pendulum clock.

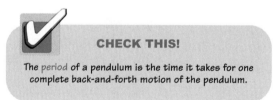

CHECK THIS!

The period of a pendulum is the time it takes for one complete back-and-forth motion of the pendulum.

1. What types of motion have you investigated so far in this chapter?

2. Give examples of events where the motion is like that of a pendulum.

Assignment

1. In **Figure 5.48**, a circle has been drawn with points evenly spaced around it. Straight lines connect all pairs of points. In order to predict the number of lines that have been drawn, you might want to start with a simpler problem and look for a pattern. Fill in the table in **Figure 5.49.** Hint: You may want to draw a circle, put the number of points on it, connect the points with lines, and then count them.

Number of Points on the Circle	Number of Lines Drawn
2	
3	
4	
5	
6	
7	

FIGURE 5.49.
Table for Question 1.

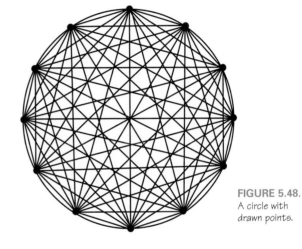

FIGURE 5.48.
A circle with drawn points.

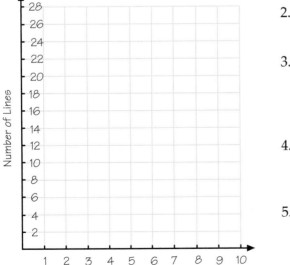

FIGURE 5.50. Graph for Question 2.

2. Graph the ordered pairs from the table on a graph like **Figure 5.50.**

3. Decide if the relationship between the number of lines and the number of points is linear or quadratic. Write a function rule that models this relationship.

4. Use your model to predict how many lines you would draw if there were 12 points on the circle.

5. Is your prediction close to the actual number of lines?

Reflections with Patty Paper

A REFLECTION WITH PATTY PAPER

1. Connect the points listed below in order on coordinate graph paper. When you see the word STOP, do not connect the point before the word STOP to the point after the word STOP.

   {(–8, 0), (–9, –2), (–3, –2), (–4, 0), (–8, 0), (–8, 8), (–4, 8), (–4, 0), STOP, (–8, 8), (–6, 10), (–4, 8), STOP}

2. Graph the line $y = x$ on the coordinate axes.

3. What do you notice about the coordinates of the points that lie on the graph of $y = x$?

4. Trace your drawing from Question 1, the line $y = x$, and the coordinate axes onto a sheet of patty paper.

5. Fold the patty paper on the line $y = x$.

6. Trace the reflection of the drawing onto the patty paper.

7. What do you notice about the reflection?

8. Trace the reflection of the drawing onto the coordinate grid. Draw the reflection with a different color pencil.

9. List the coordinates of the corresponding points of the reflected drawing in a table like **Figure 5.51**.

FIGURE 5.51.
Table for Question 9.

Coordinates of Points in Original Drawing	Corresponding Coordinates of Points in Reflected Drawing
(–8, 0)	
(–9, –2)	
(–3, –2)	
(–4, 0)	
(–4, 8)	
(–6, 10)	
(–8, 8)	

10. What do you notice about the coordinates?

11. What are the x-intercepts on the original drawing?

12. Which points in the reflection correspond to the x-intercepts in the original drawing?

13. What happens if you reflect the reflection back over the line $y = x$?

ANOTHER REFLECTION

14. Graph the line $y = 2x + 4$ on the coordinate axes.

15. Draw the graph of $y = x$.

16. Trace $y = 2x + 4$, $y = x$, and the coordinate axes onto a sheet of patty paper.

17. Fold the patty paper along the line $y = x$.

18. Trace the reflection of $y = 2x + 4$ onto the patty paper.

19. Place the patty paper back on the coordinate grid. Trace the reflection of $y = 2x + 4$ onto the coordinate grid. Draw the reflection with a different color pencil.

20. What do you notice about the reflection?

21. List three points that lie on $y = 2x + 4$ and list the coordinates of corresponding points on the reflected line.

22. What do you notice about the coordinates of corresponding points?

23. What is the slope of the line $y = 2x + 4$?

24. What is the slope of the reflected line?

25. What is the y-intercept of the line $y = 2x + 4$?

26. What is the x-intercept of the reflected line?

27. What is the x-intercept of $y = 2x + 4$?

28. What is the y-intercept of the reflected line?

29. What is the equation of the reflected line?

30. What happens if you reflect the reflection back over the line $y = x$?

A FINAL REFLECTION

31. Graph $y = x^2$ on a coordinate grid.

32. Graph $y = x$.

33. Trace $y = x^2$, $y = x$, and the coordinate axes onto a sheet of patty paper.

34. Fold the patty paper along the line $y = x$.

35. Trace the reflection of $y = x^2$ onto the patty paper.

36. Trace the reflection of $y = x^2$ onto the coordinate grid. Draw the reflection with a different color pencil.

37. What do you notice about the reflection?

38. Is the reflection a function? How do you know?

39. List three points that lie on $y = x^2$ and list the coordinates of corresponding points on the reflected graph.

40. What do you notice about the coordinates of corresponding points?

41. What are the domain and range of $y = x^2$?

42. What are the domain and range of the reflection of $y = x^2$?

43. What happens if you reflect the reflection back over the line $y = x$?

Assignment

1. Plot the following relation.

   {(2, 2), (2, 4), (–1, 4), (–3, 1), (–6, –1), (–5, –4), (–3, –6), (1, –5), (2, –2), (4.5, 0.5)}

2. What is the domain of this relation?

3. What is the range of this relation?

4. Plot the graph of $y = x$.

5. Plot the reflection of the relation from Question 1 over the line $y = x$.

6. List the coordinates of corresponding points as shown in the table in **Figure 5.52.**

Original Coordinates	Reflected Coordinates
(2, 2)	
(2, 4)	
(–1, 4)	
(–3, 1)	
(–6, –1)	
(–5, –4)	
(–3, –6)	
(1, –5)	
(2, –2)	
(4.5, 0.5)	

FIGURE 5.52.
Table for Question 6.

7. What is the domain of the reflected relation?

8. What is the range of the reflected relation?

9. What do you notice about the domain and range of the relation and its reflection?

10. If a point from the relation lies on the line $y = x$, where does the reflection of that point lie?

Inverses

The line $y = x$ acts like a mirror for a relation and its reflection across the line. When you reflect a relation across the line $y = x$, the reflection is called the **inverse**. The x- and y-coordinates of each point in a relation are reversed when you graph the reflection.

CHECK THIS!

A relation is a set of ordered pairs.

1. You may also graph a relation and its inverse on the graphing calculator. Your teacher will give you instructions on how to graph the inverse with the graphing calculator. Enter the domain of the following data set (10 members) into List 1 of your graphing calculator. Enter the range (also 10 members) into List 2.

   $\{(3, 2), (3, 3), (3, 4), (4, 1), (4, 5), (6, 1), (6, 5), (7, 2), (7, 3), (7, 4)\}$

2. Examine the scatterplot with List 1 serving as the domain and List 2 serving as the range.

3. Then activate a second scatterplot with List 1 acting as the range and List 2 acting as the domain.

4. Graph the line $y = x$. What do you observe?

CHECK THIS!

• The inverse of a relation is the reflection of the relation over the line $y = x$.

• When a relation is reflected over the line $y = x$, the x- and y-coordinates of corresponding points are reversed.

• The domain of the relation becomes the range of its inverse, and the range of the relation becomes the domain of its inverse.

• All relations have inverses.

• The term inverse is used two ways in mathematics: one to describe an opposite operation, the other to describe a type of relation.

An inverse reverses or *undoes* a previous action: A pitcher throws a ball; the catcher catches it and throws it back to the pitcher. Taking your shoes off and putting them back on is an example of an inverse. If you graph a relation, reflect it over the line $y = x$, and then reflect it back, you will have the same relation that you started with.

5. Where in mathematics have you used inverse operations?

6. Not every action can be reversed. List some examples of actions that cannot be reversed.

7. Graph $f(x) = x^2$. Graph the inverse. List five points from each graph in a table.

8. Is $f(x) = x^2$ a function?

9. What are the domain and range for $f(x) = x^2$?

10. Is the inverse of $f(x) = x^2$ a function?

11. What are the domain and range for the inverse?

Not all functions have inverses that are also functions. If you substitute $x = -2$ into $f(x) = x^2$ you get $f(-2) = (-2)^2 = 4$. If you try to undo 4 there are two possible values, 2 or -2 as shown in **Figure 5.53.**

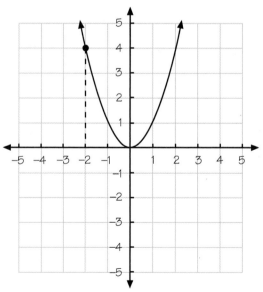

FIGURE 5.53. Inverse of a function.

In order for $f(x) = x^2$ to have an inverse that is also a function, mathematicians restrict the domain of $f(x) = x^2$ to $x \geq 0$. This gives you only the right branch of the parabola. Then the inverse is a function. The inverse of $f(x) = x^2$ needs to undo the action of squaring a number. The operation that reverses squaring is the square root. The mathematical notation for an inverse function is $f^{-1}(x)$.

If $f(x) = x^2$ for $x \geq 0$, then $f^{-1}(x) = \sqrt{x}$ for $x \geq 0$ (see **Figure 5.54**).

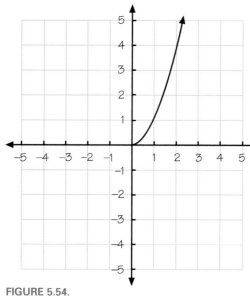

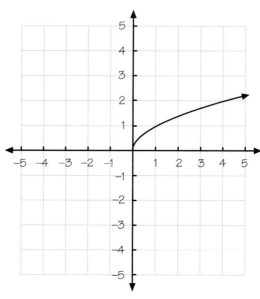

FIGURE 5.54.
Inverse of
$f(x) = x^2$ for $x > 0$.

$f(x) = x^2,\ x \geq 0,\ y \geq 0$

$f(x) = \sqrt{x}\ ,\ x \geq 0,\ y \geq 0$

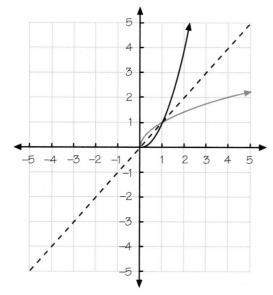

Graphing the function and its inverse on the same coordinate axes demonstrates the inverse relationship (see **Figure 5.55**).

FIGURE 5.55.
Plot of the inverse
relationship of Figure 5.54.

12. Use your graphing calculator to graph the parent function $y = \sqrt{x}$. Then graph the additional functions in **Figure 5.56** and fill in the blanks.

Function	Describe Changes to the Parent Function	Domain	Range
$y = \sqrt{x}$	Parent function	$x \geq 0$	$y \geq 0$
$y = \sqrt{x} + 2$		$x \geq 0$	$y \geq 2$
$y = \sqrt{x} - 3$		$x \geq 0$	$y \geq -3$

FIGURE 5.56.
Table for Question 12.

What do you observe?

13. Use your graphing calculator to graph the functions in **Figure 5.57** and fill in the blanks.

Function	Describe Changes to the Parent Function	Domain	Range
$y = \sqrt{x}$	Parent function	$x \geq 0$	$y \geq 0$
$y = \sqrt{x+3}$		$x \geq -3$	$y \geq 0$
$y = \sqrt{x-2}$		$x \geq 2$	$y \geq 0$

FIGURE 5.57.
Table for Question 13.

What do you observe?

14. Use your graphing calculator to graph the functions in **Figure 5.58** and fill in the blanks.

Function	Describe Changes to the Parent Function	Domain	Range
$y = \sqrt{x}$	Parent function	$x \geq 0$	$y \geq 0$
$y = 0.5\sqrt{x}$		$x \geq 0$	$y \geq 0$
$y = 2\sqrt{x}$		$x \geq 0$	$y \geq 0$

FIGURE 5.58.
Table for Question 14.

What do you observe?

15. Use your graphing calculator to graph the functions in **Figure 5.59** and fill in the blanks.

Function	Describe Changes to the Parent Function	Domain	Range
$y = \sqrt{x}$	Parent function	$x \geq 0$	$y \geq 0$
$y = -\sqrt{x}$		$x \geq 0$	$y \leq 0$
$y = -0.5\sqrt{x}$		$x \geq 0$	$y \leq 0$

FIGURE 5.59.
Table for Question 15.

What do you observe?

16. How are the transformations of $y = \sqrt{x}$ similar to what you learned about transformations of $y = x^2$?

17. Use a graphing calculator to make a table for $y = \sqrt{x-4}$, why does the word "ERROR" appear for values of x that are less than 4?

18. Graph $f(x) = x^2 + 2$ for $x \geq 0$. Graph its inverse. What is the equation of the inverse, $f^{-1}(x)$?

SUMMARY

The graph of the inverse of the graph of a function is the reflection of the function over the line $y = x$. The domain of the function becomes the range of its inverse. The range of the function becomes the domain of its inverse.

The inverse of the quadratic parent function where $x \geq 0$ is the square root function. Transformations of the square root function have effects like those of the quadratic parent function.

❖ $f(x) = \sqrt{x} + c$ results in a vertical translation.

❖ $f(x) = \sqrt{x+c}$ results in a horizontal translation.

❖ $f(x) = a\sqrt{x}$ results in a vertical compression, vertical stretch, or a reflection over the x-axis.

Assignment

1. Plot this relation and its inverse on a grid. Use a different color to distinguish the function from its inverse.

   {(–8, 0), (–7, 1), (–4, 2), (1, 3), (5, 3.5), (8, 4)}

2. Graph the inverse of the relation in **Figure 5.60** on the same grid. (Hint: You can fold your paper along the line $y = x$ to check your answer.)

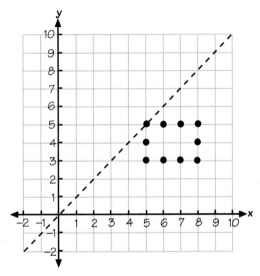

FIGURE 5.60.
Scatterplot for Question 2.

For Questions 3–8, is the statement true or false?

3. If the point (L, D) is a member of some function, then (D, L) is a member of its inverse.

4. If a function's graph intersects the graph of the line $y = x$ at a certain point, its inverse must intersect the line $y = x$ at the same point.

5. The inverse of any function is also a function.

6. A function could intersect the line $y = x$ at (5, 8).

7. The graphs of a function and its inverse are mirror images across the line $y = x$.

8. The domain of any set serves as the range of its inverse.

9. Graph $f(x) = \sqrt{x} + 3$ on a grid.

   a) State the domain.

   b) State the range.

   c) Using your knowledge of inverses, state the domain and range of the inverse (f^{-1}) of $f(x) = \sqrt{x} + 3$.

   d) Sketch the graph of the inverse on the same grid.

   e) Now find the inverse function.

10. Graph the following transformations of the square root function.

   a) $f(x) = -2\sqrt{x}$

   b) $f(x) = \sqrt{x} + 2$

   c) $f(x) = \sqrt{x+2}$

Just a Swingin'

Set up an experiment as shown in **Figure 5.61** and time the period of the pendulum for different lengths of string. Here are the steps.

Step 1: On a large sheet of chart paper draw a vertical line.

Step 2: Use a protractor to measure 10° off center of the vertical line and draw another line.

Step 3: Tape the sheet of chart paper to the edge of a desk or table.

Step 4: Tape a pencil to the surface of the desk at the point where the vertical line and the angled line intersect.

Step 5: Make sure you have enough space for a pendulum to swing freely.

Step 6: Tie a washer to the end of the string.

Step 7: Attach the string to the pencil so the length from the pencil to the center of the washer is 15 centimeters.

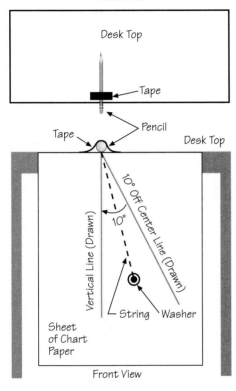

FIGURE 5.61.
Pendulum experiment.

Step 8: Pull the washer back to the 10° line. Let the washer drop freely: do not push or throw it. The washer should swing back and forth in a plane. If it appears to be swinging in a circular fashion, repeat the trial.

Length of Pendulum (cm)	Time for 10 Swings (sec)	Period (sec)
15		
25		
35		
45		
55		
65		

Step 9: Using a stopwatch or a digital watch, find the time it takes for the pendulum to make 10 full swings. Record your measurement in a table like **Figure 5.62.**

FIGURE 5.62.
Table for pendulum experiment.

Step 10: Calculate the time for one period and record it in the table.

Step 11: Continue measuring the time required for 10 back-and-forth swings as you change the length of the string as shown in the table. You may try other lengths if you wish.

1. How does changing the length of the string affect the period of the pendulum?

2. Graph the results from your experiment on a coordinate grid, and then make a scatterplot on a graphing calculator.

3. Which parent function (linear, quadratic, or square root) best fits your data?

4. Write a function rule to fit your data. Test your function with the graphing calculator.

5. The relationship between the length of a simple pendulum and the period of the pendulum is described by

$$\textit{Period of a pendulum} = \frac{2\pi}{\sqrt{\textit{Acceleration due to gravity}}} \cdot \sqrt{\textit{Length of pendulum}}.$$

If the acceleration due to gravity is 980 cm/sec^2, is this equation similar to the function you found?

$$P = \frac{2\pi}{\sqrt{\dfrac{980\ \text{cm}}{\text{sec}^2}}} \cdot \sqrt{L}\ \text{cm}$$

$$P = \frac{2\pi}{\sqrt{980}}\sqrt{L}\ \text{sec}$$

$$P = 0.2\sqrt{L}\ \text{sec}$$

6. Use your function to predict the period for a pendulum that is 200 cm in length.

7. A clockmaker wants the swing of a pendulum to match a clock's ticking of the seconds. In other words, he wants the period of the pendulum to be 2 seconds. How long should the pendulum be?

8. Ava notices that her grandfather clock is slow. To adjust it should she make the pendulum wire longer or shorter?

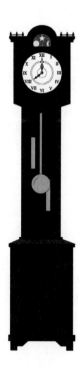

1. Sketch the inverse of each graph in **Figure 5.63.** The graph of $y = x$ is shown as a dotted line to help you sketch the inverse.

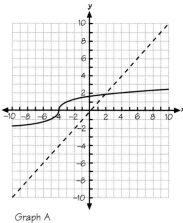

Graph A

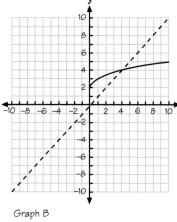

Graph B

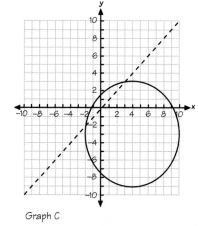

Graph C

FIGURE 5.63.
Three graphs for Question 1.

2. Look at the inverses you sketched in Question 1. Decide if each inverse is a function or a relation.

   Graph A: Function or relation?

   Graph B: Function or relation?

   Graph C: Function or relation?

3. The graph of $y = (x + 1)^2$ is shown in **Figure 5.64.** Answer these questions based on this graph.

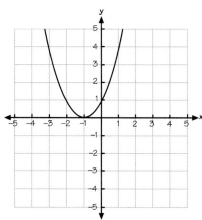

FIGURE 5.64. Graph of $y = (x + 1)^2$.

   a) State the domain and range of the function.

   b) Sketch the graph of the inverse.

   c) State the domain and range of the inverse.

   d) What two functions can be entered into your calculator in order to see the graph of the inverse?

   e) Is the inverse of $y = (x + 1)^2$ a function? Justify your answer.

   f) How could you restrict the domain of $y = (x + 1)^2$ so its inverse would be a function?

4. Graph each function.

   a) $f(x) = 2\sqrt{x}$

   b) $f(x) = \sqrt{x} - 3$

   c) $f(x) = \sqrt{x-3}$

The distance you can see from the top of a building depends on the building's height. If h is the height in meters of your viewing place, the distance you can see in kilometers on a clear day is modeled by

$S(h) = 3.532\sqrt{h}$.

5. From a height of 100 meters how far can you see?

6. Draw a graph for $S(h) = 3.532\sqrt{h}$. How can the graph of $S(h)$ be obtained from the graph of the square root parent function?

7. If you can see 14 km from the top of a ride at an amusement park, how tall is the ride?

   a) List examples of situations where this viewing model might not be accurate.

Rolling Stone

An object's acceleration on an incline is constant. The distance (d) moved from rest is related to the time (t) that a marble has been rolling by a constant k, which is unique to each incline (see **Figure 5.65**).

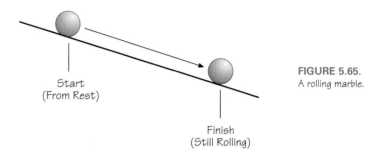

Start
(From Rest)

Finish
(Still Rolling)

FIGURE 5.65.
A rolling marble.

Trial	Distance (d)	Time (t)
A	0.25 m	1.77 sec
B	0.40 m	2.23 sec
C	0.55 m	2.65 sec
D	0.70 m	2.96 sec
E	0.85 m	3.25 sec
F	1.00 m	3.54 sec

FIGURE 5.66.
Math students' data.

1. A group of math students measured the distance, d, a marble rolled down a plane and the time, t, it took for the marble to roll each distance. They recorded their data in the table in **Figure 5.66**.

a) Make a scatterplot of the group's data.

b) Find a function that fits the data.

Trial	Distance (d)	Time (t)
G	0.25 m	1.50 sec
H	0.40 m	1.95 sec
I	0.55 m	2.25 sec
J	0.70 m	2.60 sec
K	0.85 m	2.87 sec
L	1.00 m	3.05 sec

FIGURE 5.67.
Data for Question 2.

2. Another group of students measured the distance and time for a marble to roll down a different plane. Their data are shown in **Figure 5.67**.

a) Make a scatterplot of the data.

b) Find a function that fits the data.

3. The two groups of students want to set up a marble stunt with their inclines as shown in **Figure 5.68.** At what distance should each marble be released for them to meet at the bottom exactly 4 seconds later?

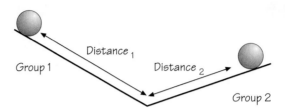

FIGURE 5.68.
Inclines for Question 3.

Assignment

The questions below are based on the relationship $k = \frac{d}{t^2}$.

1. If your value for k is 0.5 m/s², write a function for distance (d) in terms of time (t).

2. Use your function from Question 1 to calculate the distance your marble would move during the times in the table in **Figure 5.69.** Complete the table.

FIGURE 5.69.
Data table for Question 2.

Time (t)	0 s	0.4 s	0.6 s	0.8 s	1.0 s	1.2 s
Distance (d)						

3. Let time (in seconds) serve as your domain and distance (in meters) as your range. Draw a scatterplot of your data from Question 2.

4. Graph the function you wrote in Question 1.

5. What is the parent function for this graph?

6. Now switch your domain and range so that distance (now in meters) serves as your domain and time (now in seconds) as your range. Draw a scatterplot using the data from Question 2.

7. What is the parent function for this graph?

8. Are the two graphs inverses of each other?

9. Find an equation for the inverse of your function from Question 1. Hint: Solve for t.

10. Graph the equation you found in Question 9.

Modeling Project Designing The Hero's Fall

In this project you will design a stunt for a western movie in which the hero falls off a rooftop onto the roof of a stagecoach being drawn by a team of horses. In order to make your plans, you'll need to choose the height of the building, the speed of the stagecoach, and the dimensions of the stagecoach. Make sure your choices are as realistic as possible.

In order to make your stunt work so that the hero does not break any bones, it is important for your hero to know when to jump.

CHECK THIS!

Recall that when an object falls freely, its height can be modeled by the function

$$h = \frac{1}{2}gt^2 + h_0$$

h is the height, g is the acceleration due to gravity (hint: remember this is a constant), and t is time

1. What function will you use to model the motion of the hero during the fall? Explain your reasoning.

2. How long will it take the hero to reach the height of the roof of the stagecoach? Explain your plan.

3. In this situation, height is calculated in feet and time in seconds. However, the speed of the stagecoach is 20 miles per hour. Convert the speed of the stagecoach to feet per second.

4. The hero should begin the fall the instant the center of the stagecoach (not including the horses) reaches a mark in the road. Where should you place this mark so that the hero will land safely on top of the stagecoach? (Show the distance between the mark and the hero's drop point.) Explain your answer.

Practice Problems

1. Answer these questions about the function
   $y - 3\sqrt{x-2} + 1$.

   a) What is the domain?

   b) What is the range?

2. $h(t) = -5t^2 + 80$ describes the height in meters of a falling body after t seconds. Find the intercepts of the function's graph and interpret them in this context. Explain the role of the constants -5 and 80.

3. Using quadratic models sometimes requires solving quadratic equations. Among the methods you may have used to solve quadratic equations in previous courses are:

   A graphing calculator procedure such as graphing and zooming;

   A spreadsheet procedure such as zooming on a table;

   Factoring;

   The Quadratic Formula;

   Completing the square.

   The first two methods give approximate solutions and the last three give exact solutions. Solve $6x^2 + 17x = 10$ by at least two methods.

4. Solve $2x^2 - 11x + 12 = 0$ using the factoring method.

5. The table in **Figure 5.70** contains data on the distance it takes a car to stop while traveling at various speeds.

Speed (mph)	20	30	40	50	60	70
Stopping Distance (ft)	42	74	116	173	248	343

FIGURE 5.70.
Stopping distances
for different speeds.

   a) Create a mathematical model that predicts the stopping distance for any speed. Explain why you think your model is a good one.

b) A police officer at an accident scene estimates that a car needed 300 feet to stop. Write an equation for this situation, and use one of the methods you learned in this chapter to solve it. Describe the method you used.

6. Write each expression in the form stated:

a) $2(x + 4)(x - 3)$ as a general quadratic expression.

b) $3x^2 + 11x + 6$ in factored form.

7. Change the following general quadratic equations into the specified form:

a) $y = 0.5x^2 + 1.5x - 5.0$ in factored form.

b) $y = 2x^2 + 8x + 3$ in vertex form.

8. The graph of $y = 0.5x^2 - 1.5x - 2$ is shown in **Figure 5.71.**

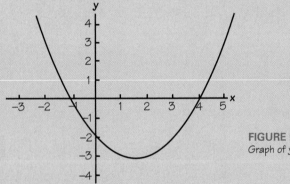

FIGURE 5.71.
Graph of $y = 0.5x^2 - 1.5x - 2$.

a) What are the x-intercepts?

b) What are the coordinates for the vertex?

c) How can you tell from looking at the original equation that the quadratic will look like a "U" (and not upside down)?

9. Given the function $y - 3 = 0.5(x + 1)^2$:

a) Explain the role that each of the three constants play in determining the graph of the function.

b) Sketch the graph of the function.

c) Stretch the graph vertically by a factor of 3 and move it 4 units to the right and 1 unit down. What equation describes the new graph?

10. Solve each of these equations. Explain the method you used.

a) $0.4(x + 3)(x - 2) = 0$

b) $1.6(x + 1)^2 - 3 = 10$

c) $2x^2 + 8x - 5 = 0$

11. A property of quadratic relationships that was explored in this chapter is that second differences are constant. You can prove that to be the case, as well as develop ways to construct the equation from patterns in the table of differences.

a) Substitute each value of x in **Figure 5.72** into $y = ax^2 + bx + c$.

b) Record the *expression* obtained for y in the column labeled y-value.

x-value	y-value	First Differences	Second Differences
0			
1			
2			
3			
4			
5			

FIGURE 5.72.
Table for Question 11.

c) Calculate first and second differences the same way you would if there were numbers in the table. Record your answers in the table.

d) Explain how the work done shows that with quadratic functions, second differences are constant.

e) Explain how to find the values for a, b, and c from the table.

f) Use your answer to e to find a function that fits the data in **Figure 5.73**.

x	y
0	2
1	9
2	20
3	35
4	54
5	77

FIGURE 5.73.
Table for Question 11f.

12. From the top of the Eiffel Tower, which is 300 meters tall, how far can you see?

13. A tsunami, a series of waves created by an undersea earthquake, hit Asia in 2004. Hundreds of thousands of people died. Now monitoring stations determine the speed and force of these waves. A key variable in the damage a wave can do is ocean depth. Ocean depth can be found using the function $s = \sqrt{gd}$ where g is 9.8 meters per second squared (the force of gravity), s is the speed of the wave in meters per second, and d is the depth of the ocean. If a wave is moving at 99 meters per second, how deep is the ocean?

Glossary

KEY CONCEPTS

Binomials: Algebraic expressions involving two terms, usually with one of them containing a variable.

Coefficient: The real number in a mathematical expression. In $3x^2$ the 3 is the coefficient.

Completing the Square: The process of placing a quadratic in vertex form. Completing the square is used to solve quadratic equations.

Dilation (graph): A transformation that stretches or compresses a graph.

Equivalent: When two expressions produce identical values and solutions for all numbers.

Factored Form of a Quadratic: A quadratic of the form $y = a(x - r_1)(x - r_2)$.

First Differences: A pattern of numbers produced by subtracting successive values from a data table in which the x-values increase by a constant amount. If first differences are constant then the equation describing the data is linear.

General Form of a Quadratic: A quadratic of the form $y = ax^2 + bx + c$.

Inverse of a Relation: A reflection of the relation over the line $y = x$.

Inverse Operations: Pairs of operations that undo each other. Addition and subtraction are inverse operations.

Polynomial Form of a Quadratic: A quadratic of the form $y = ax^2 + bx + c$.

Quadratic Formula: A formula used to solve quadratic equations of the form $ax^2 + bx + c = 0$. The solutions are:

$$x = \frac{-b \pm \sqrt{b^2 - 4ac}}{2a}.$$

Quadratic Function : A function of the form $y = ax^2 + bx + c$. The highest power of x in a quadratic is 2.

Roots of an Equation: Values that make an equation true.

Second Differences: The pattern of numbers produced by subtracting successive first differences. If the second differences are constant, then the equation describing the data is quadratic.

Square Root: A factor of a number that, when squared, gives the original number.

$\sqrt{\ }$ (Square Root Symbol): The principal square root of a number. The principal square root of a positive number is the positive square root.

Square Root Function: A function in the form $f(x) = \sqrt{x}$ is called a square root function and is defined for all $x \geq 0$.

Transformation (graph): In this chapter, a rule that changes one graph into another.

Translation (graph): A transformation that affects either the x- or y-values of an equation by adding or subtracting a number. Translations produce a "shift" or "slide" effect on a graph.

Vertex Form of a Quadratic: A quadratic of the form $y = a(x - h)^2 + k$.

Vertex of a Parabola: A point on the graph of a quadratic where the left-side and right-side (symmetric) parts meet. The vertex is either the highest or lowest point of the parabola.

x-intercept: A point where the graph of a function crosses the x-axis. The x-coordinate of the intercept is called a zero of the function.

Zero-Product Property: If $ab = 0$, then $a = 0$ or $b = 0$ or both $a = 0$ and $b = 0$. For example, if $(x + 4)(x - 3) = 0$ the Zero-Product Property states that either $x + 4 = 0$ or $x - 3 = 0$ or both. Thus, $x = -4$ and $x = 3$ are solutions to this equation.

Zeros of a Function: Values for which a function is 0. They are also the x-coordinates of the points where the function's graph crosses the x-axis.

6

CHAPTER

Growth & Decay: Exponential Functions

"For the Benefit and Enjoyment of the People"

As American pioneers settled the West in the 1800s, many of them noticed the beauty of the Great Plains, Rocky Mountains, and Pacific coast. As early as the 1830s, some people began to express concern about the impact people were having on this land and the Native Americans who lived there.

In 1872, President Ulysses S. Grant signed legislation from Congress that set aside Yellowstone Country in Wyoming and Montana Territories "as a public park or pleasuring-ground for the benefit and enjoyment of the people." Yellowstone became the first piece of land in the world to become a national park and was the start of the United States National Park Service.

The National Park Service is now almost 400 parks, historic sites, and sanctuaries. States, counties, and cities also have park services that oversee state and local parks. These parks range from campgrounds and playgrounds to cultural sites.

Park managers must make many decisions about how to balance the needs of human park visitors with the need to preserve the natural environment. In a large park such as Yellowstone, park managers must be able to survey and define each part of the park. They must also keep a careful count of the population of wildlife such as bison, wolves, moose, and fish. Managing disease and giving medicine to sick animals is important in protecting endangered species.

On the human side, park managers must deal with resource management. Renewable resources such as forests must be managed in order to balance the needs of the lumber industry with the need to preserve the park's natural setting. Non-renewable resources such as coal and oil reserves must also be carefully managed.

In a popular park such as Yellowstone, there are many visitors in a year. Park visitors can have a large impact on the park from traffic and noise pollution to the large amounts of garbage that they leave behind.

In this chapter you'll examine some of the issues that park managers face. You'll use mathematical models to solve problems such as wildlife population control and resource management. You will explore and define exponential and logarithmic functions and use them to model real-world situations. Then you will use these models to solve practical problems.

SECTION 6.1

Paper Cutting

Just about everything in our world changes over time. Sometimes the change happens quickly, such as a teenager's growth spurt over a summer or an increase of 200,000 bacteria in a container of water. Other changes occur slowly, for example, the erosion of a mountain peak or an increase in Earth's surface temperature.

Patterns of growth can be used to classify behavior. In this chapter, patterns for describing change in quantities are explored. The challenge is to understand what kind of growth patterns a quantity is undergoing and how those patterns can be modeled. Once you determine the type of growth pattern, you can apply the models to a host of other situations such as wildlife populations, radioactive decay, resource depletion, and resource harvest.

1. Cut a piece of paper in half. Lay the two sheets on top of each other. Cut each of the two sheets of paper in half again. Continue cutting, counting the number of layers of paper when the pieces are stacked up, and filling in the table in **Figure 6.1.**

Number of Cuts	Process	Number of Layers of Paper
0		
1		
2		
3		
4		
5		
6		

FIGURE 6.1.
A table for paper cutting.

CHECK THIS!

Repeated multiplication can be written with a base and an exponent. For example, $5 \times 5 \times 5$ can be rewritten as 5^3. The factor 5 is the base. The number that tells how many times the base is multiplied is the exponent.

2. Use a copy of the grid in **Figure 6.2** to make a scatterplot of your data.

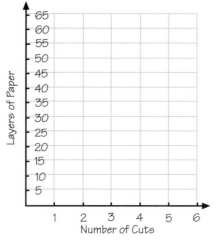

FIGURE 6.2.
Layers of paper versus number of cuts.

3. Write a function for the number of layers of paper if you cut the paper *n* times.

4. Is this function continuous or discrete? Why?

5. What are the domain and range of this function?

6. Use a graphing calculator to make a scatterplot of the data. Then sketch the graph of the function on the scatterplot and record your window.

7. A ream of paper is almost 2 inches thick. If a ream is 500 sheets of paper, about how thick is a piece of paper?

8. Complete the table in **Figure 6.3.**

Number of Cuts	Process	Thickness (in inches)
0		
1		
2		
3		
4		
5		
6		

FIGURE 6.3.
Paper cuts, process, and thicknesses.

Chapter 6 Growth & Decay: Exponential Functions

9. Write a function rule for the thickness of the stack in inches if you cut the paper *n* times.

10. How are the function that models the thickness of the stack and the function you found for the number of layers after *n* cuts related?

11. Sketch a graph for the thickness of the stack, and label the axes.

12. How is this graph transformed from the graph that you drew in Question 6?

13. Complete the tables in **Figures 6.4 and 6.5** using the data from Questions 1 through 12.

Number of Cuts	Number of Layers
0	
1	
2	
3	
4	
5	
6	

FIGURE 6.4. Paper cuts and layers.

Number of Cuts	Thickness (inches)
0	
1	
2	
3	
4	
5	
6	

FIGURE 6.5. Paper cuts and thicknesses.

14. Recall that linear functions can be written from patterns that show repeated addition. The two functions in this section are exponential functions. Exponential functions can be written from patterns that show repeated multiplication or division. Show how the tables in Figures 6.4 and 6.5 display a pattern of repeated multiplication.

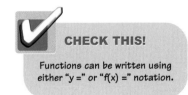

CHECK THIS!

Functions can be written using either "y =" or "f(x) =" notation.

15. A general form of an exponential equation is $f(x) = a \cdot b^x$. From the tables in Figures 6.4 and 6.5, what determines the value of *a*? How is *a* related to the graph of the function?

16. What determines the value of *b*?

1. If you cut the paper 22 times, how many layers do you have? Write an equation to help you solve this problem.

2. If you cut the paper 22 times and stack it up, how tall is the stack? Write an equation to help you solve this problem.

3. A box of paper is 5 reams deep. A ream has 500 sheets of paper. About how many cuts would you need to make a stack at least as thick as a box of paper?

4. The Eiffel Tower is approximately 1050 feet tall. If you had a big enough piece of paper, how many cuts would you need to have a stack that equals or exceeds this height?

Moose Population

When animals move to a new place, it is called migration. In 1988, Adirondack State Park in upstate New York had a moose population of about 17 moose. The park is not fenced, and moose migrate into the park from other regions. Assume that the only change in population is due to migration and that the migration rate is two moose per year.

1. Make a table like **Figure 6.6** and use it to predict the number of moose in the year 2000 (12 years later).

Year	Year Number	Number of Moose
1988	0	
1989	1	
1990	2	
1991	3	
1992	4	
1993	5	
1994	6	
1995	7	
1996	8	
1997	9	
1998	10	
1999	11	
2000	12	

FIGURE 6.6.
Table for predicting the number of moose in the park.

2. Make a scatterplot of your data.

3. Find a function rule that models the moose migration. Check it with the graphing calculator. Explain why your function is a good model for the moose migration.

4. In Questions 1–3, the only reason for population change is the migration of moose into the park. Growth also occurs due to reproduction. Babies eventually have their own babies. If you assume that the moose population is 17 in 1988 and doubles each year due to migration and reproduction, make a table like **Figure 6.7** and use it to predict the moose population in 2000.

Year	Year Number	Process Column	Number of Moose
1988	0		
1989	1		
1990	2		
1991	3		
1992	4		
1993	5		
1994	6		
1995	7		
1996	8		
1997	9		
1998	10		
1999	11		
2000	12		

FIGURE 6.7.
Table for predicting the moose population in 2000.

5. Make a scatterplot of the data in Question 4.

6. Find a function rule that models the moose migration in Question 4. Check your function with a graphing calculator. Explain why your function is a good model.

For each of these tables, decide if the data show exponential growth, linear growth, or neither. If the growth set is linear or exponential, write a function rule for the pattern. Make a scatterplot with a graphing calculator and check your function to see if it fits.

1.

Year	Population
0	3
1	12
2	48
3	192
4	768

2.

Year	Population
0	3
1	12
2	21
3	30
4	39

3.

Year	Population
0	3
1	12
2	27
3	48
4	75

4.

Year	Population
0	3
1	6
2	12
3	24
4	48

Exponential Functions

Here are the types of function models that you have seen so far in this text:

❖ A linear function is an addition function. As the *x*-values in the domain increase by a constant amount, the *y*-values increase by a constant amount. The first differences of function values are the same. An example of linear data and a function rule is shown in **Figure 6.8.**

x	f(x)
0	5
1	7
2	9
3	11
4	13

+1 +2
+1 +2
+1 +2
+1 +2

FIGURE 6.8.
A linear set of data and its function rule.

The rate of change is 2. The linear function is $f(x) = 2x + 5$.

❖ In a quadratic function the second differences are constant. An example of quadratic data and a function rule is shown in **Figure 6.9.**

FIGURE 6.9.
A quadratic set of data and its function rule.

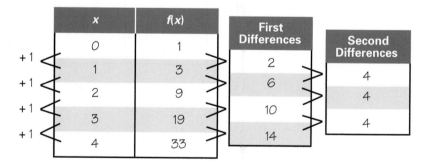

x	f(x)	First Differences	Second Differences
0	1		
1	3	2	
2	9	6	4
3	19	10	4
4	33	14	4

The quadratic function is $f(x) = 2x^2 + 1$.

❖ An exponential function is a multiplication function. As the *x*-values in the domain increase by a constant amount, the *y*-values are multiplied by a common multiplier. An example of exponential data and a function rule is shown in **Figure 6.10.**

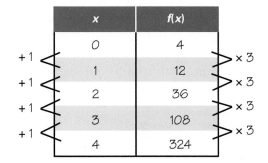

FIGURE 6.10.
An exponential set of data and its function rule.

The common multiplier is 3. The exponential function is $f(x) = 4 \cdot 3^x$.

In this same set of exponential data, notice that the first and second differences are not constants, as shown in **Figure 6.11.**

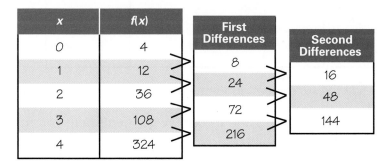

FIGURE 6.11.
An exponential set of data with first and second differences.

CHECK THIS!

The exponential parent function is written in the form $f(x) = b^x$. The constant *b* is the common multiplier, the value by which you repeatedly multiply or divide. In the paper cutting in Section 6.1, you started with 1 layer when there were 0 cuts. In your investigation of the thickness of the stack after a certain number of cuts, you started with a thickness of 0.004 inches when there were 0 cuts. In the modeling situations in this chapter, the initial value occurs when the independent variable is 0. Thus, in the exponential function $f(x) = a \cdot b^x$ that is used to model these situations, the constant *a* is the initial value of the dependent variable.

In previous sections you learned how to find a common multiplier. Look at the problem below and find the common multiplier. To find the common multiplier, you will use successive quotients. A successive quotient is the ratio of a y-value to the previous y-value.

A mosquito control scientist collected the data in **Figure 6.12** over a five-month period. Rainfall was very high during this summer, and the county did not have enough money to spray in order to control the mosquito population. Each month the scientist collected 5000 mosquitoes and tested them for West Nile Virus.

Month	Month Number	Number of Mosquitoes Found Testing Positive for West Nile Virus	Successive Quotients
May	0	400	—
June	1	600	$\frac{600}{400} = 1.5$
July	2	900	$\frac{900}{600} = 1.5$
August	3	1350	$\frac{1350}{900} = 1.5$
September	4	2025	$\frac{2025}{1350} = 1.5$

FIGURE 6.12.
Mosquito data.

1. Are the successive quotients the same?

2. How does finding the successive quotients help you find the common multiplier?

3. Find a function rule for the data in the table.

4. Check your function with a graphing calculator.

5. How are the three exponential functions listed below alike, and how do they differ?

$$f(x) = 1 \cdot 2^x \qquad f(x) = 3 \cdot 2^x \qquad f(x) = 0.5 \cdot 2^x$$

6. Use a graphing calculator to graph all three at the same time. Sketch the result on your paper.

7. How does changing a in $f(x) = a \cdot b^x$ change the graph?

CHECK THIS!

In the general exponential function $f(x) = a \cdot b^x$, if $b > 0$ and $a > 1$, the parent graph of $f(x) = b^x$ is stretched vertically. If the value of a is between 0 and 1, the graph is compressed vertically.

Assignment

Decide if a linear, quadratic, or exponential function best describes the data in each table. Find the function.

1.

x	f(x)
0	0.75
1	1.875
2	4.6875
3	11.719
4	29.297

2.

x	f(x)
-2	8
-1	2
0	0
1	2
2	8

3.

x	f(x)
0	2
1	2.44
2	2.88
3	3.456
4	4.1472

4.

x	f(x)
-3	-11
-2	-8
-1	-5
0	-2
1	1

Answer Questions 5–10 for $f(x) = 3(2.25)^x$.

5. Graph the function.

6. Fill in the table in **Figure 6.13** with 5 values for the function.

x	f(x)
0	
1	
2	
3	
4	

FIGURE 6.13.
Table of values.

7. What is the *y*-intercept of the graph?

8. What is the common multiplier?

9. Is $f(x)$ a continuous or discrete function?

10. Is $f(x) = 3(2.25)^x$ a vertical stretch or vertical compression of $f(x) = 2.25^x$?

Use **Figure 6.14** to answer Questions 11–15.

x	f(x)	Successive Quotients
0	0.5	
1	1.75	
2	6.125	
3	21.438	
4	75.031	

FIGURE 6.14.
Table for Questions 11–15.

11. Find the successive quotients for the set of data.

12. Why does an exponential function fit the data?

13. What is the initial value of the function?

14. What is the common multiplier?

15. Find an exponential function that fits the data.

 M&M's® Growth

First and second differences and successive quotients are not always exactly equal in real-world data. In this activity you will gather data and fit a function.

Start with 4 M&M's in a cup. Shake the cup, roll out the M&M's, and then count the number with "m" showing. Multiply that number by 2 and add that many M&M's to the cup. Keep a record of the population and repeat the process 5 times. Before you start, answer Question 1.

1. What would you expect the population to be at each roll? Write your predictions in a table like **Figure 6.15.**

Trial	Predicted Population
0	
1	
2	
3	
4	
5	

FIGURE 6.15.
Table for predicting the M&M's population.

2. Add a column for the actual population to your table. Conduct the experiment, and fill in your actual population column.

3. How close are your results to what you predicted?

4. Combine the data with the rest of the class, and enter these data into lists in a calculator. Use transformations to create a function to fit the data.

5. Are the results more reasonable with all of the data? Take successive quotients to confirm your answer.

6. Find a function to fit the data. Check it by graphing the function on a scatterplot. Sketch the graph.

Assignment

In 1995 there were about 60,000 centenarians in the United States. A centenarian is a person at least 100 years old. Imagine that a researcher continued to collect data through 2002 as shown in **Figure 6.16.**

Year	Year Number	Number of Centenarians	Successive Quotients
1995	0	60,000	
1996	1	64,200	1.07
1997	2	68,694	1.07
1998	3	73,503	1.07
1999	4	78,648	1.07
2000	5	84,153	1.07
2001	6	90,044	1.07
2002	7	96,346	1.07

FIGURE 6.16.
Centenarian data from 1995–2002.

1. Make a scatterplot of the data.

2. Explain which type of function (linear, quadratic, or exponential) should fit these data.

3. Find a function that fits the data well.

4. A researcher claimed that the number of centenarians would reach 232,000 by the year 2015. Verify that the researcher is correct based on the function you found in Question 3.

5. When will the number of centenarians reach 1,000,000 based on your model?

6. A scientist is trying to project deer population in a forest. The sample data are shown in **Figure 6.17.** Find successive differences, and then find the successive quotients. Write them in a copy of the table. Round quotients to the nearest hundredth.

Year	Year Number	Population	Successive Differences	Successive Quotients
2000	0	1500		
2001	1	1545		
2002	2	1591		
2003	3	1639		
2004	4	1688		
2005	5	1739		
2006	6	1791		
2007	7	1845		

FIGURE 6.17.
Sample data for
a deer population.

7. Sketch a scatterplot of the data.

8. Are the data linear or exponential? Why?

9. Determine the growth rate.

10. Find a function that models the growth.

11. Use your function to predict the population in the year 2010.

Moose Population in National Parks

Let's apply to a new situation what you have learned thus far about exponential functions.

Managers from four parks in New York, New England, and Canada are meeting to discuss how they can protect the moose population. Each of them has been recording the population of moose in their parks. The tables in **Figure 6.18** contain data that they brought to the meeting.

FIGURE 6.18.
Moose population data from four parks.

Adirondack Park (New York)		
Year	Year Number	Population
2000		50
2001		55
2002		61
2003		67
2004		73

Green Mountain National Forest (Vermont)		
Year	Year Number	Population
2000		2
2001		4
2002		8
2003		16
2004		32

Algonquin Provincial Park (Ontario, Canada)		
Year	Year Number	Population
2000		10
2001		15
2002		23
2003		34
2004		51

White Mountain National Forest (New Hampshire)		
Year	Year Number	Population
2000		50
2001		54
2002		58
2003		62
2004		66

If the moose population in each park continues to grow at the same rate, which park will have the most moose in 2015? Explain your answer.

SUMMARY

In this lesson you learned that exponential functions are good mathematical models for certain growth situations. You also reviewed other mathematical models:

❖ A linear model is an addition model.

❖ A quadratic model has second differences that are constant.

❖ An exponential model is a multiplication model.

Exponential models have these properties:

❖ Successive quotients are constant.

❖ The successive quotient is the common multiplier or the base of the exponential function.

❖ The parent function form for the exponential family is $f(x) = b^x$.

❖ A vertical compression or vertical stretch occurs when the parent function $f(x) = b^x$ is multiplied by a constant, a, $f(x) = a \cdot b^x$. This affects the y-intercept, the initial value, or a, in many modeling situations.

Fractional Parts and Area

Park managers often have to divide land into sections. One way to divide land is the rectangular survey system. This system uses rectangles or squares that are divided into equal parts. Each part is then given a name based on its location in relationship to the original rectangle or square.

In this section you will model the rectangular survey system by examining how the visible area of a sheet of paper changes as the paper is folded. You will look for patterns and make predictions.

First let's look at the part of a paper that is formed when a sheet of paper is folded.

You need an 8.5-inch by 11-inch sheet of paper. Before any folds are made, the fraction of the sheet of paper is 1 (the whole sheet).

1. Fold the sheet in half once. This fold splits the paper into regions bounded by the fold lines. Unfold the paper and count the number of regions. What fraction of the original sheet of paper is each new region?

2. Continue folding the paper and complete a table like **Figure 6.19.**

Number of Folds	Fraction of the Original Sheet of Paper
0	
1	
2	
3	
4	
5	
6	

FIGURE 6.19.
Table for paper folding data.

3. What patterns do you see in the table?

4. Based on the table values, does this relationship appear to be linear? How do you know?

5. Based on the table values, does this relationship appear to be quadratic? How do you know?

6. What is a reasonable domain here? Why?

7. What is a reasonable range here? Why?

8. Sketch what you would expect a graph of the fraction of the original sheet of paper versus the number of folds to look like. Why did you sketch the graph the way you did?

Now let's look at the area of the part of a paper that is formed when a sheet of paper is folded.

You will need a new 8.5-inch by 11-inch sheet of paper to fold. Before any folds are made, calculate the area in square inches of the sheet of paper.

9. What is the area of your sheet of paper?

10. Fold the sheet of paper one time; this fold splits the paper into regions bounded by the fold lines. What is the area of each new region?

11. Continue folding the paper and complete a table like the one in **Figure 6.20.**

Number of Folds	Area of a Region
0	
1	
2	
3	
4	
5	
6	

FIGURE 6.20.
Table for region area data.

12. What patterns do you see in the table?

13. Does the relationship between area and number of folds appear to be linear? How do you know?

14. Does the relationship appear to be quadratic? How do you know?

15. What is a reasonable domain here? Why?

16. What is a reasonable range here? Why?

17. Sketch what you expect a graph of the area of a region versus the number of folds to look like. Why did you sketch the graph the way you did?

Area of a Region

In the last section you used paper folding to break down a piece of paper into smaller regions, then you found the area of each region.

Examine the first table that you made in Section 6.6 (see **Figure 6.21**).

Number of Folds	Fraction of the Original Sheet of Paper
0	1
1	$\frac{1}{2}$
2	$\frac{1}{4}$
3	$\frac{1}{8}$
4	$\frac{1}{16}$
5	$\frac{1}{32}$
6	$\frac{1}{64}$

FIGURE 6.21. Table of values.

Number of Folds (n)	Process	Fraction of the Piece of Paper (f)
0	1	1
1	$1 \cdot \frac{1}{2}$	$\frac{1}{2}$
2	$1 \cdot \frac{1}{2} \cdot \frac{1}{2} = \frac{1}{2^2}$	$\frac{1}{4}$
3	$1 \cdot - \cdot - \cdot - = -$	$\frac{1}{8}$
4	$1 \cdot - \cdot - \cdot - \cdot - = -$	$\frac{1}{16}$
5	$1 \cdot - \cdot - \cdot - \cdot - \cdot - = -$	$\frac{1}{32}$
6	$1 \cdot - \cdot - \cdot - \cdot - \cdot - \cdot - = -$	$\frac{1}{64}$

FIGURE 6.22. Table of values with process column.

1. Use a graphing calculator to make a fraction of the original sheet versus the number of folds scatterplot. Record your window and sketch your graph.

2. What do you notice about the scatterplot?

3. How does each fraction of a sheet relate to the one before it?

4. Using the answer to Question 3, copy the table and fill in the blanks in the process column (see **Figure 6.22**).

5. What stays the same in the process column?

6. What changes in the process column?

7. Write a function rule that models this situation.

8. In the context of the paper folding activity, what does each number mean in your rule from Question 7?

9. Graph your function rule on your scatterplot. If the graph is not a good fit, change your rule. Sketch your graph.

CHECK THIS!

To find successive quotients, divide each value by the one before it.

10. What will be the fraction of the piece of paper after 9 folds?

11. If the fraction of the sheet of paper is $\frac{1}{256}$, how many times has it been folded?

12. Find the successive quotients for fraction of the sheet of paper and record them in a table like **Figure 6.23**.

Number of Folds	Fraction of the Original Sheet of Paper	Successive Quotients
0	1	
1	$\frac{1}{2}$	
2	$\frac{1}{4}$	
3	$\frac{1}{8}$	
4	$\frac{1}{16}$	
5	$\frac{1}{32}$	
6	$\frac{1}{64}$	

FIGURE 6.23.
Table of values with column for successive quotients.

13. What do you notice about the successive quotients?

14. Where do you see the successive quotients in your function from Question 7?

Now look at the second table you made in Section 6.6 (see **Figure 6.24**).

Number of Folds	Area of a Region
0	93.5 in^2
1	46.75 in^2
2	23.375 in^2
3	11.6875 in^2
4	5.84375 in^2
5	2.921875 in^2
6	1.4609375 in^2

FIGURE 6.24.
Table of values from Section 6.6.

15. Use a graphing calculator to make an area versus number of folds scatterplot. Record your window and sketch your graph.

16. What do you notice about the scatterplot?

17. How does each area relate to the area of the region before it?

Let's use a process column to help find a function.

18. Copy the table in **Figure 6.25** and fill in the blanks in the process column.

Number of Folds	Process	Area of a Region
0	93.5	93.5 in^2
1	$93.5 \cdot \frac{1}{2}$	46.75 in^2
2	$93.5 \cdot \frac{1}{2} \cdot \frac{1}{2} = 93.5 \cdot \frac{1}{2^2}$	23.375 in^2
3	$93.5 \cdot - \cdot - \cdot - = 93.5 \cdot -$	11.6875 in^2
4	$93.5 \cdot - \cdot - \cdot - = 93.5 \cdot -$	5.84375 in^2
5	$93.5 \cdot - \cdot - \cdot - \cdot - = 93.5 \cdot -$	2.921875 in^2
6	$93.5 \cdot - \cdot - \cdot - \cdot - = 93.5 \cdot -$	1.4609375 in^2

FIGURE 6.25.
Table of values with blanks in the process column.

19. What stays the same in the process column?

20. What changes in the process column?

21. Write a function rule that models this situation.

22. Graph your function rule on your scatterplot. If the graph is not a good fit, use transformations to change your rule. Sketch your graph.

23. What will be the area of the region of paper after 10 folds?

24. If the area of the region is 0.365234375 square inches, how many times has the paper been folded?

25. Calculate the successive quotients for area of a region and record them in a table like **Figure 6.26.**

Number of Folds	Area of a Region	Successive Quotients
0	93.5 in^2	
1	46.75 in^2	
2	23.375 in^2	
3	11.6875 in^2	
4	5.84375 in^2	
5	2.921875 in^2	
6	1.4609375 in^2	

FIGURE 6.26.
Table of values for calculating the successive quotients.

26. What do you notice about the successive quotients?

27. Where do you see the successive quotients in your function?

28. Write a sentence about the relationship of successive quotients to the function rule for an exponential function.

1. Rhonda is drawing a design in art class. She started by drawing a triangle. Next she drew a new triangle by connecting the midpoints of the sides of the first triangle. She shaded a new triangle. Next she found the midpoints of the sides of the unshaded triangles and connected them. Once again she shaded some new triangles. Her first three drawings are shown. Based on this pattern, complete the term value column in a table like **Figure 6.27.**

Term Number	Picture	Process Column	Term Value (Number of *Unshaded* Triangles)
0		1	1
1		$1 \cdot 3$	3
2			
3			
4			
n			

FIGURE 6.27.
Table for finding the number of unshaded triangles.

2. Use your graphing calculator to create a term value versus term number scatterplot. Record your window and sketch your graph.

3. What do you notice about the scatterplot?

4. How does each term value relate to the one before it?

5. Fill in the process column of your table.

6. What stays the same in the process column?

7. What changes in the process column?

8. Write a function rule that models this situation.

9. Graph your function rule on your scatterplot. If the graph is not a good fit, change your rule. Sketch your graph.

10. What will be the term value for the 9th term?

11. If there are 6561 new shaded triangles, what term number is this?

12. Next, Rhonda decided to examine the area of the smallest triangles she drew. She started by defining the area of the triangle for term number 0 as one square unit. So the area of the smallest triangle in her second figure is $\frac{1}{4}$ square units. Based on this pattern, complete the term value column in a table like **Figure 6.28.**

13. Use a graphing calculator to make a term value versus term number scatterplot. Record your window and sketch your graph.

14. What do you notice about the scatterplot?

15. How does each term value relate to the one before it?

16. Fill in the process column of your table.

Term Number	Picture	Process Column	Term Value (Area of the Smallest Triangle)
0	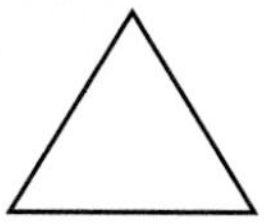	1	1
1		$1 \cdot \frac{1}{4}$	$\frac{1}{4}$
2	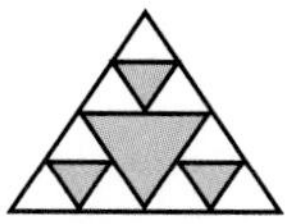		
3			
4			
n			

FIGURE 6.28.
Table for finding the area of the smallest triangle.

17. What stays the same in the process column?

18. What changes in the process column?

19. Write a function rule that models this situation.

20. Graph your function rule on your scatterplot. If the graph is not a good fit, change your rule. Sketch your graph.

21. What will be the term value for the 8th term in this pattern?

22. If the area of the smallest triangle is 0.000061 square units, what term number is this?

Characteristics of Exponential Functions

In the last sections you began to explore exponential functions. In this section you will see how and why those functions work the way they do.

Recall the paper cutting in Section 6.1. Each time the paper was cut, the number of layers of paper increased. This is an example of **exponential growth**.

1. How did the table show exponential growth?

2. How did the graph show exponential growth?

Recall the paper folding in Sections 6.6–6.7. Each time the paper was folded, the size of the region decreased. The pattern you observed is an example of **exponential decay**.

3. How did the table of data show exponential decay?

4. How did the graph show exponential decay?

5. How are the function rules for the relationship between the fraction of the paper and number of folds and the relationship between area and number of folds alike?

6. How do the function rules for the relationship between the fraction of the paper and number of folds and the relationship between area and number of folds differ?

Plant Height	
Number of Days	Height (cm)
0	2
1	5
2	8
3	11
4	14
5	17

+1 ... +3
+1 ... +3
+1 ... +3
+1 ... +3
+1 ... +3

ΔX   ΔY

Recall that linear relationships have a constant rate of change. In **Figure 6.29,** the height of a plant increases at a constant rate of 3 centimeters per day.

FIGURE 6.29.
Plant height.

7. In this linear relationship, what is the repeated operation?

8. What is a function rule that fits these data?

Let's compare the table for a linear relationship to the table for an exponential relationship. The table in **Figure 6.30** shows an exponential relationship between time and the amount of dissolved carbon dioxide (CO_2) in a can of soda.

Number of Hours	Dissolved CO_2
0	21.87
1	7.29
2	2.43
3	0.81
4	0.27
5	0.09

FIGURE 6.30.
Table of values for an exponential relationship.

9. How do these data show that this relationship is not linear or quadratic?

10. Is this relationship an example of exponential growth or exponential decay? How do you know?

11. Find successive quotients for the dissolved gas and record them in a table like **Figure 6.31.**

Number of Hours	Dissolved CO_2	Successive Quotients
0	21.87	
1	7.29	
2	2.43	
3	0.81	
4	0.27	
5	0.09	

FIGURE 6.31.
Table for recording successive quotients.

If a relationship is exponential and the rate of change of the independent variable is 1, then successive quotients of the dependent variable are constant.

12. What operation is repeated in an exponential relationship?

13. What is the function rule that fits these data?

The general function rule that models an exponential relationship is

y = (initial value) · (common multiplier)^x

$$y = a \cdot b^{\,x}$$

CHECK THIS!

The common multiplier in an exponential function is also called a common ratio because it is the ratio of successive values.

14. What must be the value of b, the common multiplier (successive quotient), in an exponential decay function?

15. What must be the value of b, the common multiplier (successive quotient), in an exponential growth function?

16. How can you find the base (b) of an exponential function in the form $y = a \cdot b^x$ from a table of values?

17. How can you find the initial value (a) for $y = a \cdot b^x$ from a table of values?

Wildlife scientists use models to predict animal populations. The data in **Figure 6.32** are for a bison population in a park.

Year	Year Number	Bison Population
1998	0	600
1999	1	570
2000	2	542
2001	3	514
2002	4	489
2003	5	464
2004	6	441
2005	7	419

FIGURE 6.32.
Bison population data.

18. Do these data show a linear relationship? How do you know?

19. Do these data show an exponential relationship? How do you know?

20. Is this relationship an example of exponential growth or exponential decay? How do you know?

21. Use your graphing calculator to make a population versus year number scatterplot. Record your window and sketch your graph.

22. Write a function rule that models this situation.

23. Graph your function rule on your scatterplot. If the graph is not a good fit, change your rule. Sketch your graph.

24. Predict the bison population in 2007.

Assignment

1. State if each of these tables shows a linear, quadratic, or exponential relationship. If the pattern is exponential, state if it is growth or decay.

a)

x	y
0	100
1	50
2	25
3	12.5
4	6.25
5	3.125

b)

x °	y
0	1
1	3
2	9
3	27
4	81
5	243

c)

x	y
0	1250
1	1350
2	1458
3	1574.6
4	1700.6
5	1836.7

d)

x	y
0	0
1	2
2	8
3	18
4	32
5	50

e)

x	y
0	1
1	$\frac{1}{3}$
2	$\frac{1}{9}$
3	$\frac{1}{27}$
4	$\frac{1}{81}$
5	$\frac{1}{243}$

f)

x	y
0	2
1	5
2	8
3	11
4	14
5	17

2. Match each window and graph to one of the tables in
Question 1, and write the function rule that fits the data.

a)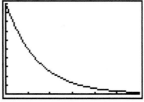

b)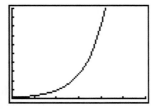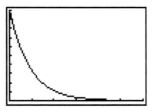

c)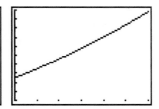

d)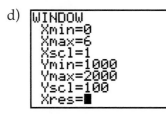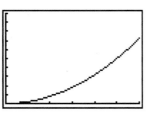

e)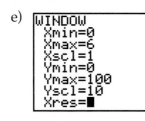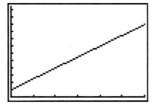

f)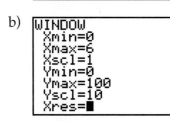

Hour	Milligrams
0	100
1	75
2	56.25
3	42.1875
4	31.6406
5	23.7304
6	17.7979
7	13.3484

FIGURE 6.33.
Medicine concentration data.

3. Park animals may need to be given medicine. The concentration of medicine in an animal's bloodstream decreases over time. **Figure 6.33** shows the concentration of a certain medicine in milligrams for each hour after an initial dose.

a) Do these data show a linear relationship? How do you know?

b) Do these data show an exponential relationship? How do you know?

c) Is this relationship an example of exponential growth or exponential decay?

d) Use your graphing calculator to make a milligrams versus number of hours scatterplot. Record your window and sketch your graph.

e) Write a function rule that models this situation.

f) Graph your function rule on your scatterplot. If the rule is not a good fit use transformations to change it. Sketch your graph.

g) How many milligrams of medication should remain in the bloodstream after 10 hours?

Newton's Law of Cooling

A national or state park is generally located around some natural attraction. For example, Yellowstone National Park contains geological interests such as the Old Faithful geyser. Crater Lake National Park in Oregon has a dormant volcano whose crater has filled with rainwater and become a deep lake.

Most lakes and pools fed by springs have a constant temperature. For example, Barton Springs in Austin, Texas, feeds a manmade pool in Zilker Park near downtown Austin. The water from the springs is always 68°F making the pool it feeds cool and popular during hot summer afternoons.

Since the temperature of the water is constant at 68°F, objects that are put in the pool cool to that temperature. Park managers can calculate how long it takes an object in the pool to reach 68°F using Newton's Law of Cooling.

To investigate Newton's Law of Cooling, we will perform two experiments. The first experiment will gather temperature data by putting a sensor in a cup of ice. The second experiment will gather temperature data by first putting a sensor in a cup of hot liquid then pulling it out and letting it cool to room temperature.

EXPERIMENT 1: CUP OF ICE

Before the start of the experiment, use a probe to record room temperature. This measurement is the temperature at time 0.

At the moment instructions tell you to PRESS ENTER TO START COLLECTING DATA, place the probe into a cup of ice. The calculator will collect 99 seconds of data.

1. Sketch a scatterplot of the data. Label your axes with units and record the window.

2. Copy the data for the first 7 seconds into a table like **Figure 6.34,** calculate the successive quotients and record them in the table.

Hour	Temperature (degrees Celsius)	Successive Quotients
0		
1		
2		
3		
4		
5		
6		
7		

FIGURE 6.34.
Table for data.

3. Do the data appear to be exponential? How do you know?

4. Use a graphing calculator to make a scatterplot of temperature versus seconds for the first 7 seconds. Sketch your graph.

5. If we continued this experiment, would the temperatures approach 0? Why or why not?

6. Write a function rule to model this situation.

7. Graph your function rule on the scatterplot. Sketch your graph and record your window.

EXPERIMENT 2: IT'S GETTING COLDER

For the second experiment, place the probe in a cup of hot water for 30 seconds. This time, at the moment instructions tell you to PRESS ENTER TO START COLLECTING DATA, press ENTER, take the probe out of the hot water, and hold it in the air.

8. Sketch a scatterplot of the data. Label your axes with units.

9. Copy the data for the first 7 seconds into a table like Figure 6.34. Calculate the successive quotients and record them in your table.

10. Do the data appear to be exponential? How do you know?

11. Use your graphing calculator to make a scatterplot of temperature versus seconds for the first 7 seconds of experiment 2. Sketch your graph and record your window.

12. If we continued this experiment, would the temperatures approach 0? Why or why not?

13. Transform your data from experiment 2 by subtracting room temperature from each temperature reading. Record the transformed temperatures in a table like **Figure 6.35.** Calculate the successive quotients and record them in the table.

Seconds	Temperature – Room Temperature	Successive Quotients
0		
1		
2		
3		
4		
5		
6		
7		

FIGURE 6.35.
Table for data and for successive quotients.

14. Do the data appear to be exponential? How do you know?

15. Use a graphing calculator to make a scatterplot of temperature – room temperature versus seconds. Sketch your graph and record your window.

16. Write a function rule to model the transformed data.

17. Graph your function rule on the scatterplot. Sketch your graph and record your window.

18. Use your knowledge of transformations to find a function rule for your original data.

19. Graph your function rule on the original scatterplot.

20. Graph both rules in the same window. What effect did the transformation have on the graph of your function rule from Question 16?

21. What does this transformation represent here?

Assignment

1. Use transformations to describe the graph of each function as it relates to the function $y = (0.93)^x$.

   a) $y = (0.93)^x + 2$

   b) $y = (0.93)^x - 4$

   c) $y = 5(0.93)^x$

   d) $y = 0.3(0.93)^x$

   e) $y = 8.3(0.93)^x + 3$

   f) $y = 0.5(0.93)^x - 6$

2. In each of these, the table represents a transformation of the function $y = (2)^x$. Write the function rule that fits the transformed data.

a)

x	y
0	6
1	7
2	9
3	13
4	21

b)

x	y
0	3
1	6
2	12
3	24
4	48

Bounce Number	Height of the Bounce (feet)
0	
1	5.231
2	4.715
3	4.436
4	4.015
5	3.788
6	3.600

FIGURE 6.36.
Rubber ball data.

3. Students in a math class collected the data in **Figure 6.36.** They dropped a rubber ball and measured the maximum height of each bounce.

   a) Do the data appear to be exponential? How do you know?

   b) Use your graphing calculator to make a scatterplot of height versus bounce number. Sketch your graph.

c) What is the average of the successive quotients?

d) Use the average of the successive quotients to estimate an initial value.

e) Write a function rule to fit the transformed data.

f) Graph your function rule on the scatterplot. Sketch your graph and record your window.

g) What would be the height of the 8th bounce?

h) Suppose the same ball is dropped from an initial height of 10 feet instead of 5.624 feet. What is a function rule that models this situation?

i) Predict how the graph of the function rule in h will differ from the graph of the function rule in e.

j) Graph both rules in the same window. Sketch your graph and record your window. What effect does changing the initial height to 10 feet have on the graph?

k) Suppose a different ball is dropped from an initial height of 4624 feet and that every bounce height is 1 foot less that the heights in the original data. What is a function rule that models this?

l) Predict how the graph of the function rule in k will differ from the graph of the function rule in e.

m) Graph both rules in the same window. Sketch your graph. What effect does subtracting 1 have on the graph?

No More Foam

Cindy, Jamal, and Juanita are discussing sodas. Jamal likes Blue Cow soda best because when he pours it in a glass the foam disappears in less time than any other soda. Juanita thinks the foam in her favorite soda, Dr. Salt, disappears in less time than any other soda. Cindy thinks the same thing about her favorite soda, Diet Dr. Salt.

The three friends decide to do an experiment on the relationship between time and the amount of foam in a glass. Their data are shown in **Figure 6.37** with foam height measured in centimeters.

Time in Seconds	Blue Cow	Dr. Salt	Diet Dr. Salt
0	17.0	14.0	14.0
1	16.1	11.8	12.1
2	14.9	10.5	10.9
3	14.0	9.3	10.0
4	13.2	8.5	9.3
5	12.5	7.7	8.6
6	11.9	7.1	8.0
7	11.2	6.5	7.5
8	10.7	6.0	7.0
9	9.7	5.3	6.2

FIGURE 6.37.
Foam data on three brands of sodas.

1. If each person drinks his or her favorite soda exactly 20 seconds after it is poured, who will be have the least foam?

2. Write a function rule that models each relationship.

SUMMARY

The general function rule that models an exponential relationship is

$y = $ (initial value) $\cdot$ (common multiplier)^x

$y = a \cdot b^x$.

If $b > 1$, then the exponential function models exponential growth where successive y-values increase by a constant factor.

If $b = 1$, then the exponential function reduces to $y = a \cdot 1^x = a$, which is a constant function.

If $0 < b < 1$, then the exponential function models exponential decay where successive y-values decrease by a constant factor.

The common multiplier b can be found from a table using successive quotients as shown in **Figure 6.38.**

Number of Hours	Dissolved CO_2	Successive Quotients
0	21.87	
1	7.29	$7.29 \div 21.87 = \frac{1}{3}$
2	2.43	$2.43 \div 7.29 = \frac{1}{3}$
3	0.81	$0.81 \div 2.43 = \frac{1}{3}$
4	0.27	$0.27 \div 0.81 = \frac{1}{3}$
5	0.09	$0.09 \div 0.27 = \frac{1}{3}$

FIGURE 6.38.
Table using successive quotients.

The value of a is the y-value when $x = 0$ if there is no vertical shift.

In Figure 6.38 the value for a is 21.87 because that is the amount of dissolved carbon dioxide (CO_2) present at 0 hours. Since the successive quotients are all $\frac{1}{3}$, $b = \frac{1}{3}$; therefore this situation can be modeled using the function $y = 21.87\left(\frac{1}{3}\right)^x$.

In the context of a problem, the value for a is the initial amount of a thing that is decaying exponentially.

For example, if the initial dosage of medication is 500 milligrams and the amount of medication in the bloodstream decreases by 90% every hour, the initial value a is 500. The constant multiplier b is 0.90. The amount of medication y in the bloodstream at time t can be modeled with $y = 500(0.90)^t$.

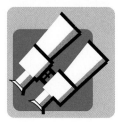

Switching Directions

A LOOK AHEAD

In Chapter 5 you learned that the inverse of a function is the reflection of the function over the line $y = x$. The domain of the function becomes the range of its inverse; the range of the function becomes the domain of its inverse. In the case of the quadratic function $y = x^2$, the inverse is the square root function $y = \sqrt{x}$. Likewise, the inverse operation of raising a number to a power is to take the root of that number. In other words, to un-square a number such as 9, you take the square root of the number; for example, $\sqrt{9}$.

Let's explore some ways we might *un-power* an equation such as $3^x = 27$. We will also investigate the inverse of an exponential function.

1. Make a table for $f(x) = 3^x$ like **Figure 6.39,** then sketch a graph of the function on a grid like **Figure 6.40.**

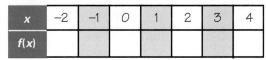

x	−2	−1	0	1	2	3	4
f(x)							

FIGURE 6.39.
Table for f(x) = 3ˣ.

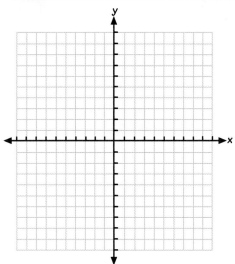

FIGURE 6.40.
Grid for graphing f(x) = 3ˣ.

2. What is the domain of this function?

3. What is the range of this function?

4. Trace the *x*-axis, *y*-axis, and the graph of *f*(*x*) onto a sheet of patty paper. Be sure to label the *x*- and *y*-axes. Reflect the graph of *f*(*x*) across the line $y = x$ by holding the top-right and bottom-left corners of the patty paper in each hand and flipping the sheet of patty paper over (see **Figure 6.41**). Sketch what you see.

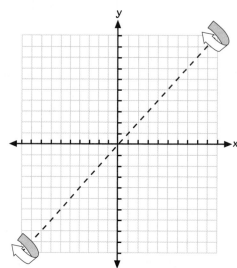

FIGURE 6.41.
Flipping over the patty paper.

CHECK THIS!

Recall that the inverse of a function is a reflection across the line y = x.

You can generate the inverse of a function by switching the domain and range values of the original function.

Now let's look at a function that undoes *f*(*x*). Let's call that function *g*(*x*). For example, when we evaluate *f*(*x*) at $x = 0$, we get a result (output) of 1. In *g*(*x*) when we evaluate *g*(*x*) at $x = 1$, we get a result of 0.

5. Complete a table like **Figure 6.42,** and sketch the graphs of both $y = f(x)$ and $y = g(x)$.

x							
g(*x*)	−2	−1	0	1	2	3	4

FIGURE 6.42.
Table for g(x).

6. Is the new curve that you sketched the graph of a function? How can you tell?

7. What is the domain of this function?

8. What is the range of this function?

The inverse of an exponential function has a special name; it is called a **logarithmic function**. In the next few sections you will explore and find some properties and uses for logarithmic functions.

It All Adds Up

In the last section you developed the inverse of an exponential function, a **logarithmic function**. This function is written as **log(x)** where x is any positive number. In the next few sections you will explore some properties and uses for logarithmic functions.

You have studied transformations of graphs of functions. In this section you will explore transformations of graphs of logarithmic functions and make some conjectures about patterns that occur in logarithmic functions.

1. On your graphing calculator, graph $y = \log(x)$. Record your viewing window and sketch your results.

2. What is the x-intercept? What is the y-intercept? Are there any other key points? Explain how you found these points.

3. In the same viewing window, graph $y = \log(x) + 2$ with $y = \log(x)$. Sketch your graph.

4. Now graph the parent function $y = \log(x)$ and $y = \log(x) - 2$ in the same window. Sketch your graph.

5. Compare the graphs of $y = \log(x)$, $y = \log(x) + 2$, and $y = \log(x) - 2$. How are they alike? How do they differ?

6. In terms of transformations, what will the graph of $y = \log(x) + k$ look like?

7. In a new viewing window, graph the parent function $y = \log(x)$ and $y = 2 \log(x)$. Sketch your graph and record your window.

8. Now graph the parent function $y = \log(x)$ and $y = \frac{1}{2} \log(x)$ in the same window. Sketch your graph.

9. Compare the graphs of $y = \log(x)$, $y = 2 \log(x)$, and $y = \frac{1}{2} \log(x)$. How are they alike? How do they differ?

10. In terms of transformations, what will the graph of $y = a \log(x)$ will look like?

11. Now enter Y1 = log(3x) and Y2 = log(3) + log(x) into the function list of your graphing calculator. Change the plot style for Y2 to a tracing ball then graph the two functions. Record your window and sketch the graphs. Explain what you saw while the calculator graphed both functions.

12. Now look at a table for these two functions. What patterns between the values for Y1 and Y2 do you see? What do these patterns suggest about the relationship between Y1 = log(3x) and Y2 = log(3) + log(x)?

13. Repeat Question 11 with Y1 = log(6x) and Y2 = log(3) + log(2x). Sketch your graphs and look at a table. What patterns between the values for Y1 and Y2 do you see? What do these patterns suggest about the relationship between Y1 = log(6x) and Y2 = log(3) + log(2x)?

14. Repeat Question 11 with Y1 = log(6x) and Y2 = log(2) + log(3x). Sketch your graphs and look at a table. What patterns between the values for Y1 and Y2 do you see? What do these patterns suggest about the relationship between Y1 = log(6x) and Y2 = log(2) + log(3x)?

15. Use your answers to Questions 12, 13, and 14 to write a sentence about log(xy).

16. Now enter Y1 = log(3x) and Y2 = log(6x) − log(2) into the function list of your graphing calculator. Change the plot style for Y2 to a tracing ball then graph the two functions. Record your window and sketch the graphs. Explain what you saw while the calculator graphed both functions.

17. Now look at a table for these two functions. What patterns between the values for Y1 and Y2 do you see? What do these patterns suggest about the relationship between Y1 = log(3x) and Y2 = log(6x) − log(2)?

18. Repeat Question 16 for Y1 = log(2x) and Y2 = log(8x) − log(4). Sketch your graphs and look at a table. What patterns between the values for Y1 and Y2 do you see? What do these patterns suggest about the relationship between Y1 = log(2x) and Y2 = log(8x) − log(4)?

19. Use your answers to Questions 17 and 18 to make a generalization about $\log\left(\frac{x}{y}\right)$.

20. Now enter Y1 = $\log(x^3)$ and Y2 = $3 \log(x)$ into the function list of your graphing calculator. Change the plot style for Y2 to a tracing ball then graph the two functions. Record your window and sketch the graphs. Explain what you saw while the calculator graphed both functions.

21. Now, look at a table for these two functions. What patterns between the values for Y1 and Y2 do you see? What do these patterns suggest about the relationship between Y1 = $\log(x^3)$ and Y2 = $3 \log(x)$?

22. Repeat Question 20 for Y1 = $\log(x^5)$ and Y2 = $5 \log(x)$. Sketch your graphs and look at a table. What patterns between the values for Y1 and Y2 do you see? What do these patterns suggest about the relationship between Y1 = $\log(x^5)$ and Y2 = $5 \log(x)$?

23. Use your answers to Questions 21 and 22 to make a sentence about about $\log(x^n)$.

1. Sketch a graph of $f(x) = 5^x$.

2. What are the domain and range of this function?

3. Sketch the graph of $g(x) = 5^x - 3$. How is this graph of $g(x)$ related to the graph of $f(x) = 5^x$?

4. What are the domain and range of $g(x) = 5^x - 3$? How do they compare to the domain and range of $f(x) = 5^x$?

5. Sketch a graph of $f(x) = \log(x)$.

6. What are the domain and the range of this function?

7. Sketch the graph of $g(x) = \log(x - 2)$. How is this graph of $g(x)$ related to the graph of $f(x) = \log(x)$?

8. What are the domain and range of $g(x)$? How do they compare to the domain and range of $f(x) = \log(x)$?

9. Find the value of each of these:

   a) $\log(3) + \log(7) =$

   b) $\log(4) + \log(10.5) =$

   c) $\log(48) - \log(16) =$

   d) $\log(60) - \log(8) =$

It's Not What You Say, But How You Say It

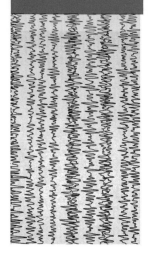

Logarithms were developed to help scientists work with large numbers in the days before calculators and computers. John Napier (1550–1617), a Scottish mathematician, developed logarithms. It has been said that science advanced quickly in the 1700s because logarithms made calculations easier.

Today, calculators and computers make calculations easy. On the other hand, logarithmic functions can still be used for modeling in science. Exponential relationships, such as energy or sound, can be expressed inversely using logarithms. For example, the Richter scale is a logarithmic scale that is used to measure the intensity of an earthquake, and the decibel scale is a logarithmic scale that is used to measure the intensity of sound.

An exponential equation has three parts as shown in **Figure 6.43**.

FIGURE 6.43.
An exponential equation.

$$y = 3^x$$

Power — Base — Exponent

As you recall, a function that undoes another function is called the **inverse** of that function. One way to find an inverse of a function is to switch y and x in its equation then solve for y. A name for a function that is the inverse of $f(x) = 3^x$ is **logarithm, base 3, of x.** It is written $f(x) = \log_3 x$. The abbreviation for logarithm is log.

To write an exponential equation as a logarithm, the base of the power becomes the base of the logarithm. The power is the quantity of which you are taking the logarithm; the logarithm of that quantity is equal to the exponent (see **Figure 6.44**).

FIGURE 6.44.
Writing an exponential equation as a logarithm.

Exponent

$$y = 3^x \qquad x = \log_3 y$$

Base

Power

Every exponential equation can be rewritten in logarithmic form and vice-versa. For example, to write $y = \log_9 81$ in exponential form.

Step 1: Identify the base as 9 and the exponent as y.

Step 2: Using the base and exponent, write an exponential expression, 9^y.

Step 3: Set the expression equal to the power in the logarithmic equation, $9^y = 81$.

To evaluate a logarithm, set it equal to x and then rewrite it in exponential form. For example, evaluate $\log_7 49$.

Step 1: Set the expression equal to x: $\log_7 49 = x$.

Step 2: Rewrite the expression in exponential form: $7^x = 49$.

Step 3: Rewrite 49 as a power of 7: $7^x = 7^2$.

Step 4: Evaluate $x = 2$.

Because logarithms can be written with any base, it is important to state the base. Our number system is base-10 (that is, place value is based on powers of 10: 1, 10, 100, etc.). Base-10 logarithms are often used; thus they are called **common logarithms**. To save time, $\log_{10}$ can be written without the 10 simply as log.

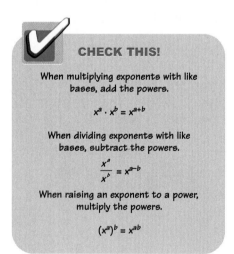

CHECK THIS!

When multiplying exponents with like bases, add the powers.

$$x^a \cdot x^b = x^{a+b}$$

When dividing exponents with like bases, subtract the powers.

$$\frac{x^a}{x^b} = x^{a-b}$$

When raising an exponent to a power, multiply the powers.

$$(x^a)^b = x^{ab}$$

There are three key properties of logarithms that you explored in Section 6.12. First, you explored $\log(xy)$.

1. Use the log key on your calculator to find the values in **Figure 6.45**. Keep a copy of your table because you will use it later in this section.

log 2	
log 5	
log 10	
log 50	
log 100	

FIGURE 6.45.
Logarithms for Question 1.

2. Use your table to evaluate and compare the quantities in **Figure 6.46.**

log 5 + log 10		log 50	
log 2 + log 5		log 10	
log 10 + log 10		log 100	

FIGURE 6.46.
Quantities for Question 2.

3. What patterns do you notice? Explain these patterns. What can you conclude?

4. Do you think this might be true for all logarithms of all bases? Explain.

Second, you explored $\log\left(\frac{x}{y}\right)$.

5. Now use your table to evaluate and compare the quantities in **Figure 6.47.**

log 10 − log 5		log 2	
log 50 − log 10		log 5	
log 100 − log 10		log 10	

FIGURE 6.47.
Quantities for Question 5.

6. What patterns do you notice? Explain these patterns.

7. Do you think this might be true for all logarithms of all bases? Explain.

Third, you explored $\log(x^b)$.

8. Use the log key on your calculator to evaluate the logarithms in **Figure 6.48.**

9. Now use your table to evaluate and compare the quantities in **Figure 6.49.**

log 2			
log 5			
log 10			
log 25			
log 100			
log 125			

FIGURE 6.48.
Logarithms for Question 8.

2 log 5		log 25	
2 log 10		log 100	
3 log 5		log 125	

FIGURE 6.49. Quantities for Question 9.

10. What patterns do you notice? Explain these patterns.

11. Do you think this might be true for all logarithms of all bases? Explain.

Assignment

1. Write each of these in logarithmic form.

    a) $x = 8^y$

    b) $x = 4^y$

    c) $x = 3^{2y}$

    d) $y = 5^x$

2. Find the value of each of these logarithms.

    a) $\log_3 27$

    b) $\log_{10} 100$

    c) $\log_2 64$

    d) $\log_8 64$

3. Simplify each of these. Leave your answers written as logarithms.

    a) $\log_3 9 + \log_3 5$

    b) $\log_2 8 + \log_2 7$

    c) $\log_2 35 - \log_2 7$

    d) $\log_7 144 - \log_7 4$

    e) $\log_{10} 125$

    f) $\log_3 64$

4. Simplify each of these as much as you can. Evaluate the logarithm when possible.

    a) $\log_2 8 + \log_2 4$

    b) $\log_2 32 - \log_2 16$

    c) $\log_2 32 - \log_2 4$

d) $\log_3 81 - \log_3 9$

e) $\log_5 125$

f) $\log_2 64$

5. Can you take the logarithm of 0? Why or why not?

6. Solve each of these for x.

a) $\log_3 x = 5$

b) $\log_3 5 + \log_3 x = \log_3 30$

c) $\log_5 x - \log_5 8 = 1$

d) $\log_7 5 + x \log_7 6 = \log_7 1080$

I Feel the Earth Move

Mount St. Helens National Volcanic Monument in Washington State has an active volcano. Active volcanoes can cause earthquakes.

Park managers work closely with geologists to monitor earthquakes. Scientists who study volcanoes use earthquake data to make predictions about volcanic eruptions. Stronger or more frequent shakes can mean that magma underground is moving toward the surface and an eruption may happen soon. By measuring the magnitude or strength of an earthquake, scientists can make decisions about an impending volcanic eruption. Such decisions could include whether or not to evacuate a park or to relocate wildlife.

In Section 6.13, you learned three properties of logarithms.

❖ $\log_b m + \log_b n = \log_b m \cdot n$

❖ $\log_b m - \log_b n = \log_b \frac{m}{n}$

❖ $\log_b mn = n \log_b m$

These properties are useful in solving exponential equations. We will solve exponential equations by taking the base 10 logarithm of each side. (We will use base 10 since this is one of two bases that the calculator uses.)

We will use $3^x = 14$ as an example.

We need a way to isolate or *undo* the exponent. To do this we need an inverse operation for exponentiation. This inverse operation is called a **logarithm**. If we take the logarithm of both sides, the logarithm undoes the exponent.

$$3^x = 14$$
$$\log(3^x) = \log(14)$$

Now we can use the properties of logarithms to solve for x. Recall that $m^n = n \log_b m$. So,

$$\log(3^x) = \log(14)$$
$$x \log(3) = \log(14)$$

Remember that log(3) and log(14) are real numbers. Therefore, we can apply division to both sides of the equation in order to solve for x. We will divide both sides of the equation by log(3) in order to undo the multiplication.

$$x \log(3) = \log(14)$$

$$\frac{x\log(3)}{\log(3)} = \frac{\log(14)}{\log(3)}$$

$$x = \frac{\log(14)}{\log(3)}$$

$$x \approx 2.402$$

The values for logarithms are often rounded to the nearest thousandth. However, sometimes you will be asked for an exact answer. In that case leave your answer in terms of logarithms.

In Section 6.12 you saw that logarithmic functions can be graphed on a graphing calculator. Most scientific and graphing calculators have two logarithm keys: LOG, which is the base-10 logarithm, and LN, which is the **natural logarithm** having a base e. The number e is similar to pi that recurs throughout mathematics and science. You can graph base-10 and base-e logarithmic functions on most graphing calculators using these keys. You can also graph other logarithmic functions, but first you must change the base to either 10 or e.

Consider the function $y = 3^x$.

1. Find the inverse function of $y = 3^x$ by switching x and y. Solve for y by taking the logarithm of both sides and using the properties of logarithms.

2. How can you write the inverse of $y = 3^x$ as a logarithmic function?

3. Based on your answer to Questions 1 and 2, what is $\log_3 x$ equal to?

4. Based on your findings in Questions 1–3, what is $\log_b x$ equal to?

The formula you found in Question 4 is called a change of base formula. It allows you to convert a logarithm of any base to a base 10. You can also use the change of base formula to convert a logarithm to any other base. In this section we are interested in changing logarithms to base 10 so that we can use the graphing calculator.

5. Use the change of base formula to graph $y = \log_5 x$ on your calculator. Record your window and sketch your results.

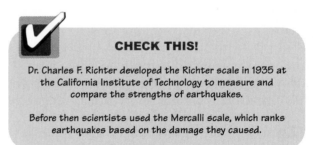

CHECK THIS!

Dr. Charles F. Richter developed the Richter scale in 1935 at the California Institute of Technology to measure and compare the strengths of earthquakes.

Before then scientists used the Mercalli scale, which ranks earthquakes based on the damage they caused.

Dr. Charles Richter

6. Use the Trace or Table feature to calculate the value of $\log_5 3$.

Logarithms can be used to compare large and small numbers. Dr. Charles F. Richter was the first scientist to recognize that the strength of a seismic wave could be used to describe the magnitude of the earthquake that caused it.

One of Richter's formulas relates the amount of energy released by an earthquake to its Richter magnitude:

$$\log E = 11.8 + 1.5M$$

In this formula, E is the seismic energy released by the earthquake and M is the Richter magnitude of the earthquake.

7. Solve Richter's formula for E in terms of M.

8. Use your graphing calculator to graph E as a function of M. Record your window and sketch your graph.

9. How useful is the graph in interpreting the relationship between energy and magnitude?

10. Use the Table feature of your graphing calculator and Richter's formula to compute the energy released for the magnitudes in **Figure 6.50.** Then find the successive ratios.

Magnitude	Energy	Successive Ratios
1		–
2		
3		
4		
5		
6		
7		

FIGURE 6.50.
Energy released by earthquake magnitudes.

11. What patterns do you notice in the ratios?

12. If the magnitude of an earthquake increases by one, by what factor does the energy increase?

13. If the magnitude of an earthquake increases by two, by what factor does the energy increase?

14. If the magnitude of an earthquake increases by four, by what factor does the energy increase?

15. The Northern Sumatra earthquake on December 26, 2004, which caused a tsunami that killed hundreds of thousands of people, had a magnitude of 9.0. In 1992, an earthquake of magnitude 4.5 struck Midland, Texas. Was the Northern Sumatra earthquake twice as strong as the Midland earthquake? Explain your answer.

Assignment

1. Solve each of these equations for x. Round to the nearest thousandth.

   a) $6^x = 8$

   b) $4^{2x} = 23$

   c) $5^x + 2 = 26$

   d) $2^x = -4$

   e) $5^x = 10$

   f) $7^x = 95$

   g) $6^x = 38$

2. Graph each of these on your graphing calculator. Record your window and sketch the graph.

   a) $y = 2 \log x + 4$

   b) $y = \log_6 x$

   c) $y = 3 \log_6 x - 2$

For Questions 3–5, use $y_1 = \log x$ and $y_2 = \log_2 x$.

3. In the same window graph $y_1 = \log x$ and $y_2 = \log_2 x$. Record your window and sketch the graph.

4. Compare the domain and range of $y_1 = \log x$ and $y_2 = \log_2 x$. How are they alike? How do they differ?

5. Use your knowledge of transformations to describe how the graphs of $y_1 = \log x$ and $y_2 = \log_2 x$ are related.

Use $10^{(11.8+1.5M)} = E$ for Questions 6 and 7.

6. On July 20, an earthquake of magnitude 2.0 was recorded on the west-southwest face of Mount St. Helens. How much energy was released by this earthquake?

7. On July 21, an earthquake of magnitude 3.4 was recorded on the same face. Compare the strength of this earthquake to the one on July 20.

8. Chemists use the pH scale to measure acidity. The pH of a solution is measured on a scale of 1–14 and can be found using the function $y = -\log H$ where y is the pH and H is the concentration of hydrogen ions. The concentration of hydrogen ions in a solution determines how acidic the solution is; the greater the concentration, the greater the acidity.

It is important for park managers to know the pH of lakes and streams. This information helps them decide how much air or water pollution is in the park. It also helps them assess the risk to wildlife.

a) Use your graphing calculator to generate a pH table for the concentrations of hydrogen ions shown in **Figure 6.51**. Round your answers to the nearest tenth.

Concentration	pH
1×10^{-13}	
1×10^{-5}	
2×10^{-13}	
6.2×10^{-10}	
7.4×10^{-5}	

FIGURE 6.51.
pH table.

b) Bunsen has a solution with a hydrogen ion concentration of 0.00001. Use the properties of logarithms to find the pH of his solution. Check your answer with a calculator.

c) The solution in beaker A has a pH of 3. The solution in beaker B has a pH of 8. How many times greater is the concentration of hydrogen ions in beaker A than in beaker B?

What Did You Say?

The intensity of sound is described with the **decibel** (dB) scale. Music producers and sound engineers use this scale to mix recordings of music and to achieve the right balance between layers of sound.

Park visitors often complain about noise. So park managers can use the decibel scale to set noise level limits and use sound meters to measure the intensity of noise.

CHECK THIS!

The human ear can detect a sound wave that displaces air particles by one-billionth of a centimeter.

The intensity of a sound wave that matches this displacement is called the threshold of hearing.

Figure 6.52 shows typical decibel levels for certain sounds.

Sound	Intensity (dB)
Refrigerator	50
Normal conversation	60
Headphones on full volume	100
Chainsaw	120
Jet engine taking off	150

FIGURE 6.52.
Sound intensities.

The decibel scale is defined using $\beta = 10 \log \left(\frac{I}{1.0 \times 10^{-12}} \right)$ where β is the intensity of the sound in decibels and I is the intensity of the sound wave in watts per square meter.

1. How many times more intense is the sound produced by a chainsaw than the sound produced during normal conversation? Explain your answer.

2. In the data in Figure 6.52, how many times more intense is the sound produced by a jet engine taking off than the sound produced by a refrigerator? Explain your answer.

SUMMARY

A logarithmic function is the inverse of an exponential function. Exponential functions can be written in logarithmic form. For example, $y = 3^x$ can be written as $x = \log_3 y$ as shown in **Figure 6.53.**

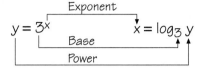

When expressions or equations are written in logarithmic form, three properties of logarithms can be used to manipulate them or to solve for a variable.

- $\log_b m + \log_b n = \log_b m \cdot n$

- $\log_b m - \log_b n = \log_b \frac{m}{n}$

- $\log_b mn = n \log_b m$

Logarithms can be used to solve exponential equations for an unknown exponent of the expression.

You can convert between logarithm bases using the **change of base** formula:

$$\log_b x = \frac{\log x}{\log b}$$

Modeling Project Noise Pollution

Noise pollution is a major issue in cities and towns around the country. Noise pollution is associated with certain illnesses, fatigue, and even hearing loss. Many places have passed laws limiting noise levels.

There may be sources of noise pollution at your school, home, or community that could be distracting or unhealthy. For this chapter's modeling project you will develop a report to the principal about sources of noise pollution and ways to lessen its impact on your school. You will need to back up your arguments with data and research about the cause of the noise pollution and what levels of noise are distracting or unsafe.

Look (and listen) around your school for sources of noise pollution. These could be the cafeteria, music room, or traffic on a nearby street.

Create a list of the sources of noise pollution you think are the worst.

Use a decibel meter at various distances to measure the noise of these objects. Record the data.

Use your library or the Internet to research about safe, unsafe, and distracting noise levels. Find out how far from these noise sources you have to be for them to be safe and non-distracting.

Develop a report for your principal about noise pollution at your school. Your report should contain recommendations for limiting noise pollution that are supported by data in tables and graphs. Your report should also summarize the research you did.

Practice Problems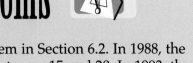

1. Recall the migration problem in Section 6.2. In 1988, the population estimate was between 15 and 20. In 1993, the population estimate was between 25 and 30.

   a) Explain how the migration rate of two moose per year was derived from these observations.

   b) The reason for using the average migration rate is that it predicts "typical" results. Concern about overpopulation might lead a mathematical modeler to use the largest migration rate instead. Based on these observations, what would be the largest rate?

   c) Estimate the largest possible moose population in the park in the year 2000 based on the observations. (We still assume that the only change in population is due to migration.)

2. In Section 6.2 a moose model was used to predict the population in the year 2000. Use the same initial population of 27 moose in 1993, and assume the growth rate is 10% per year on average.

   a) What would be the population for the year 2000 based on this set of assumptions?

   b) What would have been the yearly percentage increase if the same population reached 75 moose in the year 2000, as shown in **Figure 6.53?**

Year	Population
1993	27
1994	31
1995	36
1996	42
1997	48
1998	56
1999	65
2000	75

FIGURE 6.53.
Moose population data.

3. Reports show that satellite-based remote sensors measured a 6% decline in the area of ice covering the earth's surface during the period from 1978 to 1994.

   a) What is the overall rate of decay over the 16 years?

b) **Figure 6.54** shows the percentage of the Earth's surface covered with ice in 1978 that was still covered with ice in the given year. What is the annual rate of decay?

Year	Percentage of Ice Coverage	Year	Percentage of Ice Coverage
1978	100%	1986	97.0
1979	99.6	1987	96.6
1980	99.2	1988	96.2
1981	98.8	1989	95.8
1982	98.5	1990	95.5
1983	98.1	1991	95.1
1984	97.7	1992	94.7
1985	97.3	1993	94.4
		1994	94.0

FIGURE 6.54.
Ice coverage data.

c) Find the annual percent of decrease in the ice coverage.

d) Use 1978 as year zero and assume the amount of ice coverage to be 100% at that time. Write an equation for the percentage of ice coverage remaining after t years.

e) Graph your equation over a large domain (several centuries). If the model holds true well into the future, what is the long-term result of this decline in the ice coverage?

4. An article reported that the buffalo population in a national park grew as shown in **Figure 6.55**.

Year	Population
2000	125
2001	160
2002	205
2003	260
2004	340

FIGURE 6.55.
Buffalo population data.

a) Find the annual growth rate for the buffalo population over that time period. Explain what it means.

b) Write a function rule to predict the population of buffalo in the park over any time period. (Use the year 2000 to represent $t = 0$.)

c) Verify your function using the data from 2000 to 2004. How well does your function predict population?

d) Use the function developed in b to predict how many buffalo will be in the park in 2010.

5. The 2000 Census determined the population used to allocate seats in Congress. As of April 1, 2000, the population of the United States was around 281,422,000. That was a 13.2% increase over the 1990 census figure. This is an average annual increase of about 1.25%.

a) Write a function rule that could be used to predict the population of the United States after the year 2000 (assume a constant growth rate).

b) At the same rate of increase, what would be the population of the United States on April 1, 2003?

c) If the population increases at a yearly rate of 1.00% instead, what effect would that have on the population estimate from b?

6. A trout farm is estimated to have around 5000 fish when it opens. Each day approximately 2% of the fish in the lake are caught. At the end of each week the lake is restocked with 1200 fish.

a) How many fish are caught by the end of the first week?

b) Will the lake run out of fish? Explain.

7. Suppose the authorities at Adirondack State Park had counted 27 moose in 1988 and 42 moose in 1993.

a) If you assume that the growth is caused by migration, what is the migration rate (average number of moose migrating each year)?

b) At the same migration rate, how many moose would be in the park in the year 2013?

c) If you assume that the growth is caused by reproduction, then you can calculate an annual growth factor of 1.0924. What is the annual percentage increase?

d) Let t be the number of years since 1993. Assuming a constant growth rate write an exponential function to predict the number of moose in the park.

e) Based on your answer to d predict the number of moose in the park in the year 2013.

f) How many years would it take for the population of moose to reach 84 (double the original amount)?

8. As regional director of the Fish and Game Department you estimate that there are 6000 deer in the area, and their population grows at a rate of 9% per year. To best manage this resource you would like to keep the population constant. How many deer should you allow to be harvested by hunters next year?

Glossary

KEY CONCEPTS

Base: In an exponential expression, the base is the number that is multiplied by itself. For example, in 2^3, 2 is the base because $2^3 = (2)(2)(2)$.

Common multiplier (common ratio): When multiplication by a constant is used to get successive values, the constant is called the common multiplier.

Exponent: Number that indicates how many times the base is multiplied. In 2^4 2 is multiplied four times, $2 \times 2 \times 2 \times 2 = 16$.

Exponential decay: Negative exponential growth; a growth factor in which $0 < b < 1$.

Exponential function: A function in the form $f(x) = a \cdot b^x$.

Exponential growth: A growth pattern in which multiplication by a constant larger than 1 generates successive values

Growth factor: The common multiplier in an exponential growth or decay situation.

Logarithm: A term used to describe an exponent. For example, in 2^3, 3 is an exponent and therefore a logarithm. 2^3 can be written as $\log_3(2)$.

Logarithmic function: A function of the form $y = \log(x)$. The inverse of an exponential function is a logarithmic function.

Migration: Process by which a population changes by moving from one location to another.

Natural logarithm: A logarithm with a base of e, which has a value of about 2.718.

pH: A scale used to measure the level of acidity in a substance.

Power: The value of an exponential expression. For example, in $2^3 = 8$, 8 is called the third power of 2.

Reproduction: Process by which a population (wildlife or people) increases by births.

Richter scale: A scale invented by Charles Richter used to measure and compare the strength of earthquakes.

7

CHAPTER

What Are the Chances?
Probability

What Are the Chances?

One evening in southern California four boys are playing a game of basketball. There are two boys on each team. The stakes of this game are high. Each team is playing to raise money for its student organization, and the winning team gets a cash prize that goes into the account of its organization.

For this game the winning team is the first team to reach 50 points. To make the game simple, the boys decided that only two-point baskets would count. They would not include three-point, long-range baskets or penalty throws. This has been a really good game, and the score is 46 to 44.

Suddenly, there is an earthquake and the game stops immediately. The players and spectators agree to stop play and rush home, leaving the game incomplete. What should happen to the money that was set aside for the student organization of the winning team?

In 1494, Italian mathematician Luca Pacioli **(Figure 7.1)** posed a similar problem in his book, *Summa de arithmetica, geometrica, proportioni et proportionalita*. The solution he proposed was that each team should be awarded a portion of the prize based on the proportion of points it had scored in the game up to the time when the game was interrupted. Other mathematicians criticized this solution, however, asking questions about things like what if only one point had been scored at the very beginning of the game when the game was interrupted. It would hardly seem fair to award the entire prize to the team that scored first, before the other team had a chance to respond.

FIGURE 7.1. Luca Pacioli

A hundred and fifty years later, Blaise Pascal **(Figure 7.2)** and Pierre de Fermat **(Figure 7.3)**, two very famous French mathematicians, found a solution to the "problem of points," as the problem before

FIGURE 7.2.
Blaise Pascal

them had become known. Unlike Pacioli, who looked at the past performance of both teams to solve the problem, Pascal and Fermat looked forward — what could have happened to finish the game, and what outcome would be the most likely?

As a result, Pascal and Fermat laid the foundation for what we know today to be the study of probability. How likely is a particular outcome or event? In this chapter you will investigate various ways to answer that question. You will also investigate various applications of probability and how probability is used to evaluate risk. By the end of this chapter you will see why some mathematicians call probability the "language of uncertainty."

FIGURE 7.3. Pierre de Fermat

Are You Buying Lunch or Am I?

Based on items that archaeologists have unearthed, such as shells, pebbles, and bones, it appears that early humans may have played games of chance for thousands of years. These ancient people probably believed that the gods determined the outcome when they rolled the dice.

FIGURE 7.4.
Gerolamo Cardano

In 1545, an Italian mathematician, physician, and gambling addict, Gerolamo Cardano **(Figure 7.4)**, was the first person to use a mathematical model to predict what happens in the long run in a game of chance. More than one hundred years later, the next step in the mathematical study of probability began as a dispute between two gamblers. Two French mathematicians, Blaise Pascal and Pierre Fermat, began to study the possible outcomes of a dice game in 1654 in order to settle the dispute. The gamblers needed to decide how to divide the winnings in a game that had ended prematurely.

Mathematicians took almost 300 years to agree on a formal definition for probability. Over the course of the past 300 years, the study of probability has spread to other fields where measuring uncertainty involved more than just a game of chance, such as the insurance industry and the field of genetics.

1. Jenis takes her mother out to lunch every year for her birthday. They have a tradition of opening a bag of M&M's® before they go. If her mother draws out a blue M&M, then her mother will pay for lunch. However, if she does not draw a blue one, then Jenis will pay for lunch.

What do you predict is the probability that Jenis will pay for lunch?

2. Jenis has a plan to make sure that her mother pays for lunch this year, so she orders a special bag of M&M's from the company website. She orders a bag containing only blue M&M's. What do you predict is the probability that Jenis will pay for lunch?

3. Next year Jenis wants to pay for the birthday lunch, so she will order a special bag of yellow M&M's. What do you predict is the probability that Jenis's mother will pay for lunch next year?

4. What are some other situations in which you might be interested in the chances of an event occurring or not occurring? Explain why you or someone else might be interested in the chances.

Probability Experiments

You are going to participate in several experiments with chance. Your teacher will divide you into groups of four. Each person in the group must choose a job: recorder, observer, calculator, or experimenter.

1. The recorder creates a table and records the data collected during the experiment.

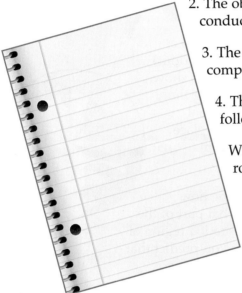

2. The observer watches to be sure that the experiment is conducted correctly with the materials provided.

3. The calculator uses a calculator to perform any required computations.

4. The experimenter actually does the experiment, following the teacher's instructions.

When you rotate to a different experiment, rotate the role assignments.

EXPERIMENT 1: Spinners

Part 1

1. The recorder creates a table similar to **Figure 7.5** on a sheet of paper.

Spinner A Lands in:	Frequency Tally	Frequency Written As		
		Fraction	Decimal	Percent
Shaded region				
Unshaded region				
Totals				

FIGURE 7.5

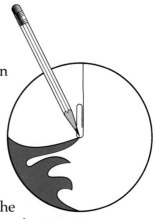

2. The experimenter places a pencil at the center of Spinner A (see handout) with an unfolded paper clip, as shown in **Figure 7.6**. Practice spinning the paper clip once or twice. Do not start the spinner at the same place every time. Try to spin it from wherever it lands.

FIGURE 7.6.
Spinner A

3. With your group, determine how often you would predict that part of the spinner will land on the shaded region of Spinner A. How often do you predict that part of the spinner will land on the unshaded region of Spinner A?

4. The experimenter spins Spinner A 20 times. The recorder uses tally marks to record the data in your table. The observer should watch to be certain that everything is done correctly.

5. The calculator should calculate the values for the last three columns **(Figure 7.7)** and the totals in the last row. The recorder records these values in the table.

Spinner A Lands in:	Frequency Tally	Frequency Written As		
		Fraction	Decimal	Percent
Shaded region				
Unshaded region				
Totals				

FIGURE 7.7

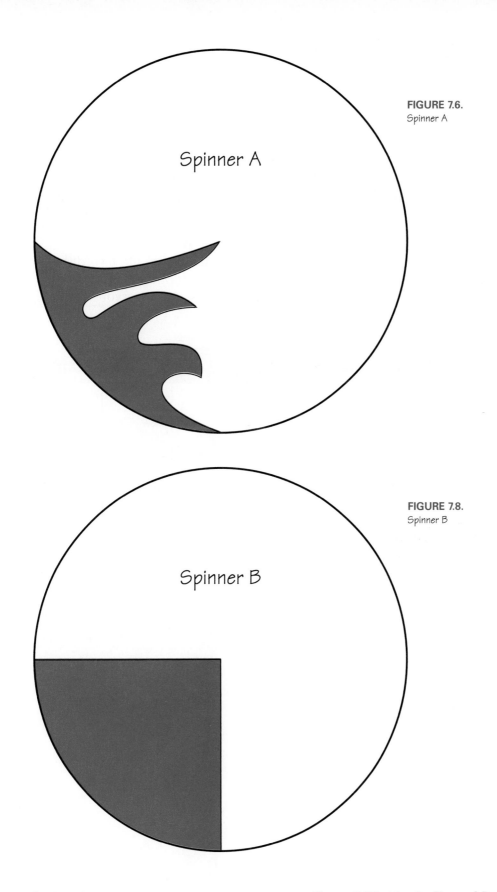

FIGURE 7.6.
Spinner A

FIGURE 7.8.
Spinner B

Spinner A

Spinner B

6. For this part of the experiment the experimenter spins with Spinner A and Spinner B **(Figure 7.8)** at the same time. The experimenter spins both spinners 16 times.

7. Before beginning to spin, with your group determine how often you would predict that both spinners will land on shaded regions at the same time. How often do you predict that both of the spinners will land on an unshaded region?

8. The recorder makes a table similar to **Figure 7.9** on a separate sheet of paper and uses tally marks to record the data in the table. The calculator will fill in the last three columns. The observer watches to be sure everyone is following the instructions.

Results of Spinning Both Spinners	Frequency Tally	Frequency Written As		
		Fraction	Decimal	Percent
Spinner A is shaded Spinner B is shaded				
Spinner A is shaded Spinner B is unshaded				
Spinner A is unshaded Spinner B is shaded				
Spinner A is unshaded Spinner B is unshaded				
Totals				

FIGURE 7.9

EXPERIMENT 2: Color Tiles

Part 1

For this experiment there are green and yellow color tiles in Bag A. Without looking in the bag, the experimenter is going to draw out a color tile. The recorder will record the color of the tile. Then the experimenter will return the tile to the bag. If you have not yet changed jobs in your group, do so now.

1. There are green and yellow tiles in Bag A. Before any tiles are drawn from the bag and without looking in the bag, with your group predict how many you think are yellow and how many you think are green. How did you make your prediction?

2. The recorder should make a table similar to **Figure 7.10**.

Results for Bag A				
Color	Frequency Tally	Frequency Written As		
		Fraction	Decimal	Percent
Green				
Yellow				
Total				

FIGURE 7.10

3. Now the experimenter draws a tile from the bag. After the recorder has made a tally mark for the color of the drawn tile, the experimenter returns the tile to the bag. The experimenter repeats this process 10 times. The experimenter should shake the bag after returning each tile to the bag. The observer should continue to ensure that all procedures for the experiment are being followed correctly.

4. The calculator will then calculate the fraction, decimal, and percentage of the draws that were green, then repeat for yellow, and calculate the totals for the last row. The recorder records these calculations in the table.

5. If there are 20 tiles in the bag, predict how many of the tiles are yellow, based on your experiment.

Part 2

6. For Part 2 of this experiment, the experimenter draws one tile from Bag A and one tile from Bag B without looking into either bag.

7. The recorder creates a table like **Figure 7.11**.

Results for Drawing both Bag A and Bag B				
Colors Drawn	**Frequency Tally**	**Frequency Written As**		
		Fraction	**Decimal**	**Percent**
Bag A: yellow Bag B: yellow				
Bag A: yellow Bag B: green				
Bag A: green Bag B: yellow				
Bag A: green Bag B: green				
Totals				

FIGURE 7.11

8. As the experimenter draws the two tiles, the recorder uses tally marks to record the colors drawn from the two bags. The experimenter should shake the bags before each drawing. The experimenter repeats this process 16 times. The observer should make sure that everyone is doing his or her job correctly.

9. The calculator calculates the fraction, decimal, and percentage of each possibility in the table, then calculates the totals for the last row. The recorder should record the calculations in the table.

10. After you have completed the experiment, look into the bags and record how many tiles of each color there are in each bag. Be sure that each bag has the original number of each color before you pass the bags to another group. Do you think someone is more likely to draw 2 yellows or 2 greens in this experiment? Why?

EXPERIMENT 3: Birthday Simulations

1. If there are 23 people in a room, do you think any of them will have the same birthday?

2. Collecting data from various classrooms can take a long time. For this experiment you are going to randomly generate a list of birthdays. Then you will look at the list to see if any of the birthdays are a match. This method will be faster than actually asking students what their birthdays are.

3. The recorder can make a copy of **Figure 7.12**.

FIGURE 7.12

Trial #	Are there any matching birthdates?
1	
2	
3	
4	

4. The calculator randomly generates a list of birthdays using the instructions below. The observer can help the calculator with the instructions.

   a. Press [STAT], then press [ENTER] to choose **1:EDIT** . Clear the lists if you have previous data in the lists. To do this, use the up arrow key [▲] to highlight the list name, press [CLEAR], then [ENTER].

Section 7.2

Chapter 7 What Are the Chances? Probability   **425**

b. To randomly generate a month for a birthday and store it in List 1, follow these instructions:

Step 1: Press [STAT], then press [ENTER] to get to the List Editor.

Step 2: Use the up arrow key [▲]. Highlight the L1 header.

Step 3: Press [MATH].

Step 4: Select the Probability menu (PRB).

Use the arrow key [▶] to select **PRB** then use the arrow key [▼] to select **5:randInt(.** Press [ENTER].

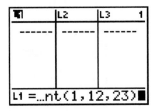

Step 5: Enter the range of random numbers to generate.
Type (1, 12, 23). Press [ENTER].

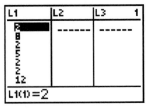

The calculator generates 23 random numbers between 1 and 12, inclusive, and places them in List 1.

426 Chapter 7 What Are the Chances? Probability

Section 7.2

c. To randomly generate a day for a birthday and store it in List 2, follow these instructions:

Step 1: Use the arrow keys ⌃ and ▸ to highlight the L2 header.

```
L1        L2      L3      2
 2      ------  ------
 8
 2
 5
 2
12
L2 =
```

Step 2: Select the Random Integer command. Press [MATH], use the arrow key ▸ to select **PRB**, then use the arrow key ▾ to select **5:randInt(**. Press [ENTER].

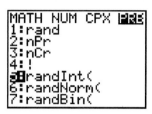

```
MATH NUM CPX PRB
1:rand
2:nPr
3:nCr
4:!
5▮randInt(
6:randNorm(
7:randBin(
```

Step 3: Enter the range of numbers to generate. Type (1, 31, 23).

```
L1        L2      L3      2
 2      ------  ------
 8
 5
 2
 2
12
L2 =...nt(1,31,23)
```

Step 4: Press [ENTER]. The calculator generates 23 random numbers between 1 and 31, inclusive, and places them in List 2.

```
L1     L2     L3      2
 2     29    ------
 8      6
 2     31
 5     24
 2     10
 2     28
12     11
L2(1)=29
```

d. To see a list of the birthdays chronologically from January to December, follow these steps:

Step 1: Use the arrow keys ⌃ and ▸ to highlight the L3 header.

```
L1     L2     L3      3
 2     29    ------
 8      6
 2     31
 5     24
 2     10
 2     28
12     11
L3 =
```

Step 2: Type 100*L1 +L2. Press [1][0][0][×][2nd][1][+][2nd][2].

```
L1     L2     L3      3
 2     29    ------
 8      6
 5     31
 2     24
 2     10
 2     28
12     11
L3 =100*L1+L2
```

Step 3: Press [ENTER].

```
L1     L2     L3      3
 2     29    229
 8      6    806
 2     31    231
 5     24    524
 2     10    210
 2     28    228
12     11   1211
L3(1)=229
```

e. As you look at List 3, what is the first date that is generated in your list? How does the equation you typed in List 3 change a month and a date from List 1 and List 2 into one number in List 3?

f. To put the dates in List 3 in ascending order, follow these steps:

Step 1: Use the arrow keys ⬆ and ▶ to highlight the L4 header.

L2	L3	🔲	4
29	229	------	
6	806		
31	231		
24	524		
10	210		
28	228		
11	1211		
L4 =			

Step 2: Copy L3 into L4. Press ⟨2nd⟩⟨3⟩.

L2	L3	🔲	4
29	229	------	
6	806		
31	231		
24	524		
10	210		
28	228		
11	1211		
L4 =L₃			

Step 3: Press ⟨ENTER⟩.

L2	L3	L4	4
29	229	**229**	
6	806	806	
31	231	231	
24	524	524	
10	210	210	
28	228	228	
11	1211	1211	
L4(1)=229			

Step 4: Use the arrow key ⬆ to highlight the L4 header.

L2	L3	🔲	4
29	229	229	
6	806	806	
31	231	231	
24	524	524	
10	210	210	
28	228	228	
11	1211	1211	
L4 ={229,806,231...			

Step 5: Select the Sort Ascending command. Press ⟨STAT⟩ then use the arrow key ⬇ to select **2:SortA(**.

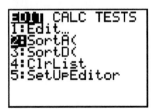

```
EDIT CALC TESTS
1:Edit…
2:SortA(
3:SortD(
4:ClrList
5:SetUpEditor
```

Step 6: Type L4. Press ⟨2nd⟩⟨4⟩⟨)⟩. Press ⟨ENTER⟩.

```
SortA(L4)■
```

Look at List 4. The birthdays from List 3 are rearranged from lowest number to highest.

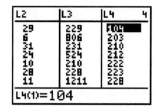

5. The experimenter should scroll down List 4 to see if any of the birthdays are a match.

6. If there are matching birthdays, the recorder will record "yes" in the appropriate column. If there are no matching birthdays, the recorder will record "no" in the appropriate column.

7. Repeat these steps three additional times. You will generate a total of 4 groups of 23 people.

8. What percentage of your simulations ended up with a matching birthday?

9. As a group, do you see any problems with this birthday simulation?

10. Based on your experiment, how often do you predict people in a group of 23 will have matching birthdays?

EXPERIMENT 4: Number Cubes

Part 1: Rolling One Number Cube

Rolling a number cube, or die, can be simulated with a graphing calculator.

1. The recorder should make a table like **Figure 7.13** and record the data as other group members do their jobs. If you have not traded jobs yet, do so now.

Number	Frequency	Frequency Written As		
		Fraction	Decimal	Percent
1				
2				
3				
4				
5				
6				
Totals				

FIGURE 7.13

2. The calculator simulates rolling a number cube by following these steps:

Press the APPS key.

Scroll down to **Prob Sim**.

Press ENTER.

Choose **2.Roll Dice**.

Press ENTER.

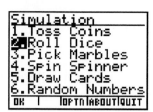

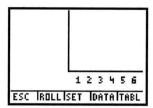

Press ZOOM to select **SET**.

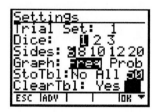

This screen tells you that we are rolling one six-sided number cube. The calculator rolls the cube one time. The data will be displayed as a frequency graph.

Press the GRAPH key to select **OK**.

As you press the WINDOW key, which selects **ROLL**, the number cube will roll once.

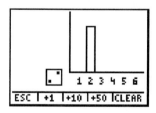

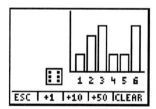

3. The recorder should record each roll of the dice in the table.

4. After you have rolled the number cube 24 times, the calculator should calculate the frequency as a fraction, decimal, and percentage. The calculator should also perform any calculations required for the last row.

5. The recorder should record all of the results in the table.

6. The experimenter should press the **+50** command. What do you think is happening?

7. What do you think would happen if you rolled the number cube 1,000 times?

Part 2: Rolling Two Number Cubes

For this portion of Experiment 4 you will be rolling two dice using the graphing calculator simulator.

8. The experimenter should choose the setting for rolling two dice.

9. The recorder should create a table similar to **Figure 7.14**.

Sum of the Two Number Cubes	Frequency	Frequency Written As		
		Fraction	Decimal	Percent
1				
2				
3				
4				
5				
6				
7				
8				
9				
10				
11				
12				
Totals				

FIGURE 7.14

10. The experimenter should choose the setting for rolling two dice.

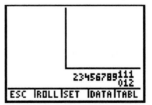

11. Roll the dice quickly 50 times. Before you actually select **+50**, what do you think the frequency bar graph will look like?

12. Which sum do you think is most likely to come up?

Press the Y= key (ESC) to see this screen.

Select **TABL** (press the GRAPH key) to see a list of the sums rolled.

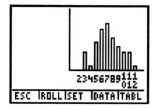 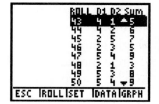

13. The experimenter reads the list of sums to the recorder. The recorder records how many of each sum was simulated by the calculator.

14. The calculator should calculate the values to fill in the fraction, decimal, and percentage columns. The calculator should also fill in the last row. If you need help with these calculations, have the observer help you.

15. Approximately how long do you think it would have taken to roll two number cubes fifty times and record the results?

Keep your data from all of the experiments.

Section 7.2

Chapter 7 What Are the Chances? Probability   **433**

Assignment

Use the graphic organizer, a Venn diagram, in **Figure 7.15** to answer the following questions about a survey of 90 high school students. Show any necessary work. The circle marked with **R** represents the number of students who like rock music. The circle marked with **C** represents the number of students who like country music. The area where the circles overlap represents the number of students who like both rock and country music. Students who do not like either rock or country music are listed outside the circles but inside the rectangle.

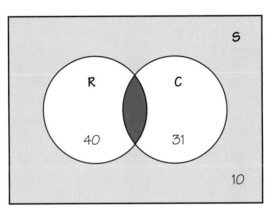

FIGURE 7.15.
90 high school students surveyed

R = Number of students who like rock music

C = Number of students who like country music

1. How many students like rock only?

2. How many students like both rock and country?

3. How many students like rock?

4. What percentage of the students surveyed didn't like either rock or country?

5. How many students didn't like country?

6. What percentage of the students surveyed didn't like country?

SECTION 7.3

What Are the Chances?

In the previous section you conducted four experiments involving probability. An experiment has an outcome, but you cannot predict what that outcome will be prior to the experiment. Probability involves measuring the likelihood of the various results of the experiment. **Probability** is defined as the ratio of the number of successful, or favorable, outcomes to the total number of outcomes.

$$\text{Probability} = \frac{\text{number of favorable outcomes}}{\text{total number of outcomes}}$$

In the four experiments in the previous section you collected data. From that data you calculated the frequencies as fractions, decimals, and percentages. The frequency ratio from an experiment is also called the **experimental probability**.

1. Look back at your data from Experiment 4, Part 1: the number cube experiment.

   a. How many 3's did your group roll?

   b. How many times did you roll the number cube?

   c. What was the experimental probability of rolling a 3 for your group?

2. Put together the collected data from all of the groups in your class for this experiment together. What was the experimental probability of rolling a 3 for your class?

Theoretical probability is different from experimental probability. In theoretical probability you actually count the number of possible outcomes. You also count the number of outcomes, or ways, that you consider a success. If you want to find the theoretical probability of rolling a 3 with a six-sided number cube, first find the total number of possible outcomes. For the number cube, there are six possible outcomes because there are six sides. If the favorable outcome is rolling a 3, you count the number of 3's on the number cube. There is one 3 on a normal number cube.

When you list all the possible outcomes, you are listing the **sample space**.

The sample space is a set of possible outcomes, so the sample space for a six-sided number cube that is numbered consecutively from 1 to 6 and written in set notation is:

{1, 2, 3, 4, 5, 6}

Probability is written as a ratio of the number of favorable outcomes to the number of total outcomes:

$$P(\text{desired outcome}) = \frac{\text{number of favorable outcomes}}{\text{total number of possible outcomes}}$$

So, written in probability notation, the theoretical probability of rolling a 3 is $P(3) = \frac{1}{6}$.

3. What is the sample space for tossing a coin?

4. What is the probability of tossing a head with a fair coin?

5. What is the probability of rolling a 10 with a six-sided number cube that is numbered from 1 to 6?

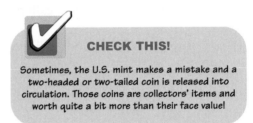

CHECK THIS!

Sometimes, the U.S. mint makes a mistake and a two-headed or two-tailed coin is released into circulation. Those coins are collectors' items and worth quite a bit more than their face value!

If there is no chance that an event will occur, the probability is 0.

6. If every student in your school rolled a number cube 50 times, what do you predict the experimental probability of rolling a 3 with a number cube might be?

The **Law of Large Numbers** says that if you collect a large amount of experimental data, the experimental probability will be close to the theoretical probability. The larger the amount of data, the closer the experimental probability is to the theoretical probability.

7. Look back at your data from Experiment 1, Part 1 of the spinner experiment.

a. What is the experimental probability of the tip of the paper clip landing in the shaded region for your group?

b. What is the experimental probability of the tip of the paper clip landing in the shaded region for your class?

c. What is the theoretical probability of the tip of the paper clip landing in the shaded region **(Figure 7.16)**? Describe how you found the theoretical probability.

d. Is the whole-class experimental probability or the small-group experimental probability closer to the theoretical probability?

8. Look back at your data from Experiment 2, Part 1 of the color tile experiment.

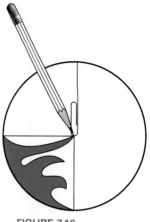

FIGURE 7.16

a. What is the experimental probability of drawing a yellow tile from Bag A for your group?

b. What is the experimental probability of drawing a yellow tile from Bag A for your class?

c. What is the theoretical probability of drawing a yellow tile from Bag A?

d. Which is closer to the theoretical probability, the whole-class experimental probability or the small-group experimental probability?

9. Look back at your data from Experiment 3, the birthday simulations.

a. What is the experimental probability of having matching birthdays in a group of 23 people, using your group's data?

b. What is the experimental probability when you combine all of the groups' data?

c. If you are predicting the theoretical probability based on the experimental probability, will you use your group's experimental probability or the entire class's experimental probability?

10. Look back at your data from Experiment 3, Part 2: rolling two number cubes.

a. What is the experimental probability of rolling a 7, using your group's data?

b. What is the experimental probability of rolling a 7, using the class data?

Sums of Two Number Cubes	Number Cube 1					
		1	2	3	4	5	6
Number Cube 2	1						
	2						
	3						
	4						
	5						
	6						

FIGURE 7.17

c. Create a table for the sample space for this experiment similar to **Figure 7.17** by filling in all of the possibilities for the sum of two number cubes. You can use this same space to determine the theoretical probabilities for rolling each sum.

d. Use the table to find the theoretical probability of rolling a 7.

e. Which is closer to the theoretical probability, the whole-class experimental probability or the small-group experimental probability?

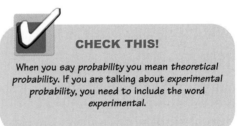

CHECK THIS!

When you say *probability* you mean *theoretical probability*. If you are talking about *experimental probability*, you need to include the word *experimental*.

11. Look back at your data from Experiment 1, Part 2: spinning two spinners.

a. What is the experimental probability of Spinner A landing in the shaded area and Spinner B landing in the unshaded area, using your group's data?

b. What is the experimental probability, using the class data?

c. Which is more likely to be close to the theoretical probability?

12. When rolling one number cube, what is the probability that you will roll a 12?

13. What is the probability that the number you roll is less than 12 when you roll a number cube?

If an event is certain to occur, the probability is 1.

Let's look at the probability of an event occurring or not occurring.

14. What is the probability of rolling a 3 with a number cube?

15. What is the probability of not rolling a 3 with a number cube?

16. What do you notice about these two probabilities?

These two events are considered to be **complementary**. The probability of an event occurring and the probability of the event not occurring will always add up to one.

$$P(\text{event occurring}) + P(\text{event not occurring}) = 1$$

The idea of complementary events is both important and useful because sometimes it is easier to find the probability that something will not occur than to find the probability that it will occur.

17. Using Spinner A, what is the probability of landing in the shaded region?

18. Using Spinner A, what is the probability of not landing in the shaded region?

19. What is the sum of the two probabilities?

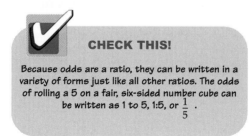

CHECK THIS!

Because odds are a ratio, they can be written in a variety of forms just like all other ratios. The odds of rolling a 5 on a fair, six-sided number cube can be written as 1 to 5, 1:5, or $\frac{1}{5}$.

Another term we use to talk about the chances of an event happening is **odds**. Odds are defined as the ratio of the number of favorable outcomes to the number of unfavorable outcomes.

$$\text{Odds} = \frac{\text{number of favorable outcomes}}{\text{number of unfavorable outcomes}}$$

20. What are the odds that you will roll a 3 with a number cube?

21. What are the odds that you will draw a green tile out of Bag A?

Odds and probability have similar characteristics but provide different information. Both are ratios but they compare different data. Probability is a part-to-whole ratio, in which the number of favorable outcomes is a part of the whole set of possible outcomes. Odds are a part-to-part ratio, in which the number of favorable outcomes is a part that is being compared to another part, the number of unfavorable outcomes.

SUMMARY

When you conduct an experiment you can find experimental probabilities. The results from an experiment are not always the same as the theoretical probabilities. As you conduct experiments and collect more data, the results will get closer and closer to the theoretical probabilities.

❖ Probability of an event occurring $= \dfrac{\text{number of favorable outcomes}}{\text{total number of outcomes}}$

❖ If an event is certain to occur, the probability is 1.

❖ If an event cannot possibly occur, the probability is 0.

❖ The sum of the probabilities for complementary events is 1.

❖ P(event occurring) + P(event not occurring) = 1

❖ Odds of an event occurring $= \dfrac{\text{number of favorable outcomes}}{\text{number of unfavorable outcomes}}$

Assignment

1. Each of the letters of the word MISSISSIPPI is written on an individual piece of paper and placed in a bag.

    a. What is the probability of drawing the letter S from the bag?

    b. What is the probability of drawing the letter P from the bag?

    c. What is the probability of drawing the letter M from the bag?

    d. What is the probability of not drawing the letter I from the bag?

    e. What is the probability of drawing the letter C from the bag?

    f. What is the probability of drawing an M, I, S, or P from the bag?

2. Susan collected data from an experiment with an eight-sided polyhedron, called an octahedron **(Figure 7.18)**. The sides are numbered from 1 to 8. Susan rolled the octahedron 24 times; her results are shown in this list:

    {1, 4, 7, 8, 2, 2, 5, 8, 6, 4, 7, 1, 6, 3, 6, 2, 5, 4, 1, 4, 6, 3, 2, 8}

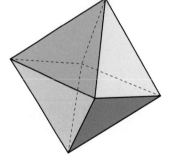

FIGURE 7.18

a. Make a frequency table **(Figure 7.19)** and find Susan's experimental probabilities for each of the numbers on the octahedron.

Number	Frequency	Experimental Probability
1		
2		
3		
4		
5		
6		
7		
8		

FIGURE 7.19

b. What is Susan's experimental probability of rolling a 6?

c. What is the theoretical probability of rolling a 6?

d. What is Susan's experimental probability of rolling an even number?

e. What is the theoretical probability of rolling an even number?

f. What is the difference between Susan's results and the theoretical probability of rolling an even number?

3. Using the table you made in this section for Question 10, fill in the table **(Figure 7.20)** with the theoretical probabilities for rolling these sums with two number cubes.

Sum of the Two Number Cubes	1	2	3	4	5	6	7	8	9	10	11	12	13
Number of ways to get this sum using the table													
Probability of rolling this sum													
Probability written as an approximate percent (%)													

FIGURE 7.20

a. What is the probability of rolling a sum of 3?

b. What is the probability of not rolling a sum of 7?

c. What is the probability of rolling a sum of 1?

d. Make a graph of the probability of rolling a sum as a percentage versus the sum of the two number cubes **(Figure 7.21)**.

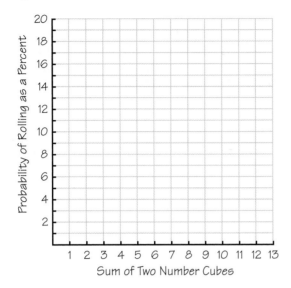

FIGURE 7.21

Independent or Dependent?

Mr. Smith uses a number cube to decide whether his students will have homework. He gives his students three choices: (1) The students will have homework if either 5 or 6 shows on the number cube, (2) The students will have homework if either 1, 2, or 3 shows on the number cube, and (3) The students will have homework if 4 shows on the number cube.

In the tables in **Figure 7.22**, the results for each of the events is shaded.

Event A: {either 5 or 6 shows on the number cube}
Event B: {either 1, 2, or 3 shows on the number cube}
Event C: {4 shows on the number cube}

Event A	
1	
2	
3	
4	
5	
6	

Event B	
1	
2	
3	
4	
5	
6	

Event C	
1	
2	
3	
4	
5	
6	

FIGURE 7.22

1. What is the probability of Event A?

2. What is the probability of Event B?

3. What is the probability of Event C?

4. Which event should the students choose to decrease the probability that they will have homework?

5. How would you find the probability of rolling an even number with a number cube?

There are times when you want to find the probability that events will happen in succession, or one right after the other.

Possible Results for Tossing a Coin		First Coin	
		Tail	Head
Second Coin	Tail	Probability =	(Head, Tail) Probability =
	Head	Probability =	Probability =

FIGURE 7.23

6. In a coin toss, to find the probability of a coin landing with heads up twice in succession with a fair coin, fill in the results in the table **(Figure 7.23)**. Find the probability for each outcome.

a. What is the sum of all of the probabilities in the table?

b. Does the outcome of the second coin toss depend on the outcome of the first coin toss? Explain.

c. Would the outcome of a second roll of a number cube depend on the outcome of the first roll? Explain.

To find the probability of either Event A or Event B occurring, you can find the probability of each event occurring and then add the two probabilities together. This is called the **additive property of probability**.

$P(A \text{ or } B) = P(A) + P(B)$ as long as there is no overlap between Events A and B.

$$P(\text{Event A or Event B}) = P(\text{Event A}) + P(\text{Event B})$$
$$= \frac{2}{6} + \frac{3}{6}$$
$$= \frac{5}{6}$$

In the coin toss, if you are not concerned about which of the coins is first and which is second but want to find the probability of tossing a head and a tail, you can add the two probabilities together.

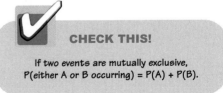

CHECK THIS!

If two events are mutually exclusive,
P(either A or B occurring) = P(A) + P(B).

The probability of tossing two coins and getting one of the coins to land heads up and the other tails up = P(Head then Tail) + P(Tail then Head) $= \frac{1}{4} + \frac{1}{4} = \frac{1}{2}$.

7. Let's look at rolling a number cube twice and find the probabilities for the following events.

   Event AA = {roll the number cube twice and get either 5 or 6 both times}

   Event BB = {roll the number cube twice and get either 1, 2, or 3 both times}

   Event CC = {roll the number cube twice and get 4 both times}

   Event AC = {roll either a 5 or 6 the first time and roll 4 the second time}

   a. Create a table **(Figure 7.24)** and shade in the squares where the result is either 5 or 6 for both rolls, and then find the probability of Event AA.

1	2	3	4	5	6

   Second Roll of Number Cube

	1	2	3	4	5	6
1						
2						
3						
4						
5						
6						

   First Roll of Number Cube

   FIGURE 7.24

   b. With a different color, shade the squares for Event BB: {roll the number cube twice and get 1, 2, or 3 both times}.

   c. With a different color, shade in the squares for Event CC: {roll the number cube twice and get 4 both times}.

   d. With a different color, shade in the squares for Event AC: {roll either a 5 or 6 the first time and roll 4 the second time}.

e. Summarize the probabilities from these four events in the table below (**Figure 7.25**).

P(A) =	P(A) =	P(A)•P(A) =	P(AA) =
P(B) =	P(B) =	P(B)•P(B) =	P(BB) =
P(C) =	P(C) =	P(C)•P(C) =	P(CC) =
P(A) =	P(C) =	P(A)•P(C) =	P(AC) =

FIGURE 7.25

f. What do you notice in the table?

Events that happen without regard to one another are called **independent events**. For example, the toss of the first coin has no effect on the second toss of the second coin. With two six-sided number cubes, the roll of one number cube has no effect on the roll of the second number cube.

You can find the probability of two independent events both occurring by multiplying the probabilities of each event occurring separately. This is called the **multiplicative rule for probability**.

$$P(A \text{ and } B) = P(A) \cdot P(B)$$

8. Find the probability of rolling a 3 with a number cube and then rolling an even number on the second roll.

P(rolling 3 and then rolling an even number)
= P(____)·P(____)
= _____ · _____
= _____

9. What is the probability of tossing three heads in a row with a fair coin?

10. Are these events independent? How do you know?

11. Look back at your results from Section 7.2 for Experiment 1, Part 2: spinning two spinners. Use the multiplication rule to make a table of the probabilities of the possible results (**Figure 7.26**).

		Spinner A	
		Shaded	Unshaded
Spinner B	Shaded		
	Unshaded		

FIGURE 7.26

a. What is the probability of both spinners landing in the shaded area?

b. What is the probability of both spinners landing in the unshaded area?

c. What is the probability of Spinner A landing in the shaded area and Spinner B landing in the unshaded area?

d. What is the probability of Spinner A landing in the unshaded area and Spinner B landing in the shaded area?

e. What is the probability of one of the spinners landing in the shaded area and the other landing in the unshaded area?

f. What is the sum of all of the probabilities in the table?

g. Are these two events independent events?

h. How do your answers from the previous questions compare to the results from your experiments?

There are experiments in which the first event has an effect on the second event. Events that are affected by each other are called **dependent events**.

12. Let's investigate some probabilities with a standard deck of playing cards **(Figure 7.27)**.

a. How many cards are in a standard deck of cards?

b. How many cards in the deck are diamonds?

c. Your math teacher uses a deck of cards to assign students to groups. Your best friend chooses a diamond. What is the probability of drawing a diamond from a standard deck of cards?

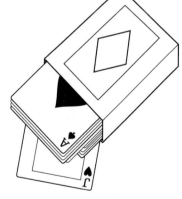

FIGURE 7.27

d. What is the probability of drawing a diamond, returning it to the deck, and drawing another diamond?

3. What does the probability mean?

13. Suppose that your teacher has already drawn one diamond from the deck and placed it face down on the table. Let's look at the probability of drawing another diamond.

    a. You want to be in the same group as your best friend. How many diamonds are left in the deck?

    b. How many cards are left in the deck?

    c. Now, what is the probability of drawing a diamond from the deck?

    d. What is the probability that you and your best friend will be in the same group? Using the multiplication property of probability, what is the probability of drawing one diamond from the deck, not returning it to the deck, and then drawing another diamond on the second draw?

    e. Was the second draw affected by the first draw? How?

    f. How do the probabilities from Questions 12d and 13e compare?

The probability of the second draw is affected by what happened in the first draw when the card from the first draw is not returned to the deck, so these events are dependent.

CHECK THIS!

If a card is returned to the deck after the draw, the words "with replacement" can be used. If a card is not returned to the deck after the draw, the words "without replacement" can be used.

14. Let's look back at Experiment 4, Part 2: rolling two number cubes, and investigate another type of probability. Here is the table you created in Section 7.3 **(Figure 7.28)**:

		Second Number Cube					
	Sum	1	2	3	4	5	6
First Number Cube	1	2	3	4	5	6	7
	2	3	4	5	6	7	8
	3	4	5	6	7	8	9
	4	5	6	7	8	9	10
	5	6	7	8	9	10	11
	6	7	8	9	10	11	12

FIGURE 7.28

Given that the first number cube rolls a 3, what is the probability that the sum of the two number cubes will be either 5 or 7?

Solution 1

a. Event A is defined as {the sum of the two numbers is 7 or 5}. Shade the squares where the sum of the two numbers is either 5 or 7. Find P(A).

b. Event B is defined as {the first number cube shows a 3}. Use a second color to shade the squares where the first number cube shows a 3. Find P(B).

c. How many favorable outcomes occur for both Event A and Event B?

d. Looking at the table, what is the probability that both Event A and Event B will occur?

e. Given that the first number cube rolls a 3, what is the probability that the sum of the two number cubes will be either 5 or 7?

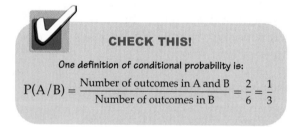

CHECK THIS!

One definition of conditional probability is:

$$P(A/B) = \frac{\text{Number of outcomes in A and B}}{\text{Number of outcomes in B}} = \frac{2}{6} = \frac{1}{3}$$

Solution 2

f. Another way to answer this question is to make a list of pairs with a 3 showing on the first number cube.

3, 1
(3, 2)
3, 3
(3, 4)
3, 5
3, 6

g. How many pairs are on the list?

h. Circle the pairs with a sum of either 7 or 5. How many pairs are there?

    i. What is the probability of rolling a sum of 7 or 5, given that the first number cube is a 3?

This type of probability is called **conditional probability**. The probability of Event A occurring with the condition of Event B occurring can be written in this shorthand notation: P(A/B).

Venn Diagrams

15. We can also use a Venn diagram to help find conditional probabilities. In the Venn diagram below **(Figure 7.29)** you will notice that the shaded area is the location of results that are in both Event M and Event S.

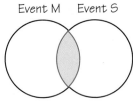

FIGURE 7.29

Event M represents an A grade in mathematics.
Event S represents an A grade in science.

12 students received an A in math but not in science.
10 students received an A in science but not in math.
2 students received an A in math and in science.

16. Fill in the Venn diagram with the information above. What is the probability of receiving an A in math, given that a student received an A in science?

Section 7.4

Chapter 7 What Are the Chances? Probability   **451**

Assignment

1. The director of a high school talent show has slips of paper numbered 1 to 60. Students who wish to try out for the talent show randomly draw one of the slips of paper to determine the order in which they will audition.

   a. What is the probability of drawing a number higher than 30?

   b. What is the probability of drawing a number lower than 10?

   c. What is the probability of drawing the number 60?

   d. What is the probability of drawing a number that is a multiple of 5?

2. What is the probability of drawing four queens in a row from a deck of cards with replacement?

3. What is the probability of drawing four queens in a row without replacement?

4. What is the probability of drawing a jack followed by a queen without replacement?

5. How many black cards are in a deck of cards?

6. If none of the cards are replaced, what is the probability of drawing three black cards in succession?

7. What is the probability of drawing five hearts in a row from a deck of cards with replacement?

8. In a game at the school fair, bills of different denominations are in a container. If a student draws two one-hundred-dollar bills in succession, she will receive the entire container of bills as a prize. The container has the following numbers of bills **(Figure 7.30)**:

Bill Value	Number of Bills
$100	2
$20	10
$10	20
$5	50
$1	100

FIGURE 7.30

What is the probability of drawing two one-hundred-dollar bills in succession without replacement?

9. One of the calculators is missing from Ms. G.'s room. A witness remembers seeing a student forget to return his calculator to the holder at the end of fifth period. The witness states that the forgetful student in fifth period is male with brown eyes and brown hair and has on a red shirt. Ms. G knows the following probabilities about her students:

$$P(\text{5th period}) = \frac{1}{7}$$

$$P(\text{male}) = \frac{1}{2}$$

$$P(\text{brown eyes}) = \frac{3}{4}$$

$$P(\text{brown hair}) = \frac{3}{4}$$

$$P(\text{red shirt}) = \frac{1}{10}$$

Ms. G. decides that Paul must be the forgetful student because he is in fifth period, has brown hair and brown eyes, and has on a red shirt. She uses the multiplicative property of probabilities to prove her conjecture.

$$P(\text{a student matches the description given}) = \frac{1}{7} \cdot \frac{1}{2} \cdot \frac{3}{4} \cdot \frac{4}{5} \cdot \frac{1}{10} = \frac{9}{2240} \approx 0.4\%$$

Ms. G. claims that the probability a student would match the description given by the witness is so low that Paul must be the forgetful student.

Do you agree or disagree with Ms. G.? Why?

Samantha's Game: A Spinner Simulation

Samantha has invented a board game. The game has a spinner that is divided into four equal sections. The sections are numbered 1, 2, 3, and 4. If a player lands on 4, he loses a turn. Samantha wants to determine approximately how many times a player would lose his or her turn in ten spins. Samantha used her graphing calculator to simulate spinning a spinner.

To simulate spinning a spinner in your graphing calculator, follow these steps:

Step 1: Use the APPS key to select Prob Sim.

Step 2: Press Enter.

Step 3: Choose 4. Spin Spinner.

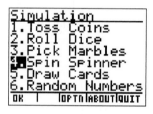

Step 4: Select TABL.

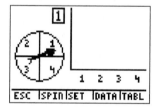

Step 5: Select SPIN.

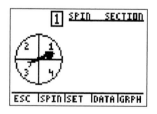

Step 6: The spinner will spin one time. Select CLEAR.

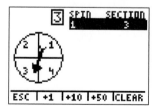

Step 7: Select YES.

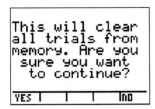

Step 8: Select +10. The spinner will spin 10 times.

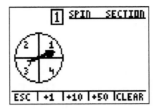

Step 9: Count the number of 4's in the list and record in your table.

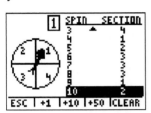

Step 10: Repeat steps 6 through 9.

Each pair of students repeats the steps for a total of ten trials of ten spins **(Figure 7.31)**. Two pairs of students should then put their data together for a total of twenty trials of ten spins each.

Number of Times "Lose a Turn" Spins (4)	Tally Marks	Frequency
0		
1		
2		
3		
4		
5		
6		
7		
8		
9		
10		

FIGURE 7.31

1. What is the theoretical probability that the spinner will land on the 4, where the player loses a turn?

2. How many times would you predict that the spinner would land on the 4 in one trial of ten spins?

3. Using your data, what is the experimental probability that the spinner will land on the 4 three times during a ten-spin trial?

4. Based on your experimental data, what is the experimental probability that the spinner will land on 4 two or more times in ten spins?

5. Graph the experimental results from your group of four.

6. Combine the data for your class.

7. Graph the experimental results from your class.

8. How are the two graphs alike? How are they different?

9. How would you find the probability that each of ten successive spins would land on the 4?

What Should I Wear?

Victoria has recently gotten a promotion at work. Because of her new position, she needs to update her wardrobe. To get the most for her money, she wants to purchase the fewest number of items she can while maximizing the number of outfits she will have to wear.

Being a savvy businesswoman, Victoria knows that she needs a variety of skirts, pants, blouses, and business suits. She also needs shoes in a variety of styles and colors.

Victoria goes to her local mall to shop. By the end of the day, she has purchased the following items **(Figure 7.32)**:

White blouse	Black jacket	Black skirt	Black pumps
Ivory blouse	Red jacket	Navy blue skirt	White pumps
Blue blouse	Tweed jacket	Tan pants	Black flat shoes
Tan blouse		Black pants	Brown flat soes

FIGURE 7.32

1. For each outfit, Victoria needs a jacket, blouse, skirt or pants, and shoes. Since she has purchased mix-and-match items, all of the pieces will go together. How many different outfits can she put together from her new purchases?

2. How did you determine the number of different outfits?

Victoria knows that decision making involves thinking about all of the possible outcomes for a given situation. Good managers make decisions only after considering all possible outcomes.

In mathematics, good decisions come from thinking about all possible outcomes as well. In the next few sections, you will examine different ways that mathematics can help people to count possible outcomes in a variety of situations.

Tree Diagrams

Victoria's son, Brad, attends Chickasaw High School. Every spring, Brad and his mother sit down to decide what classes he will take for the next school year. For his senior year next year, he has to make some decisions.

Chickasaw High School allows students not only to select their courses but also to choose which sections of each course they enroll in. Brad has looked at his transcript and his graduation requirements and knows which courses he needs to take in order to graduate. He also knows how many sections of each course are being offered. He knows which section of athletics and which section of English he will be taking. However, the other four classes, Physics, Algebra 2, Computer Programming, and U.S. Government, have multiple sections. The table in **Figure 7.33** shows the information that Brad has collected.

Physics	3
Algebra 2	3
Computer Programming	2
U.S. Government	3

FIGURE 7.33. Course enrollment information

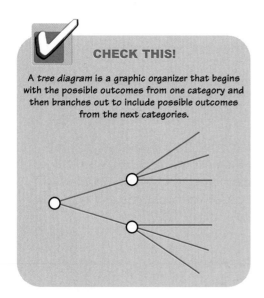

CHECK THIS!

A *tree diagram* is a graphic organizer that begins with the possible outcomes from one category and then branches out to include possible outcomes from the next categories.

To make the best decision, Brad needs to figure out how many possible schedules he could have. He decides to use a tree diagram to help him.

1. How many sections of Physics are being offered at Chickasaw High School? Begin the tree diagram on a separate sheet of paper with that number of starting points.

2. How many sections of Algebra 2 are being offered? From each starting point that represents a section of Physics, draw a branch leading to each section of Algebra 2.

3. How many sections of Computer Programming are being offered? From each section of Algebra 2, draw a branch that leads to each section of Computer Programming.

4. How many sections of U.S. Government are being offered? From each section of Computer Programming, draw a branch that leads to each section of U.S. Government.

5. From your tree diagram, how many possible schedules could Brad create for the four classes? How do you know?

6. How many possible schedules for Physics and Algebra 2 are there? How do you know?

7. How many possible schedules for Algebra 2 and Computer Programming are there? How do you know?

8. How many possible schedules for Physics, Algebra 2, and Computer Programming are there? How do you know?

9. Without constructing a tree diagram, how could you predict the total number course sections from which Brad could choose?

Assignment

The Old Dominion School District hosts a baseball tournament each spring. In the tournament, teams from eight area high schools play three games each. The eight teams are split into two divisions of four teams **(Figure 7.34)**:

Division A	Division B
Washington HS	Lincoln HS
Roosevelt HS	Reagan HS
Johnson HS	Kennedy HS
Nixon HS	Clinton HS

FIGURE 7.34

Within each division, each team plays three games: one game against each of the other teams in their division. The teams with the best record in each division play for the tournament championship.

1. Use a tree diagram to list the possible win-loss sequences for Washington H.S. for the set of three games in division play.

2. How many possible win-loss sequences are there for the three games?

The sales representatives for a technology company must attend a training session in one of two cities and then select a city on the West Coast and a city on the East Coast in which to meet with prospective clients. The cities are shown in **Figure 7.35**.

Training Session	West Coast City	East Coast City
Albuquerque	San Francisco	Richmond
Austin	Seattle	Providence
	Portland, OR	Raleigh

FIGURE 7.35

3. Use a tree diagram to show the possible sequences of cities that a sales representative may visit.

4. How many possible sequences of cities are there?

Counting Methods

In the United States, Canada, and many Caribbean countries, telephone numbers are managed and assigned by the North American Numbering Plan Administration, or NANPA. Decisions about telephone numbers, including area codes, have been made by this organization since it was created in 1951 by AT&T, which was then the only American telephone company.

In the United States, telephone numbers consist of ten digits, including a three-digit area code, a three-digit local telephone prefix, and a four-digit line number.

As telecommunications technology has evolved, the guidelines that NANPA uses have changed. Initially, the ten-digit telephone numbers were represented using notation to describe each of the three separate codes:

Area code – Prefix – Line number
3 digits – 3 digits – 4 digits

NANPA uses a string of N's and X's to represent a phone number, where N could be any digit from 2 through 9 and X could be any digit from 0 through 9.

Until 1973, NANPA used the string N(0/1)X-NNX-XXXX to represent phone numbers. There were several restrictions on the numbers: the middle digit of the area code could only be 0 or 1; the first digit of the area code could not be 0 or 1; and the first two digits of the telephone prefix could not be 0 or 1.

1. Given the area code numbering restrictions, how many possible three-digit area codes could there have been before 1973? Use **Figure 7.36** to help you determine your answer.

Digit	First Digit	Second Digit	Third Digit
Possible Values			
Number of Possible Values			

FIGURE 7.36

2. How many possible telephone prefixes could be created before 1973? Use **Figure 7.37** to help you determine your answer.

FIGURE 7.37

Digit	First Digit	Second Digit	Third Digit
Possible Values			
Number of Possible Values			

3. How many possible line numbers could be created before 1973? Use **Figure 7.38** to help you determine your answer.

FIGURE 7.38

Digit	First Digit	Second Digit	Third Digit	Fourth Digit
Possible Values				
Number of Possible Values				

4. How many possible phone numbers could be created using the pre-1973 rules? Use **Figure 7.39** to help you determine your answer.

FIGURE 7.39

Digit	Area Code	Telephone Prefix	Line Number
Possible Values			
Number of Possible Values			

5. Within a given area code, how many telephone numbers could be issued?

6. How did you determine your answers to Questions 1 through 5?

Using the ideas from tree diagrams, possible outcomes for a series of events can be counted using the **Fundamental Counting Principle**, which is called the **Multiplication Rule of Counting** in some textbooks. If you know how many possible outcomes there are for each event, you can multiply the individual totals together to find the possible number of outcomes for the whole series. In our telephone number example, each digit in the ten-digit phone number can be thought of as an event. There are a total of ten events in selecting a phone number. Using the pre-1973 rules, you can count the total number of phone numbers that NANPA believed to be sufficient to meet the needs of North American telecommunications consumers.

CHECK THIS!

The Fundamental Counting Principle states that if there are *m* ways to choose the first item and *n* ways to choose the second item, then there are *m* x *n* ways to choose outcomes of the two items together.

In **Figure 7.40**, recall that N represents the digits 2 through 9 and X represents the digits 0 through 9.

Digit	N	0/1	X	N	N	X	X	X	X	X
Number of Outcomes	8	2	10	8	8	10	10	10	10	10

FIGURE 7.40

The total number of telephone numbers available under this plan would be found by multiplying the number of possible outcomes of each event together to get over one billion possible phone numbers.

By 1973, however, telecommunications technology changed: some cities, especially large cities like New York City, began to run out of telephone numbers. As a result, NANPA changed the rules for assigning phone numbers. You will explore those changes further in Assignment 7.8.

Connections: Tree Diagrams and Probability

You may recall that the probability of an outcome, when all outcomes are equally likely, is found by taking the ratio of the number of desired outcomes and the total number of outcomes. Since the number of desired outcomes is a part of the total number of outcomes, probability is a part:whole ratio. Tree diagrams can be used to help find probabilities of a series of events, whether they are independent or dependent events.

Recall from the previous section that Brad attends Chickasaw High School. Every year, the junior class holds a carnival to raise money to help pay for the senior prom the following year. A popular booth has a game where students draw two marbles from a bag to determine their prize. The bag has two red marbles and three blue marbles. The colors and sequences in which the marbles are drawn determine the prize that the student wins.

7. Draw a tree diagram to represent all of the possible outcomes.

8. Now condense your diagram into a smaller diagram to show only the results of the drawing. Draw a tree diagram like the one shown in the figure.

9. What colors could Brad possibly draw on the first draw? Record the possibilities on your tree diagram under "Color of First Marble."

10. What is the probability that a student will draw a red marble on the first draw? a blue marble?

11. What colors could Brad possibly draw on the second draw? Record the possibilities on your tree diagram under "Color of Second Marble."

12. If a student draws a red marble on the first draw and does not replace it, what is the probability that she will draw a red marble on the second draw? a blue marble?

13. If a student draws a blue marble on the first draw and does not replace it, what is the probability that he will draw a red marble on the second draw? a blue marble?

14. Label those probabilities on your tree diagram.

By following the branches on the tree diagram, you can trace the path of events that occur. The probability that an event will occur determines the likelihood of that path being followed.

15. Brad played the game at the carnival this year, and he drew two red marbles. On your tree diagram use a highlighter to trace the path of Brad's draws.

16. What was the theoretical probability of Brad drawing two red marbles?

17. How could you use your tree diagram to find the theoretical probability of Brad drawing two red marbles?

SUMMARY

Tree diagrams can be used to graphically illustrate the **sample space** of possible outcomes for a given situation. The **Fundamental Counting Principle**, which is also called the **Multiplication Rule of Counting**, follows from the idea of using a tree diagram to count the possible outcomes in a sample space. If you know the possible outcomes for a given event, you can find the total possible outcomes for a sequence of events by multiplying the number of possible outcomes for each event in the series.

Tree diagrams can also help you find probabilities of compound events, or events in a series, occurring. For each event that occurs in the tree diagram, write the probability of that event occurring on the branch in the tree diagram. To find the probability of a particular outcome, or series of events, multiply the probabilities that occur along the path of the series of events.

Assignment

Find the number of possible outcomes resulting from selecting one item from each of the grouped categories:

1. Ice cream flavors: chocolate, vanilla, strawberry, cookies and cream
   Toppings: hot fudge, caramel, butterscotch

2. Vacation destinations: Yellowstone National Park, New York City, Chicago
   Months: June, July, August

3. Sports: football, baseball, basketball, hockey
   Colleges: University of Virginia, University of Texas, Florida State University

4. Vehicles: sports car, pick-up truck, sedan, coupe
   Colors: blue, red

Before 1973, the North American Numbering Plan Administration (NANPA) used the string N(0/1)X-NNX-XXXX, where N could be any digit from 2 through 9 and X could be any digit from 0 through 9. The restrictions on the number included: the middle digit of the area code could only be 0 or 1; the first digit of the area code could not be 0 or 1: and the first two digits of the telephone prefix could not be 0 or 1.

In 1973, NANPA changed the restrictions on telephone numbers to N(0/1)X-NXX-XXXX, removing the restriction that the middle digit of the telephone prefix could not be 0 or 1.

5. How many telephone numbers could be issued for any given area code using the NXX-XXXX system?

6. How many more telephone numbers in any given area code could be issued after 1973 than before 1973?

7. How many telephone numbers in total were available in the numbering plan after the 1973 rule change?

In 1995, NANPA removed additional restrictions on telephone numbers in response to the increasing popularity of cell phones. It removed the restriction that the middle digit of an area code must be a 0 or 1. After 1995, telephone numbers were represented with the string NXX-NXX-XXXX. This new numbering system allowed states to use new area codes in order to increase the number of telephone numbers in a region.

8. How many area codes could be generated using the NXX-NXX-XXXX system?

9. How many more area codes did the 1995 rule change create?

10. How many telephone numbers in total were available in the numbering plan after the 1995 rule change?

11. How many more telephone numbers did the 1995 rule change add to the numbering plan?

12. In the 1995 numbering plan, what is the probability that a randomly selected number will have a 0 as the middle digit of the telephone prefix?

13. Suppose that, on an average, you do your math homework four out of every five nights, or 80% of the time. Also suppose that your math teacher gives you a short quiz daily. If you do your homework the night before a quiz, the probability that you get a good score on the quiz is $\frac{5}{6}$. If you don't do your homework, the probability that you get a good score on the quiz is only $\frac{1}{3}$.

a. Draw a tree diagram to represent this situation. Label the probabilities.

b. What is the probability that you both did your homework the night before and got a good score on the quiz?

c. What is the probability that you did not do your homework the night before and got a good score on the quiz?

SECTION 7.9

Permutations and Combinations

PART 1: The Beat Goes On

Brad and his sister, Chavon, like to download music from the Internet to listen to on their MP3 players. For her American History project, Chavon needs to create a playlist of three patriotic songs: "America the Beautiful," "The Star-Spangled Banner," and "America." The playlist will play in the background of her presentation. She does not care which order the songs are played in, but she does not want the songs to repeat. How many ways can the songs on the playlist be organized?

1. How many songs could be first in the playlist?

2. After the first song is chosen, how many songs could be second?

3. After the first two songs are chosen, how many songs could be third?

4. Organize your answers to the previous questions in a table similar to **Figure 7.41**.

Song Position	1	2	3
Number of Possible Songs			

FIGURE 7.41: Playlist Possibilities

5. How many different ways can Chavon organize the songs?

6. Chavon decides to create a playlist with her five personal favorite songs. Again, she does not want the songs to repeat and does not have a preference for the order in which the songs play. How many different ways could she organize the songs?

7. In general, how can you find the number of ways to organize a group of songs that do not repeat and for which the play order does not matter?

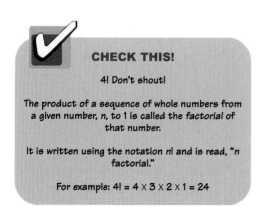

CHECK THIS!

4! Don't shout!

The product of a sequence of whole numbers from a given number, n, to 1 is called the *factorial* of that number.

It is written using the notation n! and is read, "n factorial."

For example: 4! = 4 × 3 × 2 × 1 = 24

PART 2: Does the Order Matter?

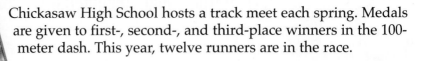

Chickasaw High School hosts a track meet each spring. Medals are given to first-, second-, and third-place winners in the 100-meter dash. This year, twelve runners are in the race.

1. Assuming that each runner has an equal chance of winning, how many possible first-place runners are there?

2. After first place has been decided, how many possible second-place runners are there?

3. After first and second places have been decided, how many possible third-place runners are there?

4. How many possible arrangements of runners are there for first, second, and third place?

5. Does the order of the winning runners matter? Why?

6. Last year at the Chickasaw High School meet, only seven runners registered for the 100-meter dash. How many arrangements of first-, second-, and third-place winners were there last year?

Arrangements of objects in a set in which the order matters are called **permutations**. In the Chickasaw meet, the set of objects was the group of runners competing in the 100-meter dash. The permutations were the arrangements of first-, second-, and third-place winners. In the Chickasaw meet, repetition was not allowed—a runner could not place both first *and* second. However, in other cases, repetition is allowed and the calculations are simpler.

Suppose that the Chickasaw High School track team has twelve members. Three of those members are to be selected to attend a special track and field camp. The order in which the members are selected does not matter.

7. How many team members could be selected for the first of the three spots at camp?

8. After one person has been selected, how many team members could be selected for the second spot? the third spot?

9. How many arrangements of the set of team members could have been chosen? Represent your answer numerically, including the operations that you used to obtain it.

10. Is it possible to have different arrangements that represent the same group of three students? If so, how?

11. Suppose that Brad, Trevor, and Jack are chosen to attend camp. How many different arrangements could have led to their selection? List those arrangements.

12. Does the order in which Brad, Trevor, and Jack were selected make a difference in the selection of the three team members that attend the camp? Why or why not?

13. How many equivalent arrangements led to the same selection of students? How could you represent that numerically?

14. Suppose that Ashley, Amanda, and Allison had been chosen to attend the summer camp. How many different arrangements could have led to their selection? List those arrangements.

15. How does the selection of Ashley, Amanda, and Allison compare with the selection of Brad, Trevor, and Jack?

16. The multiple arrangements that are equivalent to the same selection of track team members can be accounted for by counting the groups of equivalent arrangements as one selection. How many groups of equivalent arrangements are there for any set of three students that are selected to attend camp? How could you use a factorial to represent your answer?

CHECK THIS!

Recall that the operation of *division* can be used to group items. If you want to know how many groups there are, you can divide the total number of items by the number of items in a group.

17. How could you determine the number of equivalent arrangements for four students? five students? any number of students?

18. How many different selections of track team members could there have been for the Chickasaw High School track team to attend the summer camp? Complete the following division problem:

$$\frac{\text{total number of arrangements}}{\text{number of equivalent arrangements}} = \frac{\qquad}{\qquad} =$$

19. Looking at the situation another way, complete the following division problem:

$$\frac{\text{total number of arrangements}}{\text{number of equivalent arrangements}} = \frac{\times \ \times}{\times \ \times} = \frac{\qquad}{\qquad} =$$

20. The Chickasaw coach found out at the last minute that an extra slot became available at the summer camp and now he can send a total of four students to the camp. How many possible arrangements of students could he send?

21. Suppose Andrew, Wilma, Gilbert, and Katrina were selected to attend the summer camp. How many possible arrangements of those four students are there?

22. When you divide out the arrangements that are equivalent to the same selection, how many different selections of four students could the coach have sent to camp?

Selections of sets of objects in which the order *does not* matter are called **combinations**. They can be found by dividing the number of arrangements, or permutations, by the number of redundant arrangements (arrangements that all result in the same selection of objects). In the case of the Chickasaw track team, the set of objects was the group of team members. The combinations were the selections of team members chosen to attend summer camp. Also, for the Chickasaw track team, repetition was not allowed—it doesn't make sense for one team member to occupy two slots at summer camp. In other cases, repetition is allowed, and calculations become more complex.

Using Technology to Find Permutations and Combinations

Most graphing calculators have a built-in feature to quickly find the number of permutations and combinations of a set of n objects when you need to find arrangements or selections of r objects from that set. These features use calculations that assume repetition is *not* allowed. So, before using them to solve every problem situation, be sure that you determine whether or not the objects in the set can be repeated.

Permutations

The notation for finding the number of permutations for a set of n objects taken in arrangements of r objects is: $_nP_r$. For a TI-83 or TI-84, this feature is found with the MATH key. Because of the notation, you must enter the value for n first.

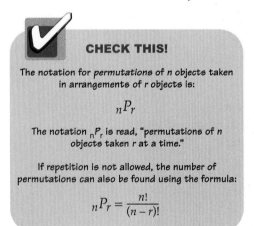

CHECK THIS!

The notation for *permutations of n objects taken in arrangements of r objects* is:

$$_nP_r$$

The notation $_nP_r$ is read, "permutations of n objects taken r at a time."

If repetition is not allowed, the number of permutations can also be found using the formula:

$$_nP_r = \frac{n!}{(n-r)!}$$

Following our earlier example, finding the number of first-, second-, and third-place winners from a set of twelve runners in the 100-meter dash, there are 12 "objects" in the set, so $n = 12$. We are interested in arrangements of 3 runners, so $r = 3$. We use the calculator to enter:

Step 1: Enter the value of n.

Step 2: Press MATH, then use the arrow keys ▶ and ▼ to select **nPr**. Press ENTER.

Step 3: Enter the value of r, then press ENTER.

Combinations

Likewise, the notation for finding the number of combinations for a set of n objects taken in selections of r objects is: $_nC_r$. For a TI-83 or TI-84, this feature is found with the MATH key. Because of the notation, you must enter the value for n first.

Following from our earlier example, finding the number of selections of groups of 3 from a set (team) of 12 track members, there are 12 "objects" in the set, so $n = 12$. We are interested in selections of 3 runners, so $r = 3$. We use the calculator to enter:

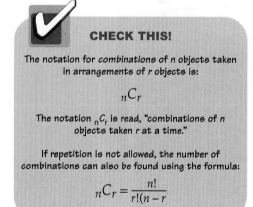

CHECK THIS!

The notation for *combinations of n objects taken in arrangements of r objects* is:

$$_nC_r$$

The notation $_nC_r$ is read, "combinations of n objects taken r at a time."

If repetition is not allowed, the number of combinations can also be found using the formula:

$$_nC_r = \frac{n!}{r!(n-r)}$$

Step 1: Enter the value of *n*.

Step 2: Press MATH, then use the arrow keys ▶ and ▼ to select **nCr**. Press ENTER.

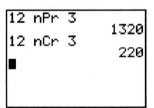

Step 3: Enter the value of *r*, then press ENTER.

PART 3: It Just Keeps Repeating!

Consider a lock that has three dials that each contain digits from 0 to 9. To open the lock, you must set each dial to the correct number. When the correct sequence is set, the lock will open.

1. In this situation, are we counting permutations or combinations? How do you know?

2. In this situation, can the digits 0 to 9 repeat on other dials?

3. What are the possible values for the first, second, and third number in the combination?

_____   _____   _____

1st Number   2nd Number   3rd Number

4. How many permutations are there to set as the combination to open the lock?

The Chickasaw High School track team has a unique incentive to encourage team members to practice regularly and often. In the spring, at the end of every week each team member who practiced more than two hours every day has his or her name put in to a drawing for a prize. A name is drawn every Friday afternoon for four weeks.

5. If all twelve team members meet the standards each week during this four-week period, how many possible permutations of winners could there be ?

_____   _____   _____   _____
1st Week   2nd Week   3rd Week   4th Week

6. What generalization can you make about finding the number of permutations for a set of n objects taken r at a time when the objects can repeat?

Now consider the ice cream bar in the Chickasaw High School cafeteria. There are five flavors to choose from: vanilla, strawberry, chocolate, mint, and caramel. For a certain price, students can have two scoops of ice cream of the flavor(s) of their choice.

7. In this situation, are we counting permutations or combinations? How do you know?

8. Is repetition allowed? In other words, can a student choose to have two scoops of the same flavor?

9. List the possible combinations of flavors that a student could choose from. Be sure to eliminate any duplicates (e.g., vanilla-chocolate is the same combination as chocolate-vanilla).

10. What patterns did you notice as you were generating your list?

SUMMARY

In counting the total number of possible groups of r objects from a set of n objects **(Figure 7.42)**, it is necessary to consider two questions:

1) Does the order matter? and 2) Is repetition allowed?

	Does the order matter? Yes	**Does the order matter? No.**
Is repetition allowed? No	This is a **permutation**. Permutations are arrangements of objects. Solution Strategies: Use the multiplication principle to determine the total number of arrangements. Use the graphing calculator to find $_nP_r$.	This is a **combination**. Combinations are selections of objects. Each selection is a group of equivalent arrangements. Solution Strategies: Use the multiplication principle to determine the total number of arrangements and the number of redundant arrangements. Then, divide the total number of arrangements by the number of redundant ones. Use the graphing calculator to find $_nC_r$.
Is repetition allowed? Yes.	This is a **permutation**. Permutations are arrangements of objects. Solution Strategies: Use the multiplication principle to determine the total number of arrangements. Use the formula n^r.	This is a **combination**. Combinations are selections of objects. Each selection is a groupof equivalent arrangements. Solution Strategy: List the possible arrangements and eliminate the redundant arrangements.

FIGURE 7.42

Assignment

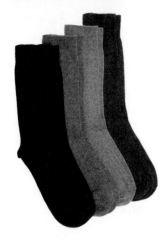

1. Find the following combinations or permutations:

   a. From 10 letters, the number of codes made with 3 letters.

   b. From 12 marbles, the number of collections of 5 marbles.

   c. From 6 socks, 2 are put together to make a pair.

   d. From 7 buttons, 4 are sewn on a blouse from the top down.

2. Different states use different combinations of letters and numbers to generate license plates. Determine the total number of possible license plates that can be generated from the following states' criteria. In this problem set, B represents any letter from A to Z and 1 represents any number from 0 to 9.

   a. Texas, BB1-B111

   b. Virginia, BBB-1111

   c. Tennessee, 111-BBB

   d. Florida, B11-BBB

   e. California, 1BBB111

   f. Rhode Island, 111-111

   g. Indiana, 11-B-1111

3. In Section 7.9, the Chickasaw High School cafeteria had an ice cream bar with five flavors of ice cream: vanilla, strawberry, chocolate, mint, and caramel. Students could choose any two scoops of ice cream.

   a. Suppose that the cafeteria runs out of caramel ice cream. If students are allowed to choose two scoops from the remaining flavors, how many possible combinations are there?

b. How does the reduction from five to four flavors change the number of possible combinations?

c. If students are allowed to choose three scoops of ice cream from the five original flavors, how many possible combinations of three scoops do students have to choose from?

d. How does the addition of a third scoop change the number of combinations?

4. A local car dealership offers customers a choice of "customer care" packages when they purchase a new car. Customers can choose one set of floor mats, one set of license plate frames, and one air freshener scent. There are four styles of floor mats, three styles of license plate frames, and five air freshener scents.

a. How many selections of customer care packages could Donna, who just purchased a new car, choose from?

b. A sales manager found a box of a fourth style of license plate frames. How many more selections of customer care packages does this additional style of license plate frames allow customers to choose from?

5. Every spring, students try out for positions in the Chickasaw High School symphonic band. There are four sections of clarinets: first clarinets, second clarinets, third clarinets, and fourth clarinets. Each section has three positions that are ranked in order: first chair, second chair, and third chair. For the selection process, the band director first chooses three clarinet players for each section. Then she assigns the chair order within each section.

a. This year there are sixteen students trying out for the twelve clarinet places in the symphonic band. How many ways could the students be selected for one clarinet section?

b. After three students have been chosen for the first clarinet section, how many different ways could the chair order be assigned?

How Much? How Many?

As you learned in the first lesson of this chapter, probability is used to make decisions about the likelihood that an event will occur. In order to determine probability, it is often useful to know how many possible outcomes of an event there are. Counting techniques can help you determine the total number of possible outcomes in order to make those decisions.

In this section you will help Brad and his family solve problems related to determining the number of possible outcomes of particular events. Your teacher will assign a particular problem to your group. To solve the problem, you can choose to use a tree diagram, the Fundamental Counting Principle, permutations, combinations, or the graphing calculator.

For each problem, follow these steps:

❖ Determine what kind of outcome the event has (permutation, combination, etc.).

❖ Choose a solution strategy.

❖ Solve the problem, showing all necessary work.

❖ Explain, using appropriate mathematical vocabulary, how you solved the problem and why you chose to solve it using that method.

❖ Present your problem to the class using the tools provided by your teacher.

PROBLEM 1: High Flying

An airline has flights from its hub in New York City to the following cities:

- Guadalajara, Mexico
- Anchorage, Alaska
- Rio de Janeiro, Brazil
- Brussels, Belgium
- Athens, Greece
- Mumbai, India

There are six pilots available for scheduling the flights: Captains Manzano, Newberg, O'Brien, Parikh, Rahmanjani, and Saobene.

a. How many possible ways could the pilots be assigned to a flight for each city?

b. Suppose that an airport strike in Belgium cancels the Brussels flight. How many possible ways could the six pilots be assigned to flights for the remaining cities?

c. Captain Manzano requests the flight to Guadalajara. How many ways could the remaining pilots be assigned to flights for the remaining cities?

d. The airline needs to send the six pilots to Washington, DC, for an aviation safety training session. They can be sent in groups of three. How many different ways can a group of three be selected?

PROBLEM 2: Lunch, Anyone?

Sal's Sub Shop specializes in making superb sandwiches. You can have a sandwich made with your choice of bread, meat, and cheese. Sal's bread choices include white, wheat, and rye. For meat, customers can choose from ham, turkey breast, salami, roast beef, and tuna. For cheese, Sal offers American, Swiss, and provolone.

a. Sal is preparing a new flyer to advertise his business. How many sandwich choices could a customer have if he or she chooses one type of bread, one type of meat, and one type of cheese?

b. On Tuesdays, Sal offers a special to attract business. Customers can choose two types of meat, including double portions of one type of meat. How many ways can customers select two portions of meat?

c. One day before he opened his shop for lunch, he discovered that the delivery truck was running late and he was out of tuna. How many sandwich choices could a customer have if he or she chooses one type of bread, one type of meat, and one type of cheese from this reduced menu?

PROBLEM 3: Spelling Bee

At the Cecil County Spelling Bee, there are twenty-four contestants. Awards are given for first through fifth places.

a. How many possible ways could the twenty-four contestants place?

b. The contestants are broken into groups of six for the initial rounds of the spelling bee. How many ways are there to form one group of six from the twenty-four contestants?

c. Suppose that two of the contestants are ill and unable to attend the spelling bee. Assuming that their spots remain vacant, how many possible ways could the remaining contestants place first through fifth?

Risky Drivers

In most states, at the age of 16 people are eligible to apply for their drivers' licenses. Teenagers are very excited when they get behind the steering wheel of their first car. That is, until they get their first auto insurance bill.

Carlos and Yesenia are no different. They are twins and recently turned 16. They each have their own gently used cars, which are similar in make and model. However, when they received their insurance bills, they were shocked at how expensive their auto insurance was. It was much more than they were expecting!

Carlos decided to investigate why his auto insurance was so expensive. He downloaded traffic fatality data from the National Highway Traffic Safety Administration (NHTSA) website for his home state of North Carolina for the year 2006. The data he found for the age of the driver and the number of fatal accidents per 100,000 people in that age group appear in **Figure 7.43**. He also generated the graph shown in **Figure 7.44**.

Traffic Fatalities for North Carolina, 2006	
Age Range of Driver	Number of Fatalities per 100,000 people
Total population 16 or older	29.9
0–15	0.6
16–20	41.3
21–34	34.0
55–69	27.5
70–74	21.8
75–79	29.0
80–84	28.7
85+	3.6

FIGURE 7.43. Traffic fatalities per age group.

Source: www.nhtsa.gov.

480 Chapter 7 What Are the Chances? Probability

Section 7.11

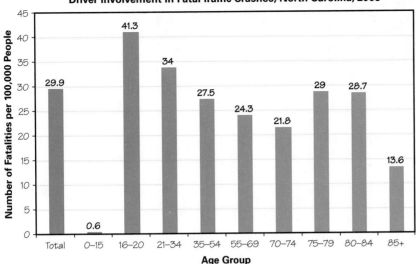

FIGURE 7.44. Traffic fatalities for North Carolina by age group.

1. Look at the table and the graph. Which age group seems to have the highest number of fatalities per 100,000 people in that age group?

2. Which age group seems to have the lowest number of fatalities?

3. How does the rate of fatalities for each age group compare to the rate for the total population of North Carolinians over the age of 16?

4. Which age group would you predict to have the highest probability of being involved in a fatal accident while driving?

5. Which age group seems to be at the highest risk of being involved in a fatal accident?

6. Why do you think there are differences among the age groups?

7. If you worked for an insurance company, which age group would you charge the most to insure against a fatal traffic accident? Use the data to explain your answer.

Yesenia bragged to Carlos that her insurance bill was lower than his. Carlos turned to the NHTSA website again and obtained data from 2006 describing the involvement of male and female drivers in fatal traffic accidents. The data he obtained from this search are shown in **Figure 7.45**.

Traffic Fatalities for the United States, 2006		
Gender of Driver	Population	Number of Fatalities per 100,000 people
Male	147,512,000	28.5
Female	151,886,000	9.6

FIGURE 7.45. Traffic fatalities by gender.

Source: www.nhtsa.gov.

8. Which gender appears to have a higher probability of being involved in a fatal traffic accident while driving?

9. Which gender appears to be at higher risk of being involved in a fatal traffic accident while driving?

10. If you worked for an insurance company, which gender would you charge more to insure against a fatal traffic accident? Use the data to explain your answer.

Evaluating risk is only one way that probability is used in the real world. In this chapter you will explore other ways that mathematicians, statisticians, actuaries, and accountants use probability to make predictions about what types of events are "likely" or "unlikely" to occur.

Square Peg, Round Hole

Carnivals often have beanbag toss games, in which the contestant throws a beanbag at a board with holes cut in it and wins a prize if the beanbag goes through the hole. Variations of beanbag toss games are played at children's birthday parties and at tailgate parties before football games.

GAME 1 Beanbag Toss

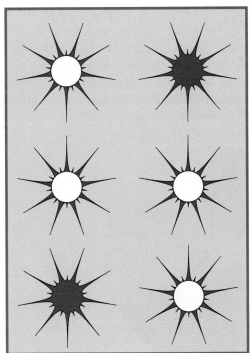

FIGURE 7.46

Some people are skilled at beanbag tosses, and others are not. Ramona is very skilled at tossing the beanbag into the hole but her friend Ralph is not. At their high school carnival, they decide to play the beanbag toss game, the board for which is shown in **Figure 7.46**. Ramona throws the first beanbag and wins a prize immediately. Ralph, on the other hand, decides to randomly throw the beanbag toward the board. What is the probability that the beanbag tossed by Ralph will go through a hole in the board?

1. What is a favorable outcome for Ralph in this situation?

2. What are the possible outcomes in this situation?

3. Thinking geometrically, what do we call the measure of the interior region in a plane that an object covers?

4. How could you determine the size of the region that could result in a favorable outcome?

5. How could you determine the size of the region that could result in any possible outcome?

6. The game board is 5 feet wide and 6 feet long. Since there are 12 inches in a foot, what is the area of the board in *square inches*?

7. Each circular hole has a diameter of 5 inches. What is the radius of each hole?

8. What is the area of each circular hole?

9. What is the total area of the circular holes in the board?

10. What would be the probability of the beanbag landing in any one of the holes? (Assume that the bag is thrown at random and lands on the board.)

GAME 2: Spin the Spinner

In Section 7.2 you used a spinner to make predictions from experimental probability. The next carnival game that Ramona and Ralph encountered is a spinner game. For one ticket, they can spin the spinner and win the prize written in the section where the arrow lands. The spinner is shown in **Figure 7.47**.

Ralph may not be good at the beanbag toss but he does know geometry. He estimates the measures of the central angles for the various sectors of the spinner to be: 120° for the sticker set, 60° for the necklace, 45° for the watch, 90° for the rubber snake, and 45° for the ring.

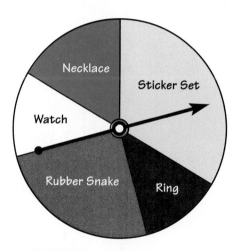

FIGURE 7.47. *Spinner game.*

1. Suppose that Ralph wants to win the rubber snake. If each degree measure of the central angle is an outcome, how many favorable outcomes could there be to win the rubber snake? How do you know?

2. How many outcomes would there be in the entire spinner? How do you know?

3. What would be the probability of winning the rubber snake?

4. Suppose that Ramona wants to win a piece of jewelry. How many possible favorable outcomes are there?

5. What would be the probability of winning a piece of jewelry?

6. What would be the probability of winning anything but the sticker set? Explain how you got your answer.

GAME 3: Tangram Puzzle

Tangrams are ancient Chinese geometric puzzles with seven tiles that can fit together in a variety of ways. One of the carnival games has contestants toss a small beanbag into a box that hides a set of tangrams **(Figure 7.48)**. A prize is awarded depending on where the beanbag lands.

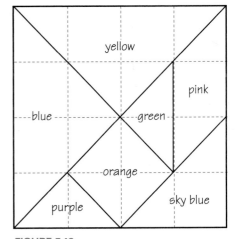

FIGURE 7.48

1. The entire tangram square is four units wide and four units long. In terms of square units, what is the area of the large blue triangle?

2. In terms of square units, what is the area of the small purple triangle?

3. What is the probability of the beanbag landing on each of the following pieces?

   a. Pink parallelogram

   b. Orange square

   c. Green triangle

4. Suppose that the box is knocked over and the tangrams fall out of their frame. If they are reassembled in a different arrangement that still makes the large square (assume that the pieces do not overlap and there are no gaps), do the probabilities of the beanbag landing on any given piece change? Explain your answer.

Assignment

Use a paper clip and pencil to create a spinner using the circle and sectors shown in **Figure 7.50**.

1. Spin the spinner twenty times (be sure to spin the same way each time) and record your results in **Figure 7.49**.

	Area 1	Area 2	Area 3	Area 4
Tally marks				
Total:				
Relative frequency (total ÷ 20)				

FIGURE 7.49

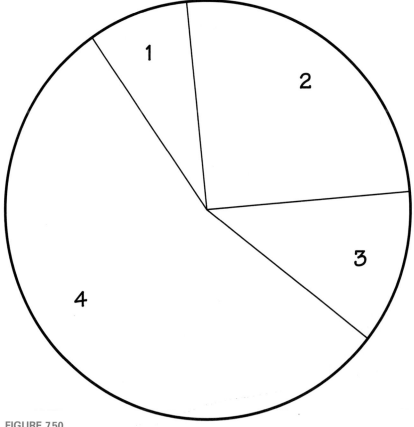

FIGURE 7.50

2. Use the data from your chart to create a bar graph of your data on a grid like **Figure 7.51**.

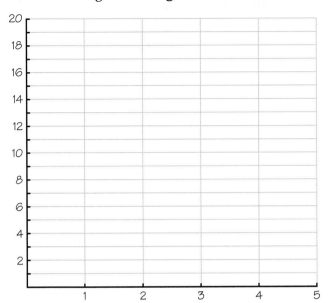

FIGURE 7.51

3. Use a protractor and measure the central angle for each sector of the circle **(Figure 7.52)**.

FIGURE 7.52

	Area 1	Area 2	Area 3	Area 4
Measure of Central Angle				
Percent of Circle (measure of central angle ÷ 360°)				

4. Compare the relative frequencies of the spins from your chart in Question 1 and the percentage of circle in your chart in Question 3. How close are the numbers? Should they be close? Explain.

Extend What You Know!

5. Create a spinner with the following sectors and percentages of the whole circle:

Red 15% = 54°
Blue 20% = 72°
Yellow 10% = 36°
Green 55% = 198°

Spin the spinner twenty times. Record the same data you recorded in the previous questions. Are your experimental results close to the assigned values? List some reasons for errors. Turn in both the actual spinner and the lab write-up.

Representations of Probability

PART 1: Geometric Probability

In the previous section you explored three different carnival games that Ramona and Ralph played at their high school carnival:

❖ Beanbag toss — Toss the beanbag onto a game board with holes. If the beanbag lands in a hole, the tosser wins a prize.

❖ Spin the spinner — Spin the spinner and win the prize in the section where the spinner lands.

❖ Tangram puzzle — Toss a beanbag into a box with tangram pieces hidden at the bottom. Win the prize that goes with the tangram tile where the beanbag landed.

Each of those games involved a target (either the beanbag or the spinner) landing in a desired area.

1. Summarize those games in a table like the one shown in **Figure 7.53**.

	Bean Bag Toss	Spin the Spinner	Tangram Puzzle
Favorable part of the game board		Sector containing the desired prize	
Whole game board	Entire rectangular game board		

FIGURE 7.53. Carnival game summary.

2. How did you determine the probability of winning for each of these carnival games?

In earlier sections we defined probability as a ratio of the number of favorable outcomes to the total number of possible outcomes:

$$P(\text{favorable outcome}) = \frac{\text{number of favorable outcomes}}{\text{total number of possible outcomes}}$$

3. Thinking about geometric probability, what does the numerator in that ratio represent for these carnival games? What does the denominator represent?

488   Chapter 7 What Are the Chances? Probability

Section 7.13

In your earlier mathematics experiences you learned that there are two kinds of ratios: part-to-part relationships and part-to-whole relationships. For example, consider Mrs. Knowles's second-period geometry class. There are thirty students in the class, eighteen of whom are girls.

4. What fraction of the class is female? What fraction of the class is male?

5. What is the sum of those fractions? What does that number represent?

6. What is the ratio of girls to boys?

7. How does the ratio of girls to boys compare to the percentage of the class that is female?

8. Is the probability of the beanbag landing in the favorable area of the game board more like the ratio of girls to boys in Mrs. Knowles's class or more like the percentage of the class that is female? Explain your thinking.

PART 2: It's in Your Genes

Sickle cell anemia is a genetic disease that is inherited from one's parents. Each person has two alleles, or pairs of genes, that determine whether or not they have sickle cell anemia. Sickle cell anemia is found most often in people of African ancestry, but it also occurs in persons of Mediterranean, Arabian, and East Indian descent. Left untreated, sickle cell anemia is almost always a fatal disease. The symptoms are now treatable, however, and people with sickle cell anemia can live relatively normal lives.

CHECK THIS!

Genes are the basic components of chromosomes that determine the characteristics of living things. Genes come in pairs, each of which is called an allele (uh-LEEL). Usually, alleles are dominant or recessive, and the dominant allele expresses the characteristic.

For example, a person's eye color is determined by one gene, or two pairs of alleles. The allele for brown eyes is dominant, and the allele for blue eyes is recessive. That's part of the reason that more people have brown eyes than blue eyes.

Malaria is a tropical, parasitic disease spread by the Anopheles mosquito. Malaria is one of the world's deadliest diseases. According to the World Health Organization, more than 1 million people die each year from the disease, and a child in Africa dies every 30 seconds from malaria. Ironically, people with sickle cell anemia are less susceptible to malaria. Scientists believe that the cell mutations associated with sickle cell anemia protect the person from the parasite that causes malaria.

Alleles are represented using letters. For this exercise, let's represent a normal allele with the letter N and a sickle cell allele with the letter S. Each person has two alleles, some combination of N and S.

1. What are the possible combinations of alleles?

A child inherits one allele from each parent. Suppose that for a given population, we know that 70% of the alleles are normal alleles, N.

2. Trace the line segment below onto your paper. If the length of the line segment is 1 unit, mark off 70% of the segment. Label the 70% P(N) to represent the probability of inheriting a normal allele, and the remaining percent P(S) to represent the probability of inheriting a sickle cell allele.

3. Since alleles are inherited from two parents, construct a congruent segment from point A that is perpendicular to the one you just drew (i.e., if segment AB is the top of a square, draw the left side of the square). Mark the portions of the segment and label them as you did in the previous question.

4. Fill in the remaining parts of the square, as shown in **Figure 7.54**. Label the four inside pieces of the square with the combinations of alleles from Question 1 in this section.

FIGURE 7.54

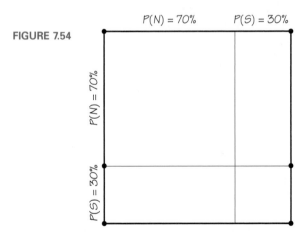

5. Are inheritance of an allele from your father and inheritance of an allele from your mother independent events? Explain.

6. Calculate the probabilities of inheriting the two alleles for sickle cell anemia. Write them in each section of your large square.

7. What is the sum of the probabilities?

In biology, people who have one dominant allele and one recessive allele are said to be *carriers* of the trait, even though they do not exhibit the trait themselves. People who have two recessive alleles will actually have that trait.

8. What percentage of this population would be carriers of sickle cell anemia? How did you get your answer?

9. What percentage of this population would actually have sickle cell anemia?

10. Suppose a second population has 80% normal alleles. Draw a probability square to represent this population. Calculate the probabilities of inheriting *NN, NS, SN,* and *SS* alleles in that population.

11. What percentage of this population would be carriers of sickle cell anemia? How did you get your answer?

12. What percentage of this population would actually have sickle cell anemia?

13. How does this model represent a geometric probability?

SUMMARY

Geometric probability is the probability of an event whose outcome is based on a ratio of geometric measures such as perimeter, area, or angle measure. Geometric probability is a part-whole ratio that is given using the definition of probability:

$$P(\text{favorable outcome}) = \frac{\text{measure of favorable region}}{\text{measure of total region}}$$

Geometric models can be used to describe real-world probability situations such as genetics. An area model can be used to find compound probabilities that two events will occur. If the model is constructed proportionally, then the area where the two events intersect indicates how the probabilities of the different events compare.

Assignment

12

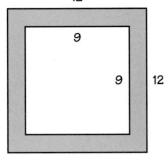

9

9

12

FIGURE 7.55

If a fly flying at random hit the board in **Figure 7.55**, what is the probability that it would hit the shaded region? This probability can be found by comparing the area of the shaded region to the total area of the board. In other words:

$$P(\text{event you're interested in}) = \frac{\text{part you're interested in}}{\text{whole}}$$

So, the probability of landing in the shaded region would be found by calculating:

$$P(\text{shaded region}) = \frac{\text{area of shaded region}}{\text{area of total region}}$$

$$= \frac{12 \times 12 - 9 \times 9}{12 \times 12} = \frac{144 - 81}{144} = \frac{63}{144} = \frac{7}{16} \approx 44\%$$

For the following problems, let's consider the same scenario: If a fly flying at random hit the board shown, what is the probability that it would hit the shaded region? Be sure to show all work. Write your answer as a fraction in lowest terms.

1. The diameter of the outer circle is 12 centimeters, and the radius of the inner circle is 4 centimeters **(Figure 7.56)**.

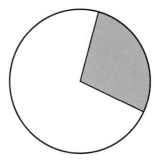

FIGURE 7.56

2. The radius of the circle is 4 inches, and the angle formed by the 2 radii is 80° **(Figure 7.57)**.

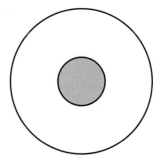

FIGURE 7.57

3.

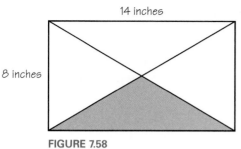

14 inches

8 inches

FIGURE 7.58

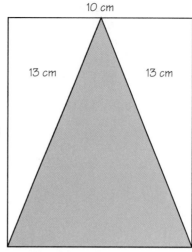

10 cm

13 cm   13 cm

12 cm

FIGURE 7.59

4. The two isosceles triangles are similar, with the measurements shown in inches. (**Figure 7.60**; Note: figure is not to scale.)

a. What is the length of a leg of the inner triangle?

b. Use the Pythagorean theorem to find the height of each triangle (don't forget to use half the length of the base as one of your leg lengths!).

c. Find the area of each triangle.

d. Find the area of the shaded region.

e. What is the probability of the fly landing in the shaded region?

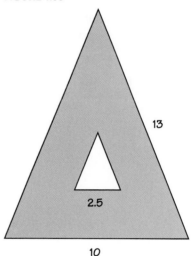

13

2.5

10

FIGURE 7.60

In this section you investigated populations of people with alleles for sickle cell anemia. Another way to represent probabilities is to use a tree diagram. A tree diagram for sickle cell anemia alleles looks like this:

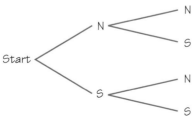

Assignment 7.13

Chapter 7 What Are the Chances? Probability   **493**

6. Suppose a population has 40% normal alleles. What is the probability that a person will inherit a normal allele from one parent? a sickle cell allele?

7. Draw a tree diagram like the one shown. Label the probability of inheriting each allele on the diagram.

8. What is the probability of inheriting the following alleles?

   f. *NN*

   g. *NS*

   h. *SN*

   i. *SS*

9. If *SN* and *NS* are both considered to be carriers of sickle cell anemia, what is the probability that someone in this population is a carrier of sickle cell anemia but does not exhibit the trait him- or herself?

10. If there are 10,000 people in this population, how many carriers of sickle cell anemia would you expect there to be? Explain your answer.

Real-World Probability—No, Really!

PROBLEM 1: Change in the Weather

Climate is the long-term average of local weather conditions. The table in **Figure 7.61** shows the minimum temperature, maximum temperature, and amount of rain for Will Rogers World Airport in Oklahoma City, Oklahoma, on March 19 from 1988 until 2007.

Forecasts based solely on climate, or past weather data, are called climatological forecasts. Meteorologists making such forecasts rely on the persistence of past weather patterns and assume that no major changes in weather patterns are coming.

1. Use your graphing calculator to make a scatterplot of maximum temperature and minimum temperature over time. Describe your viewing window and sketch your graph.

2. Based on the data, use climatological forecasting to make a forecast, for both temperature and rainfall, for the next March 19 for Oklahoma City. Justify your forecast.

Year	Maximum Temperature (°F)	Minimum Temperature (°F)	Rainfall (inches)
1988	64	30	0
1989	54	44	0
1990	55	36	0
1991	71	44	0
1992	51	36	0
1993	49	38	1.05
1994	86	47	0
1995	83	51	0
1996	47	31	0
1997	57	38	0
1998	43	35	0.07
1999	54	43	0.12
2000	59	40	0
2001	51	35	0
2002	53	45	0.61
2003	57	45	0.14
2004	83	58	0
2005	61	37	0
2006	47	42	0.45
2007	75	61	0

FIGURE 7.61. Weather data for Oklahoma City, OK.

PROBLEM 2: Game Theory

A game of dice has the following rules.

- Before rolling two dice, one player predicts the sum of the numbers rolled on the two dice.

- If the sum of the rolled numbers matches the prediction, then points are awarded equal to the sum rolled. If the sum does not match, no points are earned and the other person takes a turn.

Number Cube 1						
	1	2	3	4	5	6
1						
2						
3						
4						
5						
6						

FIGURE 7.62. Payoff table.

Mathematics can help determine a sound strategy for playing the game.

1. Copy the table in **Figure 7.62** that shows all the possible results of rolling two dice. In each cell of your table, write the payoff (sum of the two dice) that would result from each roll.

2. The **probability** of an outcome (such as getting a payoff of five) is the number of times that particular outcome can happen, divided by the total number of possible outcomes. For each payoff listed in **Figure 7.63**, find the probability for the outcome.

FIGURE 7.63. Payoff, probability, and worth.

Outcome Payoff	Outcome Probability	Outcome Worth
2		
3		
4		
5		
6		
7		
8		
9		
10		
11		
12		

3. The **probabilistic worth** of an outcome is defined as the value (or payoff) of an outcome multiplied by the probability that the outcome will occur. Complete the table in Figure 7.63 by calculating the worth associated with each outcome.

4. Use your graphing calculator to make a scatterplot of the probabilistic worth (W) versus the number that represents the guess (and the payoff) in the game (n). Describe your viewing window and sketch your graph.

5. Based on the work you've done, what strategy should you use in playing this dice game?

PROBLEM 3: Automobile Safety Risk

There is an intersection in a city where there seems to be a lot of traffic accidents. So, the city's traffic safety board began collecting data, which are shown in **Table 7.64**.

Time of Day	Number of Vehicles per Day	Number of Accidents per Month	Accident Rate per 10,000 cars per month
7:00 AM	500	4	2.67
8:00 AM	800	10	4.17
9:00 AM	650	8	4.10
11:00 AM	450	2	1.48
12:00 PM	550	6	3.64
2:00 PM	350	2	1.90
4:00 PM	450	3	2.22
5:00 PM	600	7	3.89
6:00 PM	700	12	5.71
7:00 PM	400	4	3.33

FIGURE 7.64. Traffic statistics.

1. What time of day seems to have the most traffic?

2. What time of day seems to have the most accidents?

3. Assume that accidents at this intersection occur randomly. When is a driver at the greatest risk of having an accident? What could be a possible reason?

PROBLEM 4: Medical Risk — Heart Disease

According to the American Heart Association (AHA), in 2008 an estimated 80,700,000 American adults (1 in 3) had some form of cardiovascular disease, including high blood pressure, coronary heart disease (heart attack or angina), heart failure, or stroke. The AHA estimates that cardiovascular disease cost Americans a total of $448.5 billion in 2008 alone.

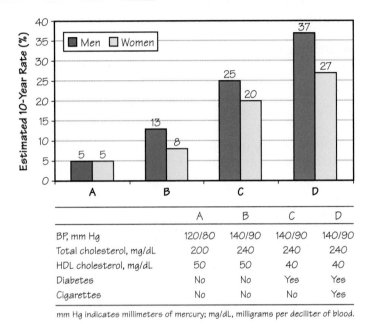

	A	B	C	D
BP, mm Hg	120/80	140/90	140/90	140/90
Total cholesterol, mg/dL	200	240	240	240
HDL cholesterol, mg/dL	50	50	40	40
Diabetes	No	No	Yes	Yes
Cigarettes	No	No	No	Yes

mm Hg indicates millimeters of mercury; mg/dL, milligrams per deciliter of blood.

FIGURE 7.65. Estimated risk of heart attack or angina.

Figure 7.65 shows the estimated ten-year risk of a new coronary heart disease event (heart attack or angina) for 55-year-old men and women with varying levels of risk factors. "BP" stands for "blood pressure," and "HDL cholesterol" stands for "high-density lipoproteins" cholesterol, commonly called "good cholesterol" because they actually help to prevent heart attacks and angina.

Use Figure 7.65 to answer the following questions:

1. Overall, do men or women have a higher ten-year risk of a heart attack or angina?

2. Which risk factors make Group B different from Group C?

3. How different is the estimated ten-year risk for Groups B and C?

4. Which risk factors make Group C different from Group D?

5. How different is the estimated ten-year risk for Groups C and D?

6. Looking at the graph, what conclusions can you draw about how risk factors influence a person's risk of suffering a heart attack or angina?

Assignment

Figure 7.66 shows the estimated ten-year risk of a stroke for the same age group for different risk factors. In the table portion of the figure, "Prior AF" stands for "prior atrial fibrillation," and "Prior CVD" stands for "prior cardiovascular disease." Atrial fibrillation is a type of heart incident, and cardiovascular disease is a range of diseases that affect the circulatory system.

Use Figure 7.66 to answer the following questions:

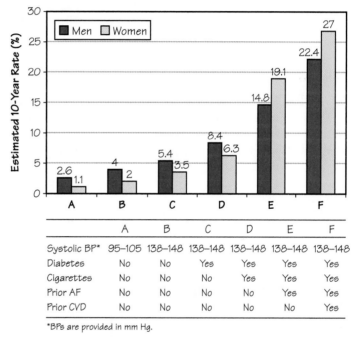

	A	B	C	D	E	F
Systolic BP*	95–105	138–148	138–148	138–148	138–148	138–148
Diabetes	No	No	Yes	Yes	Yes	Yes
Cigarettes	No	No	No	Yes	Yes	Yes
Prior AF	No	No	No	No	Yes	Yes
Prior CVD	No	No	No	No	No	Yes

*BPs are provided in mm Hg.

FIGURE 7.66. Estimated risk of stroke.

1. Compare the different groups for men and women. Which risk factors seem to affect men more than women? Which risk factors seem to affect women more than men? Explain.

2. Between which two groups do you notice the biggest change in estimated ten-year risk? What risk factors seem to influence that change?

3. Which risk factors make Group C different from Group D?

4. How different is the estimated ten-year risk for Groups C and D?

5. Looking at the graph, what conclusions can you draw about how risk factors influence a person's risk of suffering a stroke?

A popular game show has a large spinner wheel divided into twelve equal-sized sectors **(Figure 7.68)**. Each sector contains a hidden dollar amount that the contestant will win only if he or she guesses the correct dollar amount ahead of time.

6. Complete the table in **Figure 7.67**.

7. What strategy would you recommend to a contestant on this game show?

Outcome Payoff	Outcome Probability	Outcome Worth
$0		
$10		
$15		
$20		
$30		
$40		
$50		
$100		

FIGURE 7.67

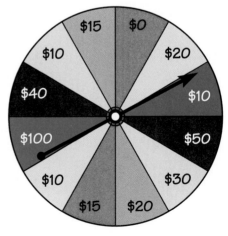

FIGURE 7.68

Interpreting Probability

For this part of the lesson you will use a random number generator (the random-integer function) on your graphing calculator to generate ordered pairs of numbers from 1 through 30.

Step 1: From the home screen, press [MATH], then use the arrow key [▶] to select **PRB**. Use the arrow key [▼] to select **5:randInt**. Press [ENTER] to return to the home screen.

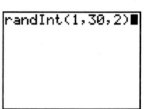

Step 2: Enter **1,30,2**, then close the parentheses. This key sequence will generate random integers from 1 to 30, inclusive, two at a time.

Step 3: Press [ENTER]. An ordered pair of randomly generated integers will appear.

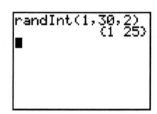

1. On your Coordinate Dalmatian (**Figure 7.69**), locate the ordered pair on the coordinate plane.

   • If the point is not located anywhere within the outline of the Dalmatian, disregard it and generate a new pair of random integers.

   • If the point is located within the outline of the Dalmatian, record the coordinates in a table like the one shown in **Figure 7.70**. Also record the coordinates if the point falls on any black portion of the Dalmatian.

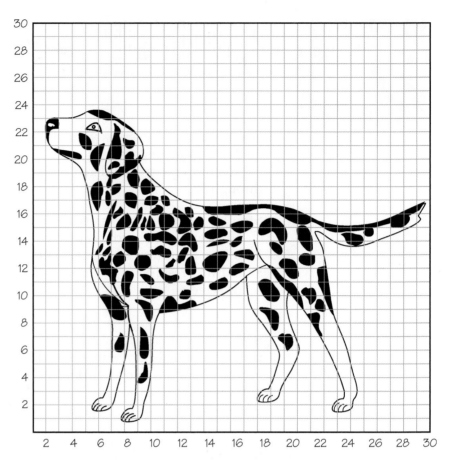

FIGURE 7.69. *Coordinate Dalmatian.*

	Ordered Pair	Black Region?
1		
2		
3		
4		
5		
6		
7		
8		
9		

FIGURE 7.70. *Dalmatian points.*

2. On the home screen of your calculator, continue to press ENTER until you have ten points that are located within the outline of the Dalmatian **(Figure 7.71)**.

	Ordered Pair	Black Region?
1		
2		
3		
4		
5		
6		
7		
8		
9		
10		

FIGURE 7.71

3. How many of the recorded points fall on a black part of the Dalmatian? What percentage of the total number of recorded points is that?

4. From the graph, estimate the percentage of the Dalmatian that is black.

5. How does your estimate compare to the percentage of points that are located within the black part of the Dalmatian? Explain your answer.

6. Generate ten more data points for a total of twenty data points on the Dalmatian **(Figure 7.72)**. Add rows to your table and record the coordinates of the points and whether they fall on a black part of the Dalmatian.

	Ordered Pair	Black Region?		Ordered Pair	Black Region?
1			11		
2			12		
3			13		
4			14		
5			15		
6			16		
7			17		
8			18		
9			19		
10			20		

FIGURE 7.72

7. How many of the twenty recorded points fall on a black part of the Dalmatian? What percentage of the total number of recorded points is that?

8. Based on your data, estimate the percentage of the Dalmatian that is black.

9. Compare your results for the set of ten points with those for the set of twenty points. Which do you think helps you make a more accurate estimate of the percentage of the Dalmatian that is black? Explain your answer.

10. How do you think a set of 500 data points would affect the confidence of your estimate of the percentage of the Dalmatian that is black? Explain your answer.

Modeling Project How Likely Is It?

You have learned about probability, theoretical and experimental, independent and dependent events, and other applications of probability.

For this modeling project, choose an event that you are interested in for investigating the probability of the event's occurrence.

Research your topic using the resources in your school or public library, interviewing people in your community, or using the Internet. If you would like to, you may create a simulation in order to investigate the likelihood of an event. Create a presentation for your class that includes the following:

- Describe the event that you chose to research.

- If you chose to collect data from a source, where and how did you collect your data?

- If you collected experimental probability data, how did you collect the data, and what are your results?

- What implications do your results have for other people in your community?

Practice Problems

1. Each letter for the words *STATISTICS* and *PROBABILITY* is written on a card. All of the cards are placed in a bag.

S	T	A	T	I	S	T	I	C	S

P	R	O	B	A	B	I	L	I	T	Y

   a. What is the probability of randomly drawing the letter *S* from the bag?

   b. What is the probability of drawing an *S*, returning it to the bag, and then drawing another *S*?

   c. What is the probability of drawing an *S*, not returning it to the bag, and then drawing another *S*?

   d. What is the probability of drawing either an *S* or a *T*?

   e. James collects some experimental data. He draws a letter from the bag with replacement 50 times. Of the 50 outcomes, 10 of them are the letter *I*. What is the difference between the theoretical probability and James's experimental probability?

2. Sarah has a game with a spinner like the one shown below.

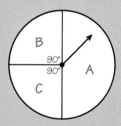

   a. What is the probability that the spinner will land on A?

   b. What is the probability that the spinner will land on B?

   c. What is the probability that the spinner will land on either A or B?

   d. What is the probability that the spinner will land on A for two consecutive spins?

e. What is the probability that the spinner will land on B for two consecutive spins?

f. What is the probability that the spinner will land on A on the first spin and C on the second spin?

3. John has three shirts — red, blue, and white — for his baseball uniform. He has two pairs of pants — grey and white. John randomly chooses a shirt and a pair of pants.

a. How many combinations of baseball uniforms does John have?

b. What is the probability John chooses the blue shirt and gray pants?

c. What is the probability John chooses any shirt and the white pants?

4. Four students have been selected to be the officers — president, vice president, secretary, and treasurer — of the student council. How many different arrangements of the four students are possible?

5. Decide if the following events are dependent or independent.

a. A number cube is rolled and a spinner is spun.

b. A piece of candy is drawn from a bag, replaced, and then another piece of candy is drawn from the bag.

c. Three coins are tossed at the same time.

d. From 5 marbles in a bag, a blue marble is drawn without replacement. Another marble is then drawn.

e. A card is drawn from a deck of cards without replacement. Another card is then drawn from the deck.

f. A person owns a white car and lives in Virginia.

6. Shawnda is on the softball team. She gets about 3 hits out of every 5 at bats. How might you design a simulation for this situation?

7. Jamie designs her own dart board. She draws four circles inside a square. The length of one side of the square is 12 inches. What is the probability that a randomly thrown dart will land in one of the shaded regions?

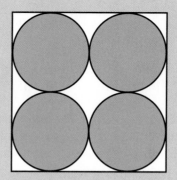

8. John spins the two spinners shown below and records the sum of the two numbers. Each number is equally likely to occur on each spinner.

 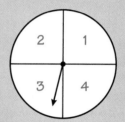

a. Construct the sample space for the sum of the numbers resulting from spinning both spinners once.

	Spin of Second Spinner			
	1	2	3	4
Spin of First Spinner 1				
2				
3				
4				

b. How many possible outcomes are there?

c. What is the probability that the sum is 2?

d. What is the probability that the sum is 5?

e. What is the probability that the sum is either 3 or 6?

Glossary

KEY CONCEPTS

Additive property of probability: If two events are mutually exclusive, the probability of one event or the other occurring can be found by adding the probability of each event occurring separately together.
P(Event A or Event B) = P(Event A) + P(Event B).

Combinations: Selections of objects, such as students chosen to attend a summer track camp, where the order *does not* matter. The notation for **combinations** of n objects taken in arrangements of r objects is: $_nC_r$.

Complementary events: Two or more mutually exclusive events that together cover all possible outcomes. The sum of the probabilities of complementary events is 1.

Conditional probability: The probability that a second event will occur given that the first event has already occurred.

Dependent events: Two events in which the outcome of the first event affects the outcome of the second event.

Experimental probability: A statement of probability based on the results of a series of trials. The frequency ratio from an experiment is also called the experimental probability.

Factorial: The product of a decreasing consecutive sequence of whole numbers from a given number, n, to 1, notated as $n!$

Frequency bar graph: A bar graph in which the height of a bar indicates the frequency.

Fundamental counting principle: If there are m ways to choose the first item and n ways to choose the second item, then there are $m \times n$ ways to choose outcomes of the two items together.

Geometric probability: The probability of an event whose outcome is based on a ratio of geometric measures such as perimeter, area, or angle measure. Geometric probability is a part-whole ratio that is given using the definition of probability,

$$P(\text{favorable outcome}) = \frac{\text{measure of favorable region}}{\text{measure of total region}}$$

Independent events: Events that happen without regard to one another.

Law of large numbers: As the sample size increases more and more, the relative frequencies of outcomes (experimental probability) more closely approximates the theoretical probabilities.

Multiplicative rule for probability: The probability of two events both occurring can be found by multiplying the probability of each event occurring separately. P(A and B) = P(A)·P(B)

Multiplication rule of counting: Another way of stating the **fundamental counting principle**.

Mutually exclusive events: Two events that cannot occur at the same time.

Odds: The ratio of the number of favorable outcomes to the number of unfavorable outcomes.

Permutations: Arrangements of objects, such as winners in a race, where the order matters. The notation for **permutations** of n objects taken in arrangements of r objects is $_nP_r$.

Probability: The chance of an event occurring. Probability is defined as the ratio of the number of favorable outcomes to the total number of outcomes,

$$\text{Probability (event)} = \frac{\text{number of favorable outcomes}}{\text{total number of outcomes}}$$

Sample space: All possible outcomes of an experiment or situation.

Simulation: A representation or model of a real-world situation.

Theoretical probability: A statement of probability based on the ratio of the number of successful, or favorable, outcomes to the total number of outcomes.

Tree diagram: A graphic organizer that begins with the possible outcomes from one category and then branches out to include possible outcomes from the next categories.

Venn diagram: A drawing that shows the relationship among sets of objects.

8

CHAPTER

Data and Statistics

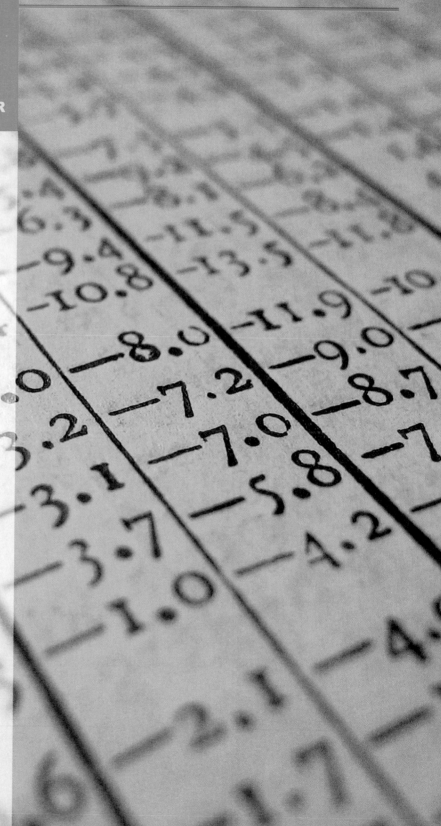

Scientists, engineers, and mathematicians often want to describe the "typical" value of a set of objects. For example, doctors may be concerned with the typical length and weight of newborn babies. Knowing about the typical, however, isn't always enough. We know that not every newborn baby is the same length and weight. Naturally, their length and weight varies. But what is that "typical" variance?

A chamber of commerce is an organization of businesses that serve a particular community. Many cities, counties, and even states have a chamber of commerce to promote business activity in their community or communities.

The chamber of commerce for a particular community serves a variety of functions. Primarily, it works to build community and business leadership. It also does a wide variety of other things to promote business. Often chambers of commerce sponsor trade shows, festivals, or other events to showcase businesses that exist in the community as well as to attract new ones. Chambers work with state and local governments to create an environment that supports businesses and professional organizations. Chambers may also provide custom research, analysis, and even local or regional economic forecasts.

In order to determine the current state of business conditions as well as attract new businesses, members of the chamber of commerce need to collect, analyze, and interpret data. Chambers of commerce are interested in information such as number of employees in the community, wages earned by employees who live in the community, tax rates, and other data that describe business conditions in the community. In places where tourism is a major industry, a chamber of commerce will look for ways to attract visitors as well as new businesses, so information about climate, including the "typical" weather for a particular season, may be important.

In this chapter you will help members of a chamber of commerce look at different ways to describe and interpret data in order to make decisions about real-world problems.

Not-So-Small Businesses

One of the top concerns for any chamber of commerce is having large employers in its city or region. Large employers, such as hospitals, factories, and national chains, can create many jobs and raise tax revenue for city and local governments.

Figure 8.1 shows the twenty largest private employers in the Richmond, Virginia, metropolitan area in 2007. Government agencies, such as city or county governments or public school districts, tend to be the largest employers in a city or region. A chamber of commerce, however, is interested primarily in attracting private business, so we are concerned here with private employers.

Rank	Employer	Industry	Number of Employees
1	HCA Inc.	Health Care	7,719
2	Capital One Financial Corp.	Banking/Finance	7,389
3	VCU Health System	Health Care	6,990
4	Philip Morris USA	Tobacco	6,100
5	Wal-Mart Stores Inc.	Retail	5,862
6	Wachovia Corp.	Banking/Finance	5,349
7	Dominion Resources Inc.	Energy	5,114
8	Bon Secours Richmond Health System	Health Care	5,021
9	SunTrust Banks Inc.	Banking/Finance	3,674
10	Ukrop's Super Markets Inc.	Retail	3,563
11	DuPont	Manufacturing	3,200
12	Bank of America Corp.	Banking/Finance	3,100
13	WellPoint Inc.	Health Care	3,028
14	Delhaize America (Food Lion)	Retail	2,553
15	Circuit City Stores Inc.	Retail	2,552
16	United Parcel Service Inc.	Distribution	2,497
17	Qimonda Richmond	Manufacturing	2,390
18	Verizon Virginia Inc.	Telecommunications	2,311
19	Genworth Financial Inc.	Banking/Finance	1,681
20	Federal Reserve Bank of Richmond Inc.	Banking/Finance	1,611

FIGURE 8.1. Largest employers in Richmond, VA for 2007.

Source: Richmond Times-Dispatch, www.inrich.com.

In your student groups, look at the data set and answer the following questions:

1. How would you describe the data? What patterns do you notice?

2. How would you describe the businesses in the top 50%?

3. How would you describe the top five largest businesses?

4. What do the data in this list tell you?

5. What do the data in this list not tell you?

6. Do you have all the information you need to describe this set of data?

7. How might graphically representing these data help you recognize patterns in the data?

8. What types of graphs might you use?

What's in a Name?

The chamber of commerce is planning to post the first names of all of the graduating seniors from the city high school on a billboard outside of town. Chamber members, however, have no idea what the typical length of a student's first name is. Your class has offered to gather data in order to make a prediction.

Your teacher will draw a number line on the board. Each student in your class will count the number of letters in his or her first name and then place a dot above the appropriate number on the line.

1. How many students are in your class?

2. Make a list of the data values for your class.

3. Which is the most common number of letters in a first name for your class?

4. Make a list of the first names in your class (or your group), then level off the number of letters until you find the average length of the first names.

5. Do you know of another way to find the average of the data? What is your method?

6. Is there a data point that is exactly in the middle of the data set for the whole class?

7. How did you find the middle value?

8. Draw a short vertical line segment at the middle of the data.

9. How many data values are on each side of the middle value in your list?

10. As you look at the list, what percentage of the data values is on each side of the middle value?

11. What fraction of the data values is on each side of the middle value?

12. Are there any data points that appear to be farther from the middle than other points?

13. If you think of the vertical line in the middle of the list as dividing the data into two parts, find the middle of the lower, or left, half of the data. Draw a short vertical line at this value.

14. If you think of the vertical line in the middle as dividing the data into two parts, find the middle value of the upper, or right, half of the data.

15. Draw a short vertical line at each end of your list.

16. What percentage of the data lies between the various vertical lines in your list? How can you tell?

17. What fraction of the data lies between the various vertical lines in your list?

18. What percentage of the data lies between the middle value of the lower half and the middle value of the upper half?

19. How would you describe the average number of letters in the first names of students in your class?

20. How would you describe the spread of your data set?

21. What recommendations would you make to the chamber of commerce about the number of letters in the first names of students for the billboard?

Assignment

The lengths of students' hand spans (in centimeters) for a class are shown in the list below. The lengths were rounded off to the nearest centimeter.

13, 14, 14, 15, 15, 15, 15, 16, 17, 18, 18, 19, 19, 19, 20, 20, 20, 20, 21, 21, 24

CHECK THIS!

A person's hand span is the distance between the thumb and pinky, or little finger, when one's fingers are spread out fully.

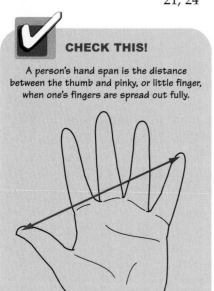

1. Make a dot plot of this set of data.

2. What do you notice about the data?

3. Find the difference between the largest and the smallest hand spans.

4. Find the average hand span.

5. Find the most common hand span.

6. Find the middle data value.

7. Find the middle data value of the lower half of the data.

8. Find the middle data value of the upper half of the data.

9. What fraction of the data is below the middle value of the lower half?

10. What fraction of the data is greater than the middle value?

11. For what occupation might a large hand span be advantageous?

12. How would you describe this collection of data to a friend?

13. How do you think having both males and females in this data set affects the average and the spread?

Box-and-Whiskers Plots

People use statistics to help them understand and use data that they collect. They describe sets of data by using terms such as *mean*, *median*, *mode*, and *range*. Here is a list of terms we use when talking about the central tendency and spread of data:

- **Statistics** is a mathematical science that studies the collection, analysis, explanation, and presentation of data.

- The **mean** is the average value of the data. To find the mean, you find the sum of the data and divide by the number of data values in the set.

- The **mode** is the value with the greatest frequency, or, the value that occurs most often.

- The **median** is the value in the middle. If there is an odd number of data values, the median is the value in the middle.

$$1 \quad 2 \quad 3 \quad \boxed{4} \quad 5 \quad 6 \quad 7$$

If there is an even number of data values, the median is the average of the two middle values.

$$1 \quad 2 \quad 3 \quad \boxed{4 \quad 5} \quad 6 \quad 7 \quad 8$$
Median = 4.5

- The **range** is the spread of the data. To determine the range, you subtract the smallest value from the largest value.

- The smallest value in the data set is the **minimum**.

- The largest value in the data set is the **maximum**.

- The **first quartile** is the median of the lower half of a data set.

- The **third quartile** is the median of the upper half of a data set.

Let's go back to the hand span data from the last section and create a **box-and-whiskers plot (Figure 8.2)**.

You may recall that the middle of the data, or the median value, was 18 centimeters. Make a short vertical line at 18. The middle, or median, of the lower half of the data, the first quartile, was 15 centimeters, and the middle, or median, of the upper half of the data, the third quartile, was 20 centimeters. Let's make a short vertical line at both 15 and 20. Then, make short vertical lines at the minimum and maximum values. Connect the first and third vertical quartile bars with horizontal bars. This is called a **box-and-whiskers plot**.

A box-and-whiskers plot divides data into four sections. Each section contains 25%, or ¼, of the data values. A box-and-whiskers plot does not tell you how many values are in each section, but it does indicate where the minimum, first quartile, median, third quartile, and maximum values are located. It can also give you an idea of how spread out the data is.

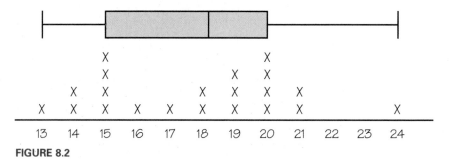

FIGURE 8.2

- A **box-and-whiskers plot** helps to summarize five values from the data set: minimum, first quartile, median, third quartile, and maximum.

1. Why do you think this type of plot is called a box-and-whiskers plot?

The owners of three shoe stores recorded the sizes of the shoes they sold last weekend. Each store owner created a box-and-whiskers plot to help identify which shoe sizes to order for the new season **(Figure 8.3)**. From the box-and-whiskers plots, the owners can identify the smallest and largest sizes, the median size, and the spread of the shoe sizes that were sold.

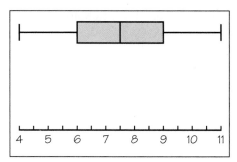

Graph 1

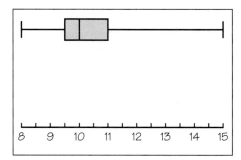

Graph 2

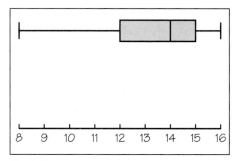

Graph 3

FIGURE 8.3

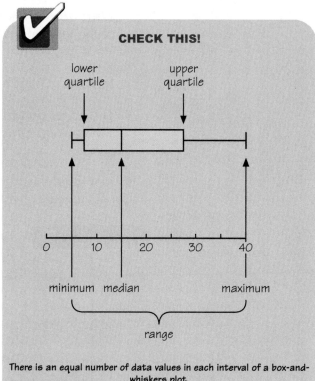

2. What do you know about the minimum, maximum, median, and range for each graph?

3. Why do you think the left section of the box in Graph 2 is smaller than the right section?

4. In Graph 3, why is the left whisker longer than the right whisker?

5. By looking at the box-and-whiskers plot, can you identify the mode of the data? If so, what is it?

6. By looking at the box-and-whiskers plot, can you identify the mean of the data? If so, what is it?

7. What do you know about the number of shoes sold in each of the four intervals in Graph 1?

8. What can you say about the data in Graph 2 compared to the data in Graph 3?

9. The upper quartile for Graph 2 is the same as the maximum shoe size for Graph 1. What does that information tell you about how the shoes sold at the two stores compare?

10. Identify the box-and-whiskers plot that matches each set of data listed in the tables. Explain your reasoning.

Men's	
8	10
8.5	10
8.5	10.5
9	11
9.5	11
9.5	11
10	14
10	15
10	15

Women's	
4	7.5
4.5	8.5
5.5	8.5
5.5	8.5
6	9
6	9
6.5	9.5
7.5	10
7.5	11

Big and Tall Men's	
8	14
11	14.5
11.5	14.5
11.5	15
12	15
12	15
12.5	15.5
13	15.5
14	16

11. Based on the data from last weekend's sales, between which two sizes should the owner of the men's shoe store order 50% of the new season shoes? Explain your reasoning.

12. If the owner of the women's shoe store plans to order 100 pairs of black dress shoes, how many pairs in each size should she order? Explain your reasoning.

A data value is considered to be an **outlier** if it is unusually small or large in relation to the majority of the data values. To determine whether a data value is an outlier, first you find the interquartile range value and multiply it by 1.5. For example, in Graph 2, the interquartile range is $11 - 9.5$, or 1.5. Multiply 1.5 by 1.5 to get 2.25. Subtract the calculated value from the first quartile value, $9.5 - 2.25 = 7.25$. Add the calculated value to the third quartile value, $11 + 2.25 = 13.25$. An outlier would have a value greater than 13.25 or less than 7.25.

13. Do you think Graph 2 has any outliers?

14. Does either Graph 1 or Graph 3 have any outliers?

The graphing calculator has a feature for making a box-and-whiskers plot. Let's use the calculator to make a box-and-whiskers plot for this set of data.

First, enter the data into List 1 in your calculator.

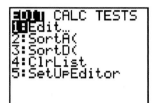 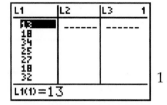

If you would like to see the data in ascending order, press [2nd][0] for [CATALOG], then select **1:SortA**. (Tip: You can avoid lengthy scrolling by pressing [ALPHA][LN], the keystrokes for the letter "S," to jump down to the commands beginning with "S.") Press [ENTER]. Insert **L1** ([2nd][1]) in the parentheses, then press [ENTER].

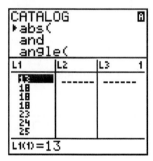  

Now when you view List 1 the values are listed in ascending order.

You can also use the LIST OPS feature:

Select [2nd][STAT] for [LIST], press the arrow key [▶] to select **1:SortA(**, then press [ENTER].

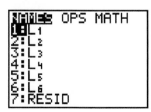 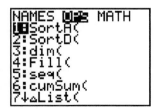

To make a box-and-whiskers plot with these data, select [2nd][Y=] for [STAT PLOT], turn the STAT PLOT on, and select the box-and-whiskers symbol.

Check to see whether you have an appropriate window, then press [GRAPH]. The window shown has an Xmin that is slightly lower than our smallest data value and an Xmax that is slightly greater than our largest data value.

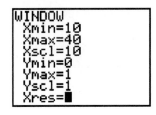 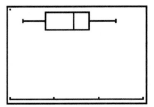

When you select the [TRACE] key and use the left ◄ and right ► arrows, you will see the five values for the box-and-whiskers plot displayed.

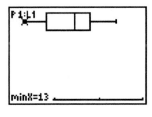 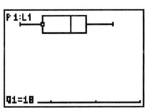 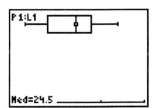

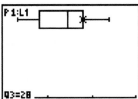 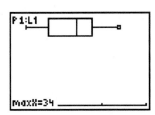

CHECK THIS!

These five values are often called the five-number summary of a data set.

If you select the [STAT] key, then use the right arrow key ► to select [CALC]. Select **1:1-Var Stats** and press [ENTER], then you will see a list of calculated values. Use the down arrow key ▼ to scroll to the bottom of the list.

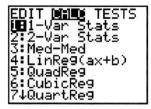 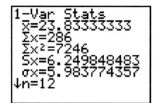

At the bottom of this list you will find the five important values, the five-number summary, for a box-and-whiskers plot. They should be identical to the values obtained using the TRACE feature of the calculator.

SUMMARY

A box-and-whiskers plot gives a summary of a set of data. It does not give individual data values. The five values that are required to make a box-and-whiskers plot are the minimum value, the maximum value, the first quartile, the third quartile, and the median.

Here are the steps for making a box-and-whiskers plot:

- Find the median of the data set and draw a short vertical line there.

- Find the medians of the lower and upper halves of the data and draw a short vertical line at each place.

- Draw a short vertical line at both the minimum value and the maximum value.

- Connect the first- and third-quartile vertical lines with horizontal lines.

Assignment

1. Generate a set of data that could be used to produce this box-and-whiskers plot of the heights of a group of basketball players **(Figure 8.4)**.

Heights of Basketball Players

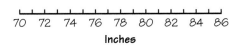

70 72 74 76 78 80 82 84 86

Inches

FIGURE 8.4

2. The box-and-whiskers plot shown in **Figure 8.5** represents the number of minutes Troy exercised each day while training for a marathon.

Duration of Exercise

70 75 80 85 90 95 100 105 110 115 120

Minutes

FIGURE 8.5

What is the range of the number of minutes Troy exercised?

a. 120 minutes

b. 90 minutes

c. 70 minutes

d. 50 minutes

3. A magazine conducted tests on two different brands of AA batteries to find out which brand has a longer battery life. The results are shown in the box-and-whiskers plots in **Figure 8.6**. Use the box-and-whiskers plots to compare and contrast the results of the experiment.

FIGURE 8.6

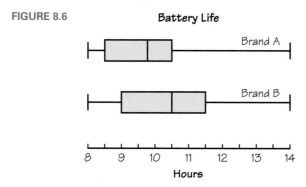

4. The box-and-whiskers plot shows the hourly pay for employees at Mega-Lo Mart **(Figure 8.7)**.

FIGURE 8.7

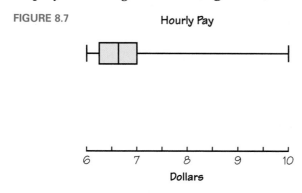

Based on this information, which of the following statements is not true about the hours worked by the ten employees?

a. The range of pay is $4.00 per hour.

b. The median pay is slightly more than $6.50 per hour.

c. More people earn between $7.00 and $10.00 per hour than between $6.00 and $7.00 per hour.

d. Seventy-five percent of the employees earn $7.00 or less per hour.

5. A warehouse manager created a box-and-whiskers plot to represent the number of hours worked each week by ten of his employees **(Figure 8.8)**.

FIGURE 8.8

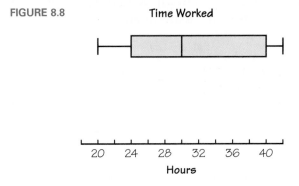

Based on this information, which of the following statements can be made about the hours worked by the ten employees?

a. More employees worked between 30 and 42 hours than between 20 and 30 hours.

b. Fifty percent of the employees work between 30 and 40 hours each week.

c. Seventy-five percent of the employees work 40 or fewer hours each week.

d. The range of the hours worked is 20 hours.

6. A doctor in our town is trying to decide which of two drugs is better for his patients for pain relief after surgery. He asks his patients to record how many minutes it takes from the time the drug is administered until they begin to feel relief from their pain. Here are the data for each drug.

Time, in minutes, until pain relief is evident:
Drug X: 12, 12, 12, 13, 14, 15, 15, 16, 16, 17, 18, 18, 19
Drug Y: 10, 11, 11, 12, 13, 13, 13, 14, 14, 15, 15, 17, 20

a. Make a dot plot for both Drug X and Drug Y.

b. Find the five values you will need to make a box-and-whiskers plot.

c. Make a box-and-whiskers plot for both Drug X and Drug Y.

d. Which of these two drugs do you think the doctor should prescribe for his patients for pain relief after surgery? Why?

Transforming Data and Histograms

PART 1: Transforming Data Sets

One of the concerns of the chamber of commerce is the increasing cost of energy. **Figure 8.9** displays fuel efficiency ratings for the twenty-two vehicles classified by the U.S. Environmental Protection Agency (EPA) as hybrid vehicles in 2008. The table shows fuel efficiency for both city and highway driving.

City	48	40	35	34	34	34	33	29	29	29	27
Highway	45	45	33	30	30	30	34	27	27	27	25

City	27	26	25	24	24	22	21	21	20	20	20
Highway	24	24	32	32	32	25	22	22	22	20	20

FIGURE 8.9. EPA fuel efficiency ratings for 2008 hybrid vehicles.

1. Use your graphing calculator to make a box-and-whiskers plot for fuel efficiency for city driving. Sketch your plot and describe your viewing window. Remember that for box-and-whiskers plots, the y-axis values do not matter.

2. Label the critical values, including the minimum value, first quartile, median, third quartile, and maximum value.

3. Create a table like **Figure 8.10** on your paper. Record the information for 2008 fuel efficiency.

Critical Value	2008 Fuel Efficiency	Proposal #1
Minimum		
First Quartile		
Median		
Third Quartile		
Maximum		

FIGURE 8.10. Critical values for data.

Suppose the EPA is considering various proposals to increase vehicles' fuel efficiency. One proposal is that every hybrid vehicle must increase fuel efficiency by five miles per gallon.

4. What do you think a box-and-whiskers plot for the increased fuel efficiency would look like? Explain.

Use your graphing calculator to investigate the EPA proposal.

5. Begin by using the List Editor to transform the data. Use List 2 to add 5 to each List 1 value. (Hint: Use the List Header as a shortcut!)

6. Make a box-and-whiskers plot of the increased fuel efficiency. Display the new box-and-whiskers plot with your original plot. Sketch your plot and describe your viewing window.

7. Label the critical values, including the minimum value, first quartile, median, third quartile, and maximum value.

8. How do the two box-and-whiskers plots compare?

9. Record the information for the increased fuel efficiency in your table like in Figure 8.10 in the "Proposal 1" column. How do the critical values for the box-and-whiskers plots compare?

10. How do the box-and-whiskers plots and table values compare to your prediction?

11. What do you think would have happened to your graphs if the EPA had proposed increasing fuel efficiency by eight miles per gallon instead of five? Test your prediction.

One member of the chamber of commerce complains that an increase in fuel efficiency of five miles per gallon simply isn't enough. She claims that in order to make a significant reduction in fuel expenses, the EPA should at least double the 2008 fuel efficiencies.

12. What do you think a box-and-whiskers plot for her suggested doubling of fuel efficiency would look like? Explain.

13. Use your graphing calculator to transform your data. Use List 2 to double each List 1 value. (Hint: Use the List Header as a shortcut!)

14. Make a box-and-whiskers plot of the doubled fuel efficiency. Display the new box-and-whiskers plot with your original

2008 fuel efficiency plot. Sketch your plot and describe your viewing window.

15. Label the critical values, including the minimum value, first quartile, median, third quartile, and maximum value.

16. How do the two box-and-whiskers plots compare?

17. Record the information for both the 2008 fuel efficiency and the increased fuel efficiency in your table like in **Figure 8.11** in the "Proposal 2" column. How do the critical values for box-and-whiskers plots compare?

Critical Value	2008 Fuel Efficiency	Proposal #2
Minimum		
First Quartile		
Median		
Third Quartile		
Maximum		

FIGURE 8.11. Critical values for data.

18. How do the box-and-whiskers plots and table values compare to your prediction?

19. What do you think would have happened to your graph if the chamber of commerce member had suggested increasing fuel efficiency by a factor of three instead of two? Use List 3 to test your prediction.

20. How does adding the same value to each element in a data set change the measures of central tendency?

21. How does multiplying the same scale factor to each element in a data set change the measures of central tendency?

22. How do the changes in the box-and-whisker plot relate to transformations that you can perform on functions or geometric figures in the coordinate plane?

PART 2: Frequency Tables and Histograms

Another function of the chamber of commerce is to promote tourism. Professional sports attract a lot of business to a town. When teams play well, more people come to the games and spend money, increasing the amount of business revenue.

Figure 8.12 shows some 2007 statistics for the Norfolk Tides minor league baseball team in Norfolk, Virginia. The table shows the number of runs scored by each team member during the season.

Position	Player	Runs Scored
1B	Mike Cervenak	69
3B	Terry Tiffee	45
C	J.R. House	52
2B	Eider Torres	38
OF	Jason Dubois	40
SS	Brandon Fahey	37
OF	Cesar Crespo	32
OF	Tike Redman	53
OF	Adam Stern	40
OF	Jon Knott	42
OF	Luis Montanez	27
CA	Iberto Castillo	24
OF	Val Majewski	16
OF	Sebastien Boucher	13
2B	Bo Hart	6
C	Eli Whiteside	5
C	Ryan Hubele	8
OF	Ruddy Yan	4
3B	Travis Brown	5
OF	Matt Cepicky	3
SS	Luis Hernandez	4
C	Morgan Clendenin	2
SS	Gerardo Alvarez	0
OF	Jay Payton	3

FIGURE 8.12. Stats for 2007 Norfolk Tides.

Interval (class)	Number of Players (frequency)
0–9	
10–19	
20–29	
30–39	
40–49	
50–59	
60–69	

FIGURE 8.13. Frequency Table 1.

Interval (class)	Number of Players (frequency)
0–4	
5–9	
10–14	
15–19	
20–24	
25–29	
30–34	
35–39	
40-44	
45-49	
50-54	
55-59	
60-64	
65-69	

FIGURE 8.14. Frequency Table 2.

1. Create a table like **Figure 8.13** on your paper. Count the number of players (the **frequency**) scoring a number of runs that falls in that interval (called the **class**). Record the information in your table.

2. Create a table like **Figure 8.14** on your paper. Count the number of players scoring a number of runs that falls in that frequency and record the information in your table.

3. Compare the two frequency tables. What information about the 2007 Norfolk Tides does each table suggest?

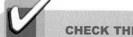

CHECK THIS!

Frequency tables and histograms are special types of data representations. In both frequency tables and histograms, the interval that you designate is called the class and the number of times that data points fall within a certain class is called the frequency.

The chamber of commerce wants to use these data to encourage people to attend Norfolk Tides games. Many people are visually oriented; they may be more likely to read a graph than to read the numbers in a table. There are many ways to represent these data graphically. A histogram is one way. Your graphing calculator has a histogram option in the STAT PLOT menu.

4. Enter the data for the number of runs scored into List 1 of the Stat Editor of your graphing calculator.

5. Follow the steps shown below to create a histogram that matches the frequency table in Figure 8.13.

Step 1: Press 2nd Y= to get to the STAT PLOT menu.

Step 2: Use the arrow keys ▾ and ▴ to select **1:Plot1**. Press ENTER.

Step 3: Turn the plot on. Use the arrow key ▾ to select **On**, then press ENTER.

Step 4: Choose the Type. Use the arrow key ▾ to move down to **Type**, then use the arrow key ▸ to select the Histogram type. Press ENTER.

Step 5: Verify the Xlist. If necessary, use the arrow key ▾ to move down to **Xlist**, then press 2nd 1 for List 1, [L3].

Step 6: Set the viewing window. Press WINDOW. Use the arrow keys ▾ and ▴ to scroll up and down the list as you set the domain and range of your viewing window. Be sure that the domain (Xmin to Xmax) includes all data points in your Xlist. Xmin should be the lowest class boundary and Xscl should be the interval width. Be sure that the range (Ymin to Ymax) includes your highest frequency. The window shown will contain the sample data.

Step 7: View the graph. Press GRAPH.

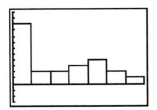

6. Sketch the histogram that you created in the previous step. Label the x-axis with the appropriate intervals, which are also called **class widths**, and the y-axis with the appropriate values.

7. Use the TRACE feature to determine the number of players contained in each bar, also called the **class**. Label that information on the sketch of your graph.

8. How does the histogram compare to the frequency table in Figure 8.13?

9. Now, repeat the steps listed earlier to generate a histogram from the data in Figure 8.14. Notice that the interval is different; consequently, you will need to change Xscl accordingly. Sketch your histogram, labeling the axes appropriately.

10. How does the histogram compare to the frequency table in Figure 8.14?

11. How do the two histograms compare to each other?

12. Which histogram would you include to boost attendance at Norfolk Tides games? Why?

CHECK THIS!

A histogram is a bar graph with data represented in intervals, or classes. Each class has a lower class limit and an upper class limit that describes each boundary of the bar representing the class. The class width represents the width of the bar.

Sometimes, class boundaries, or the boundaries of both sides of the bar, are a half-unit above or below the class limits so that all data points clearly fall within the area of the bar. At other times, class boundaries are chosen so that a data point may fall on the boundary. In that case, the data is usually considered to be in the next higher class (to its right).

Histograms are useful graphical displays that show variation within a data set. Statisticians looking for the most common element or the distribution of a data set might find a histogram helpful. However, as with any graphical display of data, there are some limitations to the use of histograms. If the class width is too wide or too narrow, the histogram might result in some misleading conclusions. Also, the histogram only shows the distribution of one set of data. A statistician looking for changes over time or patterns within a data set might not find a histogram to be very helpful.

CHECK THIS!

There are many ways to label a histogram. Some histograms label the midpoint of the class. Some histograms label the class boundaries. Labels are important to consider when interpreting histograms or using technology to create histograms.

Assignment

Ms. Santos's English Literature class is participating in the Read-a-Thon competition sponsored by the local library over the summer. Her students recorded the number of books that each student read over the summer. Their results are indicated in the table below.

3	6	4	2
8	1	4	3
9	4	7	5
11	4	7	3
1	12	6	4

1. What is the five-number summary for this data?

2. Create a box-and-whiskers plot to represent the number of books read by students in Ms. Santos's class.

3. Mr. Santarelli told Ms. Santos that his students also participated in the summer Read-a-Thon and that his students read twice as many books as her students. If we assume that each of Mr. Santarelli's students read twice as many books as one of Mrs. Santos's students and that there are also twenty students in his class, what would be the five-number summary for his class's data?

4. Ms. Santos assigns four more books for her students to read. Assuming that every student completes his or her assignments, what would be the five-number summary for the new set of data?

The local chamber of commerce is interested in promoting a circus in the community. One Saturday, they randomly surveyed people attending the circus to determine their ages. Following are random ages from forty circus attendees who entered the house of mirrors.

5	4	17	12	10	18	21	35
38	7	11	15	22	27	10	8
6	31	30	39	6	8	19	13
15	22	27	31	37	39	34	20
18	5	8	11	15	18	33	8

5. Create a histogram with intervals of width 5.

6. Create a histogram with intervals of width 10.

7. How do the two histograms compare?

8. For your data set calculate:

   a. The mean age

   b. The median age

   c. The mode age

   d. The range of the data

9. Using your first histogram, mark the mean in green, the median in red, and the mode in blue. If colored pencils or markers are not available, be sure to label the lines you drew in pencil.

10. Which one of the measurements of central tendencies seems to best represent these data? Explain your choice.

How Many Pizza Restaurants Are There?

Lawrence, Kansas, is the home of the University of Kansas. Like most college towns, it has its fair share of pizza places. In 2007, the university newspaper ran an article describing the town's saturated pizza market. How many pizza restaurants does a "typical" town have?

To investigate this question, we will investigate the number of pizza restaurants by state. The U.S. Department of Commerce and the U.S. Census Bureau maintain information about types of businesses, such as how many of a particular type of business there are in a city or state. **Figure 8.15** shows the number of pizza restaurants and the estimated 2007 population for all fifty states.

Your class has a contract with the Pizza Wacky Restaurant Group to investigate ways to expand the restaurant chain.

In your groups, determine a reasonable way to compare the number of pizza restaurants with the population for each state. Then create the following data representations:

✓ Box-and-whiskers plot

✓ Histogram

✓ Five-number summary (i.e., find the minimum value, first quartile, median, third quartile, and maximum value)

✓ Mean, median, mode, range, and interquartile range

✓ Outliers (if appropriate)

Use the data to make a presentation to the board of directors of the Pizza Wacky Restaurant Group about the current state of the pizza market. What recommendations might you make to the board about potential opportunities for expanding or reducing their presence in the pizza markets of various states? Use your data representations to defend your recommendations.

State	Number of Pizza Restaurants	Population (2007 estimated)	State	Number of Pizza Restaurants	Population (2007 estimated)
Alabama	1071	4,627,851	Montana	236	957,861
Alaska	149	683,478	Nebraska	471	1,774,571
Arizona	919	6,338,755	Nevada	406	2,565,382
Arkansas	776	2,834,797	New Hampshire	119	1,315,828
California	6524	36,553,215	New Jersey	1182	8,685,920
Colorado	929	4,861,515	New Mexico	454	1,969,915
Connecticut	732	3,502,309	New York	2574	19,297,729
Delaware	133	864,764	North Carolina	1673	9,061,032
Florida	2505	18,251,243	North Dakota	165	639,715
Georgia	1515	9,544,750	Ohio	2387	11,466,917
Hawaii	217	1,283,388	Oklahoma	1034	3,617,316
Idaho	298	1,499,402	Oregon	806	3,747,455
Illinois	3047	12,852,548	Pennsylvania	1682	12,432,792
Indiana	1394	6,345,289	Rhode Island	136	1,057,832
Iowa	838	2,988,046	South Carolina	1011	4,407,709
Kansas	708	2,775,997	South Dakota	158	796,214
Kentucky	879	4,241,474	Tennessee	1652	6,156,719
Louisiana	952	4,293,204	Texas	5200	23,904,380
Maine	212	1,317,207	Utah	469	2,645,330
Maryland	721	5,618,344	Vermont	128	621,254
Massachusetts	620	6,449,755	Virginia	1701	7,712,091
Michigan	1838	10,071,822	Washington	1357	6,468,424
Minnesota	933	5,197,621	West Virginia	314	1,812,035
Mississippi	685	2,918,785	Wisconsin	1286	5,601,640
Missouri	1195	5,878,415	Wyoming	108	522,830

FIGURE 8.15. Number of pizza restaurants in all fifty states.

Sources: U.S. Department of Commerce, U.S. Census Bureau.

SECTION

8.6

Well, It Varies...

Belinda's father was recently transferred to a company located in your town. She will soon be one of the newest students in your school. But before she arrives for her first day in her new school, she would like to know what to expect. She calls her new counselor and asks what a typical day at her new school might be like.

How would you describe a "typical" day at your school? Would you talk about your friends? your favorite teacher? a boring class? What does the lunch period look like at your school?

Mathematicians also have ways to describe numerical sets of data. For example, how would you describe the "typical" height of someone in your class?

Measure the height, in feet and inches, of each student in your class. Record the heights in a table like the one shown in **Figure 8.16**, adding rows as necessary. Be sure to separate the heights of boys and girls in the table.

Female		Male	
Name	**Height**	**Name**	**Height**

FIGURE 8.16. Height-recording chart.

1. Make a histogram of the heights of the female students and a histogram of the heights of the male students. Be sure to convert feet and inches into feet. Sketch each histogram.

2. How do the two histograms compare?

3. Find the mean, median, and mode height for female students and male students. How do those measures compare?

4. How would you describe the height of the "typical" female student in your class?

5. How would you describe the height of the "typical" male student in your class?

6. Which data set seems to be more spread out? Explain your answer.

7. How do the heights of the female students in your class vary? How is that variation reflected in your histogram?

8. How do the heights of the male students vary? How is that variation reflected?

Not Your Typical Height

Various groups of people may have different "typical" heights. If you measured the heights of members of the girls' and boys' basketball teams in your school, how do you think their "typical" heights would compare to the "typical" heights of female and male students in your class?

Consider the Washington Wizards, the professional National Basketball Association (NBA) team for Washington, DC. The heights of members of the 2007-2008 team are shown in the table in **Figure 8.17.**

1. Enter the heights of the members of the Washington Wizards into List 1 of the List Editor of your graphing calculator. Be sure to convert feet and inches into feet.

2. Make a histogram to display the heights of the Washington Wizards team members. Sketch your histogram.

3. Find the mean, median, and mode heights of the Washington Wizards team members. If there are any outliers, identify them. How do these measures compare to those for the heights of students in your class?

Name	Height
Gilbert Arenas	6 ft. 4 in.
Andray Blatche	6 ft. 11 in.
Caron Butler	6 ft. 7 in.
Antonio Daniels	6 ft. 4 in.
Brendan Haywood	7 ft. 0 in.
Antawn Jamison	6 ft. 9 in.
Roger Mason	6 ft. 5 in.
Dominic McGuire	6 ft. 9 in.
Oleksiy Pecherov	7 ft. 0 in.
Darius Songaila	6 ft. 9 in.
DeShawn Stevenson	6 ft. 5 in.
Etan Thomas	6 ft. 10 in.
Nick Young	6 ft. 5 in.

FIGURE 8.17. Professional basketball players' heights

4. Describe the spread of the heights of the Washington Wizards team members.

5. How do the heights of the Washington Wizards team members compare to the heights of the boys and girls in your class? Explain.

6. The graph in **Figure 8.18** shows the heights of the Washington Wizards team members. Where does the mean height appear on this graph? Sketch a graph similar to the one in Figure 8.7.2 and draw in the horizontal line representing the mean height.

7. How does the height of an individual player deviate (in other words, is different) from the mean height of the team?

8. How much would you say that an individual player's height typically deviates from the mean height of the team?

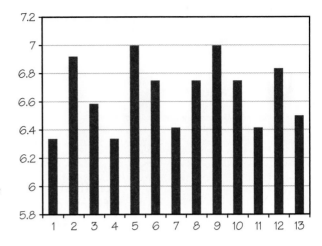

FIGURE 8.18. Heights of Washington Wizards basketball players

9. Use the List Editor of your graphing calculator to subtract the height of each player from the mean height of the team. Perform that calculation in List 2.

10. Make a graph like the one shown in **Figure 8.19**, plotting the line representing the mean as well as the height of each player. Draw in each segment that represents the shortest distance from each point to the line representing the mean.

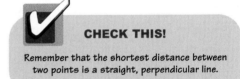

CHECK THIS!

Remember that the shortest distance between two points is a straight, perpendicular line.

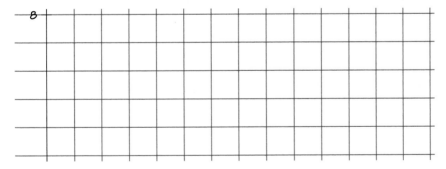

FIGURE 8.19. Graph of mean height and players' heights

11. Use your graphing calculator to find the sum of the differences between players' heights and the team's mean height from List 2. What do you notice?

12. Divide the sum of the differences by the number of players to find the mean of the differences. How well does the mean

of the differences describe the typical variation from the mean height of the team?

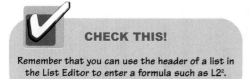
Since the sum of the differences turns out to be a special number, statisticians have found a way to work around that number in their quest to find a way to describe the typical deviation from the mean value of a data set.

13. On your graph from Question 10 (Figure 8.19), construct a square for each player's height. The side length of each square should be equal to the distance each player's height is above or below the mean height.

14. In your graphing calculator's List Editor, use List 3 to find the square of the differences between each player's height and the mean height of the team; i.e., square the values in List 2 and place them in List 3. How do these values compare to the squares that you constructed in the previous question?

15. Use your graphing calculator to find the sum of the squares of the differences between players' heights and the team's mean height from List 3. What do you notice? Why do you think that might be?

16. Look at your graph of the squares. What do you think the area of the "average" square would be?

17. Use the home screen of your graphing calculator to find the average square size by finding the sum of the squares in List 3 and then dividing by the number of players on the team (you may want to refer back to Figure 8.17).

18. If you know the area of a square, how do you find the length of its side?

19. Find the length of the side of a square whose area is what you calculated in Question 16.

20. How does this value describe the "typical" deviation of an individual player's height from the mean height of the team?

What's Normal?

As you collect sets of data and find the mean, median, or mode, the description of the data is sometimes incomplete. In the last section you found a typical deviation from the mean for the heights of members of the Washington Wizards basketball team. The term statisticians use for a typical deviation from the mean is **standard deviation**, and the typical square size is the **variance**. The standard deviation is the square root of the variance. Determining how much data varies from the mean gives you a more complete description of the data. Statisticians use computer software programs and calculators to help them calculate the mean, standard deviation, and variance in order to describe and interpret sets of data quickly and efficiently. In the last section you found the standard deviation and the variance using the "long" method.

The data we have used to think about mean and standard variation are quantitative. Data that can be represented using measurements or numbers are called **quantitative** data. Data that are categorical, such as favorite color, occupation, or marital status, are called qualitative data. You have made circle graphs and bar graphs to represent qualitative data in previous sections.

1. Let's take a small set of data and calculate the mean and standard deviation for the data. Mr. Jones has test grades for five students; he wants to analyze the test results. The grades are 50, 62, 78, 80, and 100.

Fill in a table similar to the one shown in **Figure 8.19** with the appropriate information.

2. What do the mean and standard deviation tell you about this set of data?

Imagine what the computations might have looked like before graphing calculators were available to statisticians!

X_i	Test Scores, L1	L2 = L1 − mean	L3 = L2²
X_1	50		
X_2	62		
X_3	78		
X_4	80		
X_5	100		
	Sum of L_1 =		Sum of L_3 =
n =	Mean of L_1 =		Variance: $\dfrac{\text{Sum of } L_3 =}{n}$
			Standard deviation: $\sqrt{\text{variance}}$ =

FIGURE 8.19. Calculation of standard deviation

Monday's homework assignment for Ms. Smith's students is to measure how much time it takes for their dead cell phone battery to completely recharge. On Friday the students return with their data. The results for the amount of time (to the nearest quarter hour) for each student's complete battery recharge are shown in the list below.

3.75	3.25	4	4.5	4.75
3.75	4	3.5	4.25	5
4.25	4	3.75	4.5	2.5
4	4.5	3.5	4	4.25

Let's use your graphing calculator to find the average amount of time and the typical variation for the time it takes for Ms. Smith's students' cell phones to recharge by finding the mean, median, mode, standard deviation, and variance for this set of data.

3. First, enter the values into a list in the calculator.

4. Sketch a histogram using the window shown below. What do you notice?

  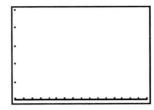

5. Then press [STAT], use the arrow key ▶ to select **CALC**, then press [ENTER] to select **1: 1-Var Stats**. Notice that the calculator screen displays several calculated values.

  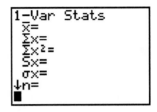

The first value, $\bar{x}$, is the mean of the data set.

The second value, $\sum x$, is the sum of the data set.

The third value is the sum of the squares of the data.

The fourth value, s, is the standard deviation of the sample.

The fifth value, σ, is the standard deviation of the population.

The sixth value, n, is the number of entries in List 1.

Remember, if you press the down arrow you get additional information.

CHECK THIS!

Letters from the Greek alphabet are often used in statistics. Capital sigma, Σ, represents a sum. Lowercase sigma, σ, represents the standard deviation.

> Notice that minX is the minimum value for x in your list.
> Q_1 is the first quartile.
> Med is the median for the set of data.
> Q_3 is the third quartile.
> Finally, maxX is the maximum value for your list.

6. What is the mean amount of time it takes for a student's cell phone to recharge?

7. If you knew only the values of the sum of the data set, $\sum x$, and n, how could you find the mean, $\bar{x}$?

Notice that the calculator has calculated a standard deviation for a sample and a population. What is the difference? Statisticians use the term **population** to describe individuals, items, or data they are interested in studying. It is sometimes possible to study an entire population. For example, you might want to calculate the mean GPA for the seniors in your high school and then see how the GPAs vary from the mean. At other times, the population is so large that it would be impossible to measure the variable that you are interested in for every single person or event. Statisticians will then pick a subset of the population, called a **sample**, and study the data from this subset in order to make a prediction for the population. For example, Ms. Smith's class is a sample of the population of all cell phone users. A sample should be randomly selected if you want to use the results to make predictions for a population.

During presidential election years, pollsters collect data from a sample of the population of the United States and use the information to try to predict who the next president of the United States will be. George Gallup was a pioneer in predicting presidential elections by conducting surveys of Americans. For example, a poll conducted on a sample of voters in New Hampshire predicted that Barack Obama would win the New Hampshire Democratic primary in January 2008. After the results were counted, Hillary Clinton had won the state of New Hampshire. If you are interested in poll predictions and politics you might want to investigate the presidential races between Al Landon and Franklin Roosevelt or between Thomas Dewey and Harry Truman.

8. Do you think that a sample will always accurately predict results for a population? Why or why not?

9. How might you choose your sample in order to best make a prediction for the population?

The formula statisticians use for the standard deviation of a population is:

$$\sigma = \sqrt{\frac{1}{n}\sum_{i=1}^{n}(x_i - \mu)^2}.$$

The formula statisticians use for the standard deviation of a sample is:

$$s = \sqrt{\frac{1}{n-1}\sum_{i=1}^{n}(x_i - \overline{X})^2}.$$

10. How are a sample and a population different?

11. How are the formulas for the standard deviation of the sample and the standard deviation of the population different and how are they alike?

12. Using your calculator, find the median value for Ms. Smith's set of data.

13. What is the value of the mode for Ms. Smith's set of data?

14. What is the range of the data in List 1?

15. If we think of Ms. Smith's class as a population, what is the standard deviation?

16. If we think of Ms. Smith's class as a sample from the population of cell phone users, what is the standard deviation?

17. What does the standard deviation mean for this set of data?

18. Find the variance using the information you have on your calculator.

You may have noticed that not all sets of data have the same shape when you plot the frequency. There is one particular shape that occurs often. Look at the histogram in **Figure 8.20**, which was made using a very large set of data. The graph plots the frequency of one thousand 18-year-old girls vs. their heights in inches at a college campus.

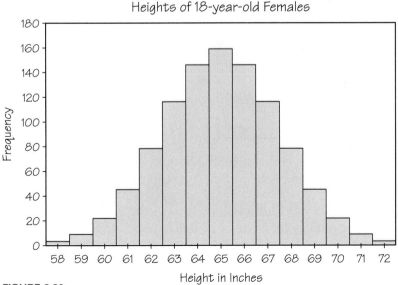

FIGURE 8.20

FIGURE 8.20. Heights of 1,000 18-year-old females

19. What do you notice about the shape of the histogram?

20. The mean of the data is 65 inches and the standard deviation is 2.5 inches. What can you say about the heights of this group of 18-year-old females?

21. What do you think is the mode of this set of data?

22. What is the median of this set of data?

23. **Figure 8.21** contains a table with the frequency of occurrence for each height. When the height listed is 65 inches, this includes all females between 64.5 and 65.5 inches tall. What percentage of the females are 65 inches tall? What percentage of the females are 69 inches tall? What percentage of the females are 61 inches tall?

Height (±.5)	Frequency
58	3
59	10
60	22
61	45
62	78
63	116
64	146
65	160
66	146
67	116
68	78
69	45
70	22
71	10
72	3

FIGURE 8.21.
Frequency chart

24. If the total area covered by the bars in the histogram is 1, what is the area of the bar for a height of 64 inches?

If you connect the midpoints of the tops of the bars in **Figure 8.22**, the graph takes on more of a "bell" shape, which is the reason some people call it a bell curve. Statisticians also call it a **normal curve** because data sets that can be represented graphically using a normal curve are said to follow a **normal**

distribution. In a normal distribution, the mean, median, and mode are all the same value, which is indicated by the peak of the bell curve. Normal curves are also symmetric.

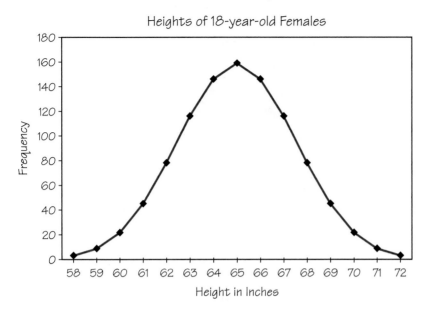

FIGURE 8.22. *Graph of heights*

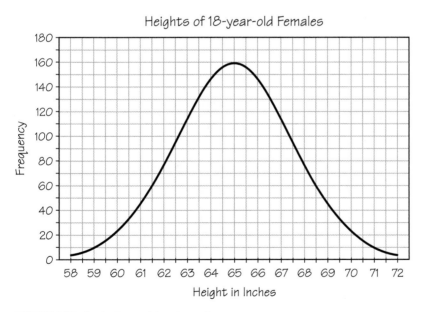

FIGURE 8.23. *Graph of normal distribution function*

As you collect more data, the graph becomes even smoother, as seen in **Figure 8.23**.

If you know the mean and the standard deviation of a normal curve, you can graph the normal curve with your graphing calculator.

If the set of data has a mean of 0 and a standard deviation of 1, use these steps to graph the normal curve.

Press the [Y=] key.   [2nd][VARS]([DISTR])[ENTER]

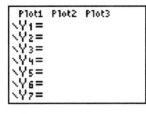 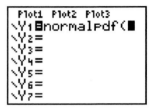 

Enter x, mean of 0, standard deviation of 1. Set the WINDOW. Then press [GRAPH].

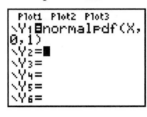 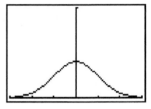 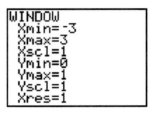

24. What do you think will happen to the graph if we change the standard deviation to 0.5?

In the Y= screen, graph Y2=normalpdf(x, 0, .5). Press [GRAPH].

 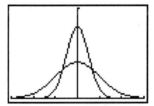

25. What did the change in the standard deviation do to the graph of the normal curve?

26. How do you think two graphs will compare if they have the same standard deviation but different means?

Try graphing two normal curves with the same standard deviation but different means. One curve has a mean of 0 and the other has a mean of 1, but they both have the same standard deviation, 1.

Enter these two functions in the Y= screen. Press GRAPH.

 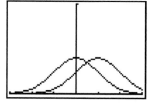

27. What do you notice about these two graphs?

How would you graph a normal curve with a mean of 65 and a standard deviation of 2.5?

Enter the normal distribution function into Y1. If you press GRAPH, you will probably not see the graph. This means that you will need to change the WINDOW.

 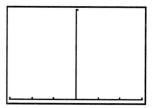

To change the window, use these values:
The Xmin value is the mean minus 3 times the standard deviation.
The Xmax value is the mean plus 3 times the standard deviation.
The Xscl value is the standard deviation.

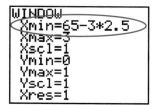 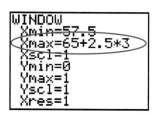 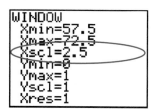

The Ymin value is 0.
The Ymax value is 1 divided by 2 times the standard deviation.
The Yscl value is 0.

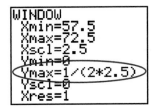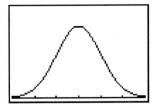

SUMMARY

The **standard deviation** for a set of data measures the spread about the **mean**. The standard deviation is the square root of the **variance**. So the variance is the square of the standard deviation. The standard deviation can be found by paper and pencil calculations or by using a graphing calculator.

Statisticians distinguish between a **sample** and a **population** and have slightly different formulas for calculating the standard deviation for each.

Some sets of data (but by no means all) can be described by a **normal curve**. The mean of the normal curve is right in the middle, as are the mode and the median. The normal curve is also symmetrical. Normal curves with smaller standard deviations are taller, less spread out, and have sharper peaks than those with larger standard deviations. However, they all have the characteristic normal bell shape.

Assignment

1. How can you spot the mean of a normal curve?

2. If one normal curve is low and spread out and another is tall and skinny, which curve has the larger standard deviation?

3. How many movies have you seen this month? This question was asked of six tenth graders and six eleventh graders. Here are their responses.

Tenth graders:	5	1	2	5	3	8
Eleventh graders:	4	2	0	2	3	1

Calculate the mean, the variance, and the standard deviation of each of these sets of data. Make a graph of each set. What do you notice about the two graphs? Which of the sets is more spread out?

4. Suppose that we add 2 to each of the numbers in the tenth-grade data set in Exercise 1. That gives us 7, 3, 4, 7, 5, 10.

   a. Find the mean and the standard deviation of this new set of numbers.

   b. Compare your answers with the tenth graders from Exercise 1. How did adding 2 to each number change the mean? How did it change the standard deviation?

   c. Without using the calculator, can you guess what will happen to the mean and standard deviation of the eleventh graders if we add 10 to each number in the set? Why?

5. The army wants to describe the distribution of head sizes of its soldiers to plan orders of helmets. Here are the head sizes in inches of 30 male soldiers, obtained by putting a tape measure around each soldier's forehead.

23.0	22.2	21.7	22.0	22.3	22.6
22.7	21.5	22.7	24.9	20.8	23.3
24.2	23.5	23.9	23.4	20.8	21.5
23.0	24.0	22.7	22.6	23.9	21.8
23.1	21.9	21.0	22.4	23.5	22.5

a. Do you think that this set of data is considered a sample or a population? Why?

b. Give a graphical description of these data. Do these data appear to be normally distributed? Explain.

c. Find the mean and the standard deviation for the sample for these head sizes. Be sure to include the units in which the numbers are measured.

d. What is the standard deviation of head sizes for the population of male soldiers?

6. Using a graphing calculator, graph the normal curve with a mean of 100 and a standard deviation of 15. Then graph the normal curve with a mean of 100 and a standard deviation of 10. How are the two graphs alike, and how are they different?

Area Under the Curve

As you saw in the previous section, normal distributions are described by symmetric, bell-shaped curves. The center of a normal curve is the mean, and the spread is controlled by the standard deviation.

The population of high school students' scores on the math portion of the SAT also falls into the shape of a bell curve **(Figure 8.24)**. The scores are approximately normal with a mean of 500 points and a standard deviation of 100 points. The normal curve for SAT math scores is shown below.

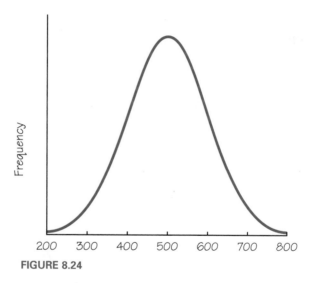

FIGURE 8.24

1. Use your graphing calculator to find out what happens to the graph of high school students' SAT math scores if the mean changes to 600 but the standard deviation remains 100.

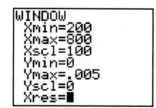

2. What would happen to the graph of high school students' SAT math scores if the mean remains 500 but the standard deviation changes to 50?

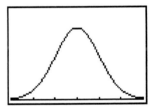

```
WINDOW
 Xmin=200
 Xmax=800
 Xscl=100
 Ymin=0
 Ymax=1/(2*50)■
 Yscl=0
 Xres=1
```

```
Plot1 Plot2 Plot3
\Y₁■normalpdf(X,
500,100)
\Y₂■normalpdf(X,
500,50)
\Y₃=
\Y₄=
\Y₅=
```

3. How are these transformations similar to transformations of functions that you have studied previously?

4. Which scores are within one standard deviation of the mean?

5. Which scores are within two standard deviations of the mean?

6. Which scores are within three standard deviations of the mean?

If you want to find out what percentage of high school students score between 500 and 600, you can use your graphing calculator. First, graph the normal distribution with a mean of 500 and a standard deviation of 100.

```
Plot1 Plot2 Plot3
\Y₁■normalpdf(X,
500,100)
\Y₂=■
\Y₃=
\Y₄=
\Y₅=
\Y₆=
```

```
WINDOW
 Xmin=200
 Xmax=800
 Xscl=100
 Ymin=0
 Ymax=.005
 Yscl=1
 Xres=1
```

Next, shade the portion of the normal distribution in which you are interested by using the Draw tools. Press [2nd] [VARS] ([DISTR]), arrow right using the [▶] key to select **DRAW**, then select **1:ShadeNorm(**. Press [ENTER].

```
DISTR DRAW
1■normalpdf(
2:normalcdf(
3:invNorm(
4:invT(
5:tpdf(
6:tcdf(
7↓Χ²pdf(
```

```
DISTR DRAW
1■ShadeNorm(
2:Shade_t(
3:ShadeΧ²(
4:ShadeF(
```

Enter four values in the parentheses after ShadeNorm(lower bound, upper bound, mean, standard deviation). The lower bound of data we are interested in is 500; the upper bound is 600. The mean of the entire data set is 500, and the standard deviation is 100. Press [ENTER] to see the graph with the area shaded.

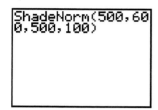
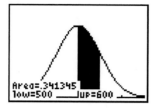

The area under the entire normal curve is considered to be one. The calculator finds the area of the shaded region in terms of a part of the entire curve. So the area of 0.341345 represents approximately 34% of high school students' scores between 500 and 600 on the math portion of the SAT.

7. Continue using this feature of your graphing calculator to fill in the table in **Figure 8.25**.

Range of SAT math scores	Approximate percent of students scoring in this range
$200 \leq score < 300$	
$300 \leq score < 400$	
$400 \leq score < 500$	
$500 \leq score < 600$	
$600 \leq score < 700$	
$700 \leq score < 800$	

FIGURE 8.25

8. What percentage of students' scores are within one standard deviation of the mean?

9. What percentage of students' scores are within two standard deviations of the mean?

10. What percentage of students' scores are within three standard deviations of the mean?

The population of high school students' ACT math scores is also approximately normal. The mean is 18 and the standard deviation is 6. This normal distribution is shown in **Figure 8.26**.

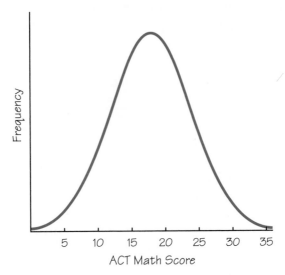

ACT Math Score

FIGURE 8.26

11. Use your graphing calculator to fill in the table in **Figure 8.27** with the percentage of students in each range of scores for the ACT math test.

Range of ACT math scores	Approximate percent of students scoring in this range
$0 \leq x < 6$	
$6 \leq x < 12$	
$12 \leq x < 18$	
$18 \leq x < 24$	
$24 \leq x < 30$	
$30 \leq x < 36$	

FIGURE 8.27

12. What do you notice about the percentage of students within each standard deviation range?

13. What percentage of the students score below the mean?

Statisticians have noticed that if data from a population are normally distributed, the percentage of data within one, two, or three standard deviations of the mean remains fairly constant, as shown in the graph below. This pattern is called the 68-95-99.7 rule **(Figure 8.28)**.

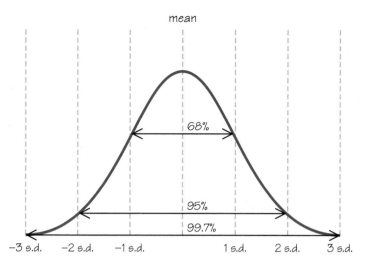

mean

68%

95%

99.7%

−3 s.d.   −2 s.d.   −1 s.d.   1 s.d.   2 s.d.   3 s.d.

FIGURE 8.28

14. In the standard normal distribution shown above, what percentage of data is more than three standard deviations from the mean?

15. What percentage of students score higher than 750 on the math portion of the SAT?

16. What percentage of students score lower than 16 on the ACT math test?

17. The normal distribution can also be used to compute probabilities if the data set is very close to normal. For example, if you randomly choose a high school student, what is the probability that his or her SAT math score will be lower than 500?

Statisticians often need to compare scores from one test to scores from a different test. In order to compare scores from different tests, you need to standardize the values. Let's see how we can use standardized scores, also called z-scores, to compare an SAT score to an ACT score.

Melissa scored 625 on the math portion of the SAT. Her friend Arthur scored 25 on the ACT. Melissa claims that her score is higher because it is more than one standard deviation away from the mean. Arthur claims that his score is just as good because he is also more than one standard deviation from the mean.

You can use standardized scores to see who is right whenever the data is very close to a normal distribution.

$$\text{z-score} = \frac{\text{score} - \text{mean of the population}}{\text{standard deviation of the population}}$$

$$\text{Melissa's z-score} = \frac{625 - 500}{100} = \frac{125}{100} = 1.25$$

$$\text{Arthur's z-score} = \frac{25 - 18}{6} = \frac{7}{6} \approx 1.17$$

A z-score tells you how many standard deviations above or below the mean a particular data point is. Melissa's z-score is 1.25 standard deviations above the mean while Arthur's z-score is 1.17 standard deviations above the mean. So Melissa's score really is higher than Arthur's score.

18. What is the z-score for a score of 430 on the math portion of the SAT if we continue to use a mean of 500 and a standard deviation of 100?

You can also describe performance on a test using percentiles. For example, if a score on the math portion of the SAT falls in the 90th percentile, it means that 90% of the test scores were lower than that score. You can use your graphing calculator to find percentiles.

Earlier in this section you used the ShadeNorm command on the calculator to find the percentage of data between two values. The invNorm command performs the opposite function. So, instead of finding the percentage of data that is less than, greater than, or between two scores, we can find the score value when we know the percentage, helping us find percentile values.

To do so, use the Distribution tools. Press [2nd][VARS] to pull up the Distribution menu, [DISTR], then arrow down using the [▾] key to select **3:invNorm(**. Enter three values in the parentheses after invNorm(percentile, mean, standard deviation). The percentile we want to find is the 90th percentile, so use the decimal equivalent of 0.90. The mean of the entire data set is 500, and the standard deviation is 100. Press [ENTER].

In the screen below, you can see that 90% of the high school students scored below approximately 628 on the math portion of the SAT. So, the 90th percentile is approximately 630.

19. What is the score that corresponds to the 15th percentile for SAT math scores?

20. Using your knowledge of SAT scores and your graphing calculator, find the value for each of the percentiles listed below and draw a box-and-whiskers plot on the same screen as the graph of the normal distribution for SAT math scores.

   a. 0%

   b. 25%

   c. 50%

   d. 75%

   e. 100%

   f. What do you notice about the box-and-whiskers plot and the normal distribution graph?

There are times when data are not normally distributed. The data may not be symmetric with respect to the mean. As shown in **Figure 8.29**, the data may be asymmetric.

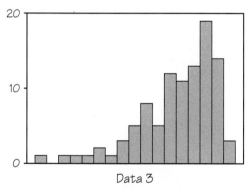
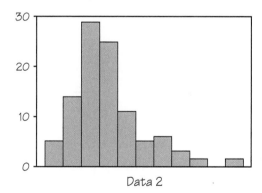

FIGURE 8.29

Asymmetric data sets might include a chemical plant's emissions or kindergarteners' reading scores. The mean, median, and mode are all the same value in a normal distribution. Let's investigate the mean, median, mode, and standard deviation in the following two distributions.

21. Listed in the table below are Joe's and Mary's math test scores for this year.

Joe	70	80	62	75	80	60	66	90	71	72	73	65
Mary	70	85	100	50	86	92	86	92	95	89	95	95

a. Make a histogram for each student's scores.

b. Make a box-and-whiskers plot for each student's scores.

c. What do you notice about Joe's and Mary's test scores?

d. Find the mean, median, mode, interquartile range, range, and standard deviation for each student.

e. What grade would you assign to each student for the year?

Distributions of data with a long tail on the right are called **right-skewed**, or skewed to the right **(Figure 8.30)**.

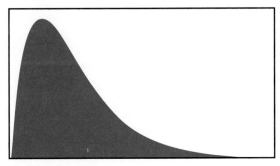

FIGURE 8.30

Distributions of data with a long tail on the left are called **left-skewed**, or skewed to the left **(Figure 8.31)**.

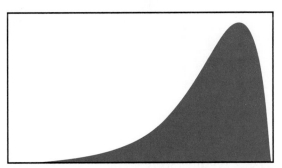

FIGURE 8.31

Some data distributions have more than one mode and may be termed **bimodal (Figure 8.32)** or **multimodal (Figure 8.33)**.

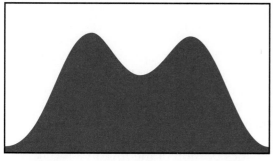

FIGURE 8.32

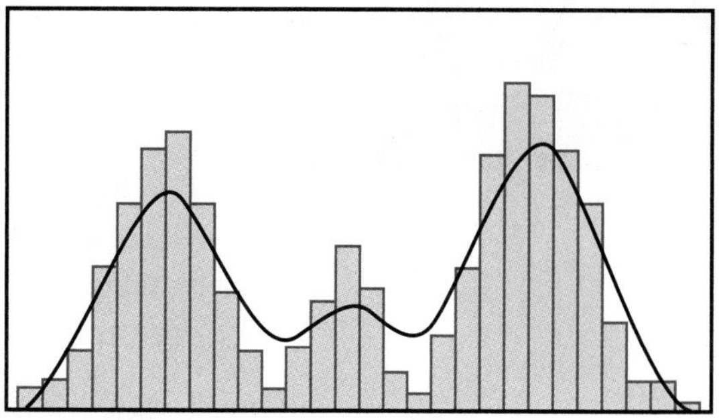

FIGURE 8.33

22. Would you describe Joe's and Mary's test scores as normally distributed, right-skewed, left-skewed, or bimodal? Why?

SUMMARY

Data sets come in all shapes and sizes. If a data set is very close to being normally distributed, you will be able to calculate z-scores in order to compare scores from different tests. You will be able to find what percentage of the data is between two values. With the help of a graphing calculator, you can find the nth percentile, the value below which n percent of the scores lie.

Not all data sets are normally distributed. If you plot the data, you will be able to decide if the data set is right-skewed, left-skewed, or some other shape.

Assignment

1. The heights of young women follow the normal distribution, with a mean of 65.5 inches and a standard deviation of 2.5 inches. What percentage of women are between 66 and 68 inches tall?

2. Scores on the mathematics portion of the SAT in a recent year were approximately normal with a mean of 476 and a standard deviation of 96

   a. What percentage of students scored between 400 and 600?

   b. What percentage of students scored above 600?

   c. How high a score on the mathematics portion of the SAT is needed to place in the top 10%?

3. Students in two class periods have different test grades on Ms. Smith's test. Both classes' grades are normally distributed. First period has a mean of 70 and a standard deviation of 10. Second period has a mean of 66 and a standard deviation of 8. What score is at the 75th percentile for each of the classes?

4. Ty Cobb's batting average in 1911 was .420. A player's batting average is computed by dividing the number of hits by the number of official at-bats. So, 42% of Ty Cobb's official at-bats resulted in a hit in 1911. The mean for all of the players in the league in 1911 was .266, and the standard deviation was .037. George Brett's batting average in 1980 was .390. The mean for the entire league in 1980 was .260, and the standard deviation was approximately .0317. Find the z-score for both players in their particular years. Who, in your opinion, is the better batter? Justify your statement using the data.

5. If a normally distributed set of data has a mean of 225 and a standard deviation of 12, what percentage of the data is between 200 and 250?

6. What does the 68-95-99.7 rule mean in relation to the graph of the normal curve?

7. What percentage of observations from a standard normal distribution (mean of 0 and standard deviation of 1) are

    a. Less than –1 standard deviation from the mean?

    b. Greater than +2 standard deviations from the mean?

    c. Between –1 and 2 standard deviations from the mean?

8. What percentage of the data in a normally distributed population is more than three standard deviations from the mean?

9. A diabetic patient reports, "My blood sugar level is at the 95th percentile so I must be very healthy." How would you respond to this patient?

Ice Cream Variance

The Our Town Ice Cream Plant sells ice cream in one-gallon containers. Customer satisfaction is important to the company. If a container has less than one gallon, customers might purchase less ice cream. If a container has more than one gallon, the company will lose money.

Our Town Ice Cream has had a reduction in sales so the company is hiring a quality control manager. Quality control managers collect samples, analyze the results, and make recommendations for improving manufacturing processes.

The quality control manager collected data from three different machines, each of which filled 250 half-gallon (0.5-gallon) containers of ice cream. The results are shown in a frequency table in **Figure 8.34**.

Use what you know about central tendency and spread as well as variance to compare the three runs of ice cream.

1. Make a histogram for each ice cream machine. How do the histograms compare? What type of distribution (normal, left-skewed, right-skewed) does each machine have? How do you know?

2. Make a box-and-whiskers plot for each ice cream run on the same grid. How do the box-and-whiskers plots compare?

3. Choose one run for which to graph a histogram and a box-and-whiskers plot on the same screen. How do the histogram and box-and-whiskers plot compare?

4. As the quality control manager, what recommendations would you make with regard to ice cream operations?

Volume of Ice Cream (gallons)	Machine #1 Frequency	Machine #2 Frequency	Machine #3 Frequency
0.490	0	0	0
0.491	9	0	0
0.492	38	2	1
0.493	30	1	2
0.494	29	4	3
0.495	24	3	2
0.496	23	4	5
0.497	21	5	17
0.498	15	10	30
0.499	11	11	42
0.500	10	15	46
0.501	9	17	42
0.502	10	25	30
0.503	5	28	17
0.504	6	29	5
0.505	4	40	2
0.506	3	27	3
0.507	2	16	2
0.508	1	8	1
0.509	0	5	0
0.510	0	0	0

FIGURE 8.34. Results of ice cream machines

How's the Weather?

The board of directors for the chamber of commerce has decided to start an annual festival on March 19, which is an important date in the local community's history. In order to promote the festival, the chamber has set up a committee to put together a brochure and design a web page. Part of each document will be a description of the weather on a "typical" March 19.

1. You are on the design committee for the brochure and web page. What information do you need to collect in order to describe the typical weather on March 19?

2. Where might you find that information?

3. March 19 is in the spring, so the weather can change quickly. How much variance is there for the weather on March 19?

Climatology is the long-term study of weather. Meteorologists, or scientists who study the weather, like to say that *weather* is something that happens from day to day, but *climate* is a much bigger picture over a long period of time. The U.S. National Weather Service (NWS) uses a thirty-year average to describe the "normal" temperatures and rainfall that are reported on the evening news.

Santa Fe, New Mexico, is the oldest city that has served as a regional center of government, or capital city, in North America. It was founded in 1607 and became the capital of the Spanish Kingdom of New Mexico in 1610. Santa Fe has been the capital of New Mexico ever since.

4. How many times has March 19 occurred since Santa Fe was founded?

5. The Pueblo Indians lived in what is now northern New Mexico for several hundred years before the Spanish founded Santa Fe. How many times did March 19 occur in that location before Santa Fe was founded?

6. Why do you think that the NWS uses only thirty years of data to describe a normal temperature?

7. If all of the days called March 19 that have occurred in Santa Fe are thought of as the **population**, what would you call the subset of days that the NWS uses to determine a normal temperature?

8. What other ways can you think of to describe the typical weather on March 19, other than using the thirty-year average?

We Need to Study This

Recently, three important issues have come before the chamber of commerce:

- A new local business is planning to install digital music player and cell phone charging stations around town, including at the high school and the local shopping mall.

- The city council is considering a proposal to install a city-wide wireless network.

- A movie theater company wants to open a new theater in town.

To investigate these issues, the chamber of commerce has hired a research consulting firm, Questionnaires, Etc., to conduct surveys to determine the feasibility of each of the three issues.

CHECK THIS!

Recall that a *population* consists of the entire group that is being studied. A *sample* is a small portion, or subset, of the population.

A *census* is a survey of the entire population. Sometimes it is not possible or it is very expensive to survey an entire population so a *sample survey* is used to collect data to describe the entire population.

ISSUE #1: Low Battery?

Brandon has noticed that many of his friends have digital music players or cell phones whose batteries run out at inconvenient times during the day when they are away from home. He wonders if he could provide charging stations at school or at the shopping mall where people could charge the batteries of their digital music players or cell phones for a small fee. He thinks this is a great business opportunity but he needs to do some consumer research before jumping into it. His research question is, "Are enough people interested in charging their batteries to justify the expenses of the business?"

1. What population of people does Brandon need to survey?

2. Is it possible for Brandon to survey every member of the population? If not, how might he decide which members to survey?

3. Who should be included in the sample of the population that Brandon intends to survey?

4. Would it make more sense for Brandon to survey high school students or senior citizens at a local retirement home? Why?

5. Brandon is trying to decide on a location to survey people. How likely is Brandon to get a representative sample of his population in the following locations? Explain.

   a. Airport

   b. Shopping mall

   c. History museum

   d. High school cafeteria

   e. City park

Brandon decides to go to the electronics store at the shopping mall and survey the first fifty people who will talk to him.

6. How representative are those fifty people of the population that Brandon wants to study?

7. Did each member of the population of the study have an equal chance of being surveyed? How do you know?

8. If each survey takes about five minutes to complete, how much time do you think it might take Brandon to complete his study?

9. Do you think that Brandon's survey will answer his original research question? Explain.

ISSUE #2: We're Going Wireless!

In 2007, Corpus Christi, Texas, became the first city in the United States to install a citywide wireless computer network. Although the network was originally developed to connect the city's automated parking meters in a wireless network with each other, the city government decided to open the network up to wireless Internet service providers and customers. Today residents and visitors to Corpus Christi can access this wireless computer network anywhere inside the city limits.

Many other cities, such as New Orleans, Houston, Atlanta, and Boston, have explored or partially implemented citywide wireless computer networks. Our chamber of commerce has recently become interested in this trend, since several businesses that are members of the chamber have pointed out the e-commerce aspects of the Internet. How might a city decide if there is enough interest to make it worth the expense to create a citywide wireless network?

1. What population should the chamber of commerce survey in order to determine the level of interest across the city?

2. Who should be included in the sample of the population that is surveyed?

3. What are some potential locations for finding a representative sample of the population?

4. How likely is the chamber of commerce to get a representative sample of the population in the following locations? Explain.

   a. City park

   b. Country club

   c. Library

   d. Bus station

   e. Over the telephone

Because the chamber of commerce is interested in how the entire city population feels about a wireless computer network, the research team decides to assign each person who lives in the city a number and then use a random number generator to generate 200 random numbers. The research team will then call all of these 200 people on the telephone and survey them.

5. How representative are those 200 people of the population in the study?

6. Did each member of the population of the study have an equal chance of being surveyed? How do you know?

7. If each survey takes about five minutes to complete, how much time do you think it might take to complete the study?

8. Do you think that this survey will answer the original research question? Explain.

ISSUE #3: Two Tickets for the 9:00 Show

According to the Motion Picture Association of America, in the United States in 2007, 1.4 billion movie theater tickets were sold, generating a total of $9.69 billion in revenue. The chamber of commerce has noticed this trend and is wondering if there is enough demand in our city to build a new movie theater. A group of business owners in the chamber recently posed the question, Is there enough interest in the community to justify building a new movie theater?

1. What population should the chamber of commerce survey in order to determine the level of interest in a new movie theater?

2. Who should be included in the sample of the population that is surveyed?

3. What are some potential locations for finding a representative sample of the population?

4. How likely is the chamber of commerce to get a representative sample of the population in the following locations? Explain.

   a. City park

   b. Science museum

   c. Library

   d. Existing movie theater

The chamber of commerce decides to survey 150 people from a randomly generated list of people who have "frequent moviegoer" accounts at the existing movie theater. The surveyors will make telephone calls to every fourth person on the list.

5. How representative are those 150 people of the population in the study?

6. Did each member of the population of the study have an equal chance of being surveyed? How do you know?

7. Do you think that the survey will accurately describe the demand for a second movie theater? Explain your answer.

8. If each survey takes about five minutes to complete, how much time do you think it might take to complete the study?

9. Do you think that this survey will answer the original research question? Explain.

For each of the three surveys described in this section, fill in a table like the one shown in **Figure 8.35** to summarize the surveys. You will need this table for Section 8.13.

Issue	Who was the population?	Who was the sample?	How was the sample chosen?	Where was the survey conducted?
Digital Music Players/Cell Phone Chargers				
Citywide Wireless Network				
New Movie Theater				

FIGURE 8.35. Summary table

Sampling and Bias

PART 1: Methods of Sampling

In the previous section you examined three issues that had come before the Chamber of Commerce:

- A new local business planning to install digital music player and cell phone charging stations around town, including at the high school and the local shopping mall.

- The city council considering a proposal to install a city-wide wireless network.

- A movie theater company wanting to open a new theater in town.

For each of those issues, a survey was conducted. You summarized some information about the surveys in a table like the one shown in Figure 8.35.

1. Look at the responses in your table. Which of the surveys used a randomly generated sample?

CHECK THIS!

Random methods of sampling are also called probability methods of sampling because each member of the population has an equal chance of being selected for the sample.

Nonrandom methods of sampling are also called nonprobability methods of sampling because every member of the population may not have a chance of being selected for the sample.

Statisticians distinguish between various methods of sampling from a population by sorting the methods into two categories. **Probability methods** of sampling are methods in which each member of the population has an equal chance of being selected for the sample. Some kind of randomization is typically used to ensure an equal probability of being selected in the sample.

2. For which survey(s) does each member of the population have an equal chance of being selected for the sample? How do you know?

A **simple random sample** is one in which the participants in the sample are chosen from the population using some kind of random selection. The citywide wireless network survey used a simple random sample because the sample was randomly chosen from the population, residents of the city, and every member of the population had the same chance of being selected for the sample.

A **systematic random sample** is one in which participants are ordered and then chosen in certain intervals from a randomly selected starting point. Samples obtained using this method are also called **interval samples** because the sample is selected in regular intervals from a randomly chosen starting point. The movie theater survey used a systematic random sample because the members of the "frequent moviegoer" club were listed in random order, and then every fourth person on the list was surveyed (i.e., the interval of the sample was 4).

Nonprobability methods of sampling are methods in which each member of the population does not have an equal chance of being selected for the sample.

3. For which survey(s) does each member of the population not have an equal chance of being selected for the sample? How do you know?

Sometimes it is impractical or even impossible to randomly generate a sample from a larger population. In such cases, surveyors can use **convenience samples** to conduct their survey. Convenience samples are just that — chosen out of convenience. The digital music player/cell phone charger survey used a convenience sample because Brandon went to the electronics store and surveyed the first fifty people that he could find who were willing to talk to him. Each member of the population of his survey did not have an equal chance of being selected for the survey sample because he chose to use a convenience sample.

4. What are some advantages and disadvantages of simple or systematic random samples?

5. How does a convenience sample compare with a random sample?

Suppose that there are approximately 1,800 students at River Bottom High School. Of those, 36% are freshmen, 26% are sophomores, 20% are juniors, and 18% are seniors. The cafeteria manager plans to make some changes to the school lunch menu and wants to seek student input. She obtained a list of students with their grade-level classifications and then randomly selected 36 freshmen, 26 sophomores, 20 juniors, and 18 seniors to survey.

6. How is this method of sampling different from the method used for a simple random sample?

7. Why might the cafeteria manager have chosen this method of sampling?

This method of sampling is called **stratified sampling.** Things that are stratified, like rocks or cakes, have layers. Each layer is called a **strata**. Stratified sampling has "layers" that are categories within the population of the study. Within each category, sample participants are chosen randomly. In this case, the cafeteria manager chose categories of grade-level classification. Other stratified samples often include categories such as gender (male or female), education level (high school, college, graduate school), or type of employee (support, professional, managerial).

PART 2: Can You Really Say That?

Consider the following situation:

A school district wants to determine if there is enough community support to pass a bond issue (which means that local taxes will increase to support the sale of the school bonds) in order to build a new baseball stadium. The school board asks a high school math class to survey community members about whether or not they would support raising money to build a new baseball stadium.

Class members decide to attend the next five high school baseball games and survey 100 participants randomly from the stands. They determine that 75 out of the 100 people they surveyed agreed that they would be willing to pay more taxes for school bonds if they got a new baseball stadium in return. The math class reports back to the school board that 75% of community members in the district support the issue.

1. What was the population that the school board asked the math class to survey?

2. Did the people that the math class surveyed represent this population? Why or why not?

3. How did the choice of location for the survey affect the results of the survey?

4. Where else could students have surveyed people in order to get a more representative sample?

5. What kind of sampling method did the students use? Explain.

Sometimes a survey produces results that may accurately describe the sample but not the population. When that is the case, statisticians say that the survey has **bias** that causes the results for the sample to differ (to be either higher or lower) from the results for the population. Several factors can cause bias. In the baseball stadium example, the bias resulted from the selection of the sample, which is called **selection bias**. Only a portion of the population was sampled, resulting in inadequate representation of the entire population. This type of selection bias is called **undercoverage** because parts of the population were "under-covered," or underrepresented, in the survey sample.

Suppose that the math class now decides to expand its survey. Class members obtain a list from the school district's central office of all residents in the district. From that list they randomly select 800 people and mail them a survey. One hundred surveys are returned and this time the results are different. Sixty of the residents who returned surveys are against the new baseball stadium. The class reports to the school board that 60% of the community is against the new baseball stadium.

6. What percentage of the surveys that were mailed out were actually returned?

7. What might have happened to the other 700 surveys that were not returned?

8. Who might have been more motivated to return their surveys, people who support the stadium or people who do not want to pay higher taxes?

9. How representative of the population of the survey would you say that the new sample is? Explain.

You can't force people to respond to a survey; they must be willing to respond on their own. People usually respond to a survey if they feel passionately about an issue, either in support of it or against it. For a variety of reasons people can also choose not to respond to a survey. Because their opinions are not represented in the survey, the survey results could have nonresponse bias because a segment of the population is not represented in the survey results.

Other types of bias result from the survey itself rather than from the sample. Consider this scenario:

A daytime talk show host recently did a show about the national problem of teenage drug use. Members of a parents' group at a local high school saw the show and were alarmed. They want to know how bad the problem is in their community. The parents decide to survey students about their drug use so they ask a uniformed police officer to survey 100 students randomly selected from the student body. The police officer calls the students into the principal's office and asks them if they have used illegal drugs within the last six months.

10. How likely do you think the students are to be truthful in this survey?

11. Do you think the results of the survey would have been different if a casually dressed college student were conducting the survey rather than the uniformed police officer? Why or why not?

Bias that results from the way in which a survey is conducted is called **response bias**. In the case of the drug use survey, the unspoken threat of legal authority is very likely to cause students to respond that they have not used illegal drugs even if they have. Response bias can also result from the questions themselves. For example, a children's cancer research foundation wants to determine how many people in the community support its charitable cause. The foundation randomly selects 220 people to survey over the telephone. One of the questions in the survey is, "If you support our cause, you can help children with cancer. Would you like to help sick children?"

SUMMARY

There are many methods of selecting a sample from a population:

* **Simple Random Sample** — Each member of the population has an equal chance of being selected for the sample. Also, each sample from the population has an equal chance of being drawn from the population. In this method, each member of the population is usually assigned a number, and numbers are randomly drawn until a sample is created.

* **Systematic Random Sample** — If the members of the population are listed in no particular order, a starting point is randomly chosen and then every nth person is selected for the sample.

* **Convenience Sample** — People who are easy to reach are chosen for the sample. Surveyors use this method when they need quick, inexpensive results to portray an approximation of

the truth. Convenience sampling is a nonrandom or nonprobability method of sampling because all members of the population do not have an equally likely chance of being chosen for the sample. Convenience sampling is prone to bias because the sample is not randomly chosen, and there may be other factors that skew the results.

❖ **Stratified Sample** — Similar to a simple random sample but the population is broken into categories, called strata, before the random selection occurs. For example, in a high school, if a survey question may get different results from students in different grades, a surveyor might want to categorize the population by grade level and then randomly select a certain number of students from each grade level.

There are also several forms of bias that can appear in the survey:

❖ **Selection bias** — This type of bias results from how the sample was selected from the population.
  • **Undercoverage** results when some groups within the population are not represented in the sample.
  • **Nonresponse bias** results when a significant number of people selected for a sample, usually from one group within the population, do not respond to the survey.

❖ **Response bias** — This type of bias results from the way the survey is conducted.
  • **Social desirability** may motivate people being surveyed not to respond honestly because they want to appear in a better light than they otherwise might.
  • **Leading questions** can make a person more likely to respond in a certain way that may not reflect his or her true beliefs.

Assignment

1. Suppose that a nationwide video game retail store wants to determine if there is enough customer demand to open a second store in town. The store owner hires a consumer research company to conduct and analyze a survey. The consumer research company decides to ask customers of the existing store questions about their video game use. Some of their questions include:

- How much time per week do you spend playing video games?
- How many new games a month do you buy?
- How many of your friends play video games?
- What kinds of video games do you like the most?

The research company prepares its final report for the video game store owner. The report states that 200 customers of the existing store were surveyed and the following results were obtained (**Figure 8.36**):

How much time per week do you spend playing video games?					
0–3 hours	3–6 hours	6–9 hours	9–12 hours	12–15 hours	15+ hours
10	25	25	20	40	80

How many new games a month do you buy?					
0 games	1 game	2 games	3 games	4 games	5+ games
8	30	75	42	25	20

How many of your friends play video games?					
0–1 friends	2–3 friends	4–5 friends	6–7 friends	8–9 friends	10+ friends
10	50	40	60	30	10

What kinds of video games do you like the most?					
Action	Strategy	Role-Playing	Arcade-style	Sports	Flight Simulator
43	35	36	32	27	27

FIGURE 8.36. Video game survey results

a. From what population did the research company draw its sample?

b. How well do the people who were surveyed represent the group of people in whom the video game store is interested? How do you know?

c. What other questions should the research company have asked? How would that help strengthen the results of the survey?

A high school counselor wants to survey students to determine prizes that might appeal to students so she can use them as an attendance incentive. Match the following surveys with their method of sampling.

2. Survey the first 100 students who enter the library on a randomly selected day.

3. Have 25 teachers each randomly select 4 students to survey.

4. Assign each student a number. Use a random number generator to generate 100 random numbers and then survey each student whose number is selected.

5. While students are standing in line to get lunch in the cafeteria, randomly choose a student to begin with and then survey every third student in line until 100 students have been surveyed.

A. Stratified sample

B. Simple random sample

C. Convenience sample

D. Interval sample

Answer the following questions:

6. The student council wants to determine which types of music students want to hear at the Homecoming dance. Which of the following samples would best represent the entire student body? Explain your answer.

a. Survey the teachers.

b. Survey the captain from each sports team.

c. Randomly survey two people from each homeroom class.

d. Randomly survey fifty people from the freshman class.

7. The student council also wants to plan lunchtime activities for Spirit Week, which precedes the Homecoming dance. They decide to survey students to find out which activities might be the most popular. Which of the following groups would give them the most representative survey sample? Explain your answer.

a. The freshman, junior varsity, and varsity football teams

b. The dance team and the band

c. The speech club and the drama club

d. One English class at each grade level

8. In her computer class Hyacinth learned that 28 of the 32 students have computers at home. She knows that there are 800 students in her school, so she concluded that 700 of them must have computers at home. Is her conclusion valid? Why or why not?

9. Barney was surprised to read in the newspaper that the average teenager earns $6.00 per hour while working a part-time job. He surveyed twelve of his friends and calculated that the average wage is really $7.50. What kind of bias does his survey have? Explain.

10. The county parks department plans to survey residents to determine whether they would use a new community center. The survey must represent all people who live in the county. Three different survey locations were proposed: a day care center, a tennis club, and a shopping mall. Every fourth person identified at the location would be asked to take part in the survey. Of the three proposed locations, which would have the least amount of bias? Why?

11. The Honor Society of Middle Neck High School wants to know how students get to school. Alicia conducted a survey by arriving at school at 7:00 a.m. and then surveying the first sixty students to arrive. Zachary conducted a survey by using a random number generator to select sixty students in the school to survey. Both of their results are shown in **Figure 8.37**.

Alicia's Survey (first 60 arrivals)		Zachary's Survey (number generator)	
Method of Transportation	Number of Students	Method of Transportation	Number of Students
Walk	10	Walk	10
Bicycle	12	Bicycle	13
Car	10	Car	22
Bus	28	Bus	15

FIGURE 8.37

a. Which method of sampling did Alicia use? Zachary?

b. Which of the two surveys is more representative of the entire student body? Explain your answer.

c. Suppose that there are 900 students at Middle Neck High School. Based on the results of the more representative sample, how many students would you expect to use a car to get to school? Explain how you determined your answer.

Experimental Design

For schoolchildren, summertime has always been a time of fun. When the weather is hot, many people like to swim in lakes and rivers. Prior to the 1950s, however, the fun of swimming in the 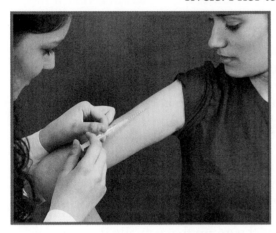 summer had a dark side to it — the ever-present threat of polio. Polio is a crippling disease caused by a virus that used to be present in some lakes and ponds. President Franklin Roosevelt contracted polio as an adult in this way. Most Americans feared the dreaded disease and its terrible consequences.

In 1954, Dr. Jonas Salk began testing a vaccine for polio that he had developed two years earlier. Over 1.8 million children in the United States, Canada, and Finland participated in the largest clinical trial of a medical procedure in history. Because Dr. Salk set up the experiment very carefully, by the end of the trial he was able to clearly demonstrate that his vaccine was highly effective. On April 12, 1955, he and Dr. Thomas Francis announced that they had indeed discovered a "safe, effective, and potent" vaccine for a terrible disease. By 1979, polio had been all but eradicated in the United States and in 1994 all of the Americas were declared "polio free."

Scientists and researchers today still use processes similar to those that Dr. Salk used to clearly show that his vaccine was safe and effective. Through a process called **experimental design**, experiments can be set up in a way that allows a researcher to look for how one variable might cause a second variable to respond.

CHECK THIS!

Variables other than the independent and dependent variables that influence the outcome of an experiment are called *lurking variables*.

Suppose that a medical researcher is interested in finding out whether taking vitamin C daily leads to improved health, and if so, to what extent.

1. What are the variables in this situation?

2. What are the independent and dependent variables?

3. Write a dependency statement that relates the independent and dependent variables. For example, "The amount of postage I

have to put on a package depends on how much the package weighs."

4. How might you measure the two variables?

5. Are there any other variables that might influence the relationship?

Part of an experimental design study is that half of the group being researched receives the **treatment**, or different levels of the independent variable, and the other half does not. Now, suppose the medical researcher is ready to begin her experiment. She gets 240 volunteers for her study — 120 men and 120 women. Since she has an equal number of men and women, she plans to give a certain amount of vitamin C each day to the women, and the men receive a sugar pill that they think may be vitamin C.

6. What is the treatment in this experiment?

7. The **control group** is the group that does not receive the treatment — they continue with business as usual. In the current plan, which group is the control group?

8. The **treatment group** is the group that actually does receive the treatment. In the current plan, which group is the treatment group?

9. A **placebo** is a substitute for the treatment that has no effect on the variables being studied. What is the placebo in this study?

10. If the researcher implements her plan as it is and notices differences between the two groups, what factors other than the vitamin C might have caused the differences? Explain.

Our medical researcher thought about your answers to that last question, and she has reconsidered her plan. Rather than place all of the men in the control group and the women in the treatment group, she has decided to randomly assign her participants to one of two groups: Group A and Group B. She does not tell the participants which group receives the treatment and which group does not.

11. If she randomly assigns a person to each group, does each person have an equal chance of being assigned to the control or treatment group? How do you know?

12. Approximately how many men and women would you expect to be in each group?

13. Since the researcher did not tell the participants in the study if they were in the control group or the treatment group, how will they know if they are taking vitamin C or a sugar pill each day?

CHECK THIS!

The *placebo effect* is when participants think they are experiencing the benefits of the treatment even when they are not receiving the treatment. In medical research, the placebo really is often simply a sugar pill.

14. How do you think that knowledge might influence the results of the study?

Not telling the participants whether they are receiving the treatment or not is a procedure known as **blinding**. In large studies, such as Dr. Salk's polio vaccine study, the people administering the treatment or placebo also cannot know whether they are administering the treatment or not. Such studies are said to be **double-blind** studies, in which neither the participants nor the people administering the treatment know who is receiving the treatment.

EXPERIMENTAL ERROR

Scientists describe two types of numbers: **exact numbers**, whose values are known exactly and **inexact numbers**, whose values are obtained by measurement. Exact numbers are usually obtained by counting. For example, by definition we know that there are 3 feet in 1 yard, 12 eggs in 1 dozen, or exactly 2.54 centimeters in 1 inch. We can count the number of chickens in a chicken coop, tires on a heavy truck, or cars in a parking lot. However, when scientists need to measure a quantity, like the temperature of the air, they work with inexact numbers. In measurement, there is always some source of error. The instrument may not be as precise as it could be or people may read the instrument differently. Any time a quantity is measured there an error can occur.

In chemistry class, Freda and Bob conducted an experiment involving the boiling points of different solutions. They know that water has a boiling point of 212°F. Yet they took the temperature of the water several times while it was boiling. They recorded their findings:

$$214, 213, 215, 214, 212, 216$$

1. What was the average temperature reading?

2. What is the difference between the average temperature reading and the theoretical boiling point of water?

3. What percentage of the theoretical boiling point of water is this difference?

$$\text{Experimental Error} = \frac{(\text{Actual Value} - \text{Theoretical Value})}{\text{Theoretical Value}} \times 100$$

The difference between the theoretical value and the measured value is called the **experimental error** of the measurement. Experimental error is usually expressed as a percentage of the theoretical value.

SUMMARY

An experimental study seeks to explain a causal relationship between an independent variable and a dependent variable. In order to do so, lurking variables must be accounted for. There are several strategies that can control the lurking variables so that the relationship between the independent and dependent variables can be explained.

* **Use of a control group**, which is the group in the experiment that does not receive the treatment.
* **Use of a placebo**, which helps to conceal which group receives the treatment and which group does not.
* **Blinding** a group under study, when the research team does not tell the participants who is receiving the treatment and who is not.
* **Randomization** of the treatment and control groups, which helps to distribute the participants more evenly between the two groups so that the effects of any lurking variables are more evenly distributed between the two groups.

$$\text{Experimental Error} = \frac{(\text{Actual Value} - \text{Theoretical Value})}{\text{Theoretical Value}} \times 100$$

Data obtained from measurements always contain experimental error, which is the difference between the actual (measured) value and the theoretical value expressed as a percentage of the theoretical value.

1. In a study of each of these questions, determine whether a survey or an experimental study was used:

   a. Are gas prices affecting your drive to work or school?

   b. Do airplane delays affect the amount of lost luggage?

   c. Does a new skin patch help increase the number of people who can successfully quit smoking?

   d. How much weight are people losing, and what diets do they use?

2. Australian doctors are concerned about an increase in the rate of skin cancer in Australia. A recent study included 588 men and women, half of whom received a skin cream with sunscreen and half of whom received a skin cream without sunscreen. After seven months, the men and women who used the skin cream with sunscreen had fewer new precancerous skin lesions.

   a. What were the independent and dependent variables?

   b. What was the treatment?

   c. What was the placebo?

   d. What lurking variables may have existed in this study?

   e. How could randomization have helped to control those lurking variables?

3. The federal government wants to test the effectiveness of a new airport security system in removing suspicious material from carry-on luggage. To do so, they plan to study six airports — three with the new system and three with the old system.

   a. What are the independent and dependent variables?

   b. What lurking variables may exist?

   c. What is the control group in this study?

d. What is the treatment group?

e. How can the federal government use randomization to select the control and treatment groups?

4. Benita collected data with her group using a calculator and a calculator-based laboratory (CBL). They used a light sensor to measure the intensity of a lightbulb that was five feet away from the sensor to be 255 watts per square centimeter. However, they used a formula to calculate that the intensity should have been 270 watts per square centimeter. What is Benita's group's experimental error?

Survey Says!

Earlier in this chapter you saw how a consumer research company handled three important issues that have come before the chamber of commerce:

- A local business is planning to install digital music player and cell phone charging stations around town, including at the high school and the local shopping mall. Is there enough demand to justify the charging stations?

- The city council is considering a proposal to install a city-wide wireless network. Is there enough demand to justify the network?

- A movie theater company wants to open a new theater in town. Is there enough demand to justify the new theater?

Most businesses do a lot of research before making a decision to invest money in a new product or service. Is the product or service really necessary? Will people really spend money to use the service? One of the best ways for businesses to collect data to help them make decisions is by surveying potential customers to determine answers to questions like these.

The chamber of commerce has come to your class for help. They need researchers to investigate the three issues that business groups have brought to them. In your student group, choose one of the three issues that are before the chamber of commerce. You will design, conduct, and evaluate a survey of these issues.

Your study will consist of the following tasks:

- Decide how you will conduct your survey. Who will you survey? How many people will you survey? How do those selections reflect the population your survey seeks to describe?

- Collect the data.

- Analyze the data in terms of central tendency, spread, and variability. Represent the data using appropriate numerical and graphical representations.

- Make a recommendation for the issue your group studied.

- Present your findings to the class. Be sure to use visual (technology-based or nontechnology-based) aids with your oral presentation.

Use an outline similar to the outline below to help you design, conduct, and evaluate your survey.

Design

1. What is your topic of study?

   What do you need to know about the topic in order to make an informed decision?

2. What **population** will you be studying? In other words, what group of people might be interested in using your product? Is it the general population or a group with a special interest, like video gamers?

   a. Who is in your population of study?

   b. How many people are in your population of study?

3. How will you choose the people that you will survey?

   a. Where will you find people to survey?

   b. How will you decide whom to survey?

4. What questions do you want to ask?

   a. What kind of data do you want to generate (numerical, categorical, etc.)?

   b. What kinds of questions do you need to ask in order to generate those data?

Collect the Data

5. Ask the people in the sample you identified earlier the survey questions. Record their responses.

Analyze the Data

6. For any numerical data,

   a. What are the measures of central tendency and spread?

b. How can you represent those measures graphically using a box-and-whiskers plot or a histogram?

7. For any numerical data, what are the measures of variance (including standard deviation)?

8. For any categorical data, how can you best display the information graphically?

9. What steps did you take to ensure that your survey was not biased?

Recommendations

10. What recommendations do you have with regard to your topic of study?

Class Presentations

11. How will you generate your visual displays?

    a. What types of graphs are the best to use?

    b. What technology can you use (spreadsheet, graphing calculator, etc.)?

    c. If you use paper-and-pencil, how will you construct your graphs?

12. What are the key points that you want to communicate to your classmates?

As you watch your classmates present their studies, answer the following questions on a sheet of paper that you can turn in to your teacher:

1. How did the group choose its sample for the survey?

2. What types of graphs did the group choose to display its results? How meaningful were those choices?

3. Do you agree with the group's recommendations? Why or why not?

Modeling Project What Is "Normal" Anyway?

You have learned that some natural distributions follow a normal distribution, where the mean, median, and mode are all equal. The properties of a normal distribution allow us to make important inferences about one member of the population as compared to the other members of the population.

- How does my college entrance exam score compare to other seniors around the country?

- How does my height or weight compare with the general population?

- What percent of my crop would I expect to fall within a certain range of distributions?

Of course, not everything is normally distributed. Sometimes, distributions are skewed in one direction or another.

For this modeling project, you will choose something that you believe to be normally distributed for a given population. Research your topic using the resources in your school or public library, interviewing people in your community, or using the Internet. Create a presentation for your class that includes the following:

- Describe the measurement that you chose to research. For what population do you believe your measure is normally distributed?

- What are the critical attributes of your measurement (that is, what are the mean, median, mode, standard deviation, and other statistical measures)?

- How would you use percentiles, area under the curve, and z-scores to make meaningful conclusions from your distribution? Give several examples.

- What implications do your findings have for other people in your community?

Practice Problems

1. The table below shows the ages, in years, of the pitchers for the 2008 Houston Astros and the 2008 Boston Red Sox.

| Houston Astros | 30 | 31 | 41 | 35 | 31 | 32 | 37 | 31 | 30 | 29 | 27 | | |
| Boston Red Sox | 27 | 28 | 24 | 26 | 24 | 31 | 28 | 33 | 28 | 25 | 35 | 42 | 42 |

    a. Find the mean, median, and mode ages for each team.

    b. Find the range of ages for each team.

    c. Find the five-number summary of the data for each team.

    d. Make a box-and-whiskers plot of the ages of the pitchers for each team.

    e. Which team has the wider spread in the middle 50% (between the first and third quartiles) of the ages of its players?

    f. How do the ages of pitchers on the Astros and Red Sox compare? Explain.

2. A box-and-whiskers plot for the heights in centimeters of students in their freshman year in high school and their senior year in high school is shown.

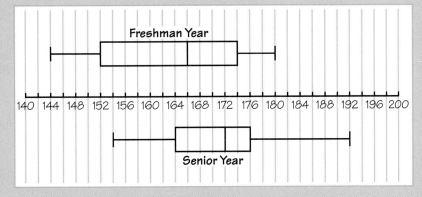

    a. From the graph, find the five-number summary for the students' heights in both years.

    b. Find the range of students' heights in both years.

c. What is the difference in the ranges of heights from students' freshman year to their senior year?

d. What is the difference in the median height of students from their freshman year to their senior year?

e. Compare the middle half (between the first and third quartiles) of the heights of students in their freshman year to their senior year? Explain your answer.

3. Bobby made a box-and-whiskers plot of the 30 top per-game point scorers in a women's basketball league. His graph is shown.

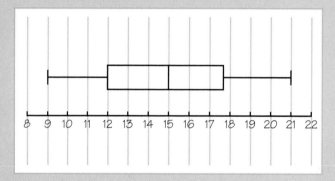

Based on the data in the box-and-whiskers plots, which of the following statements MUST be true? Explain your reasoning for each statement.

a. The mean number of points scored in a game is 15 points.

b. Half of the 30 top per-game point scorers scored at least 15 points.

c. Only one woman scored 21 points in a game.

d. Twenty-five percent of the top per-game point scorers score between 9 and 12 points in a game.

e. Half of the 30 top per-game point scorers score between 12 and about 17.7 points in a game.

f. The range of the points scored per game in this group of players is 14.

4. The school band sells chocolate bars each year as a fundraiser. The table below shows the number of candy bars that students in the clarinet section sold.

63	74	102	63	42	96
73	68	88	82	61	79
84	67	56	49	63	94

a. Complete the following frequency table.

Number of Candy Bars Sold	Frequency
40 – 49	
50 – 59	
60 – 69	
70 – 79	
80 – 89	
90 – 99	
100 – 109	

b. Use the data in your frequency table to make a histogram of the data.

c. As an incentive, the band booster club agreed to put each student's name who sold at least 80 candy bars in a drawing for a free digital music player. How many students will be in the drawing from the clarinet section?

d. If there are a total of 28 students' names in the drawing, what is the probability that a clarinet player will win the digital music player?

5. A plant nursery advertises a certain type of rose to have a typical flower size that is 3 inches in diameter. A gardener at the nursery randomly selected 20 roses to measure, and she recorded the actual sizes, in inches, of the flowers in the table shown.

3.1	3.15	2.8	2.5	3.5
3	2.75	3.25	3.75	3
3.4	2.6	2.75	2.5	3
2.85	3.4	3.15	2.65	2.5

a. Find the mean, median, and mode flower size.

b. What is the standard deviation of the flower diameter?

c. How many flowers are within one standard deviation of the mean flower size?

6. The annual corn crop per acre for a Midwestern state in a particularly good year was normally distributed with a mean of 150 bushels per acre and a standard deviation of 22 bushels per acre.

   a. Use your graphing calculator to make a graph of this normal curve. Describe your viewing window and sketch your graph.

   b. What percent of farmers harvested between 130 and 180 bushels per acre?

   c. How many farmers had a yield of more than 180 bushels per acre?

   d. By contrast, a neighboring state also had a mean yield of 150 bushels per acre but a standard deviation of only 10 bushels per acre. What percent of the neighboring state's farmers had a yield between 130 and 180 bushels per acre?

   e. Compare the percentage of farmers with a crop yield of between 130 and 180 bushels per acre in the two states. Use mean and standard deviation in your response.

7. According to the U.S. Department of Agriculture (www.usda.gov[1]), in 2002, the mean corn crop yield in Ohio was 89 bushels per acre. In 2003, the mean corn crop yield in Ohio was 156 bushels per acre. Assume that the standard deviation in both years was the same at 25 bushels per acre.

   a. Farmer Jones had a crop yield of 95 bushels per acre in 2002. Find his z-score for that crop.

   b. In 2003, Farmer Jones had a crop yield of 150 bushels per acre. Find his z-score for that crop.

   c. According to the z-scores, in which year did Farmer Jones have a better crop in comparison to his colleagues? Explain your answer.

8. Identify the methods of sampling that were used in each of the following surveys (stratified, simple random, convenience sample, interval sample).

[1]Data for Problem 7 were obtained from www.nass.usda.gov

a. To study the amount of time students spend doing homework each day, use a random number generator to randomly select 25 students from the student enrollment database.

b. To study the amount of time students spend doing homework each day, use a random number generator to randomly select 25 freshmen, 25 sophomores, 25 juniors, and 25 seniors.

c. To determine people's favorite websites, go to an Internet café and ask the first 25 people who walk in what their favorite website is.

d. To find out what people's preferred ice cream flavor is, wait outside an ice cream parlor and ask every 4th person who exits the store what their favorite flavor of ice cream is until you have a total of 25 responses.

e. To determine the level of interest in a professional soccer team, go to the university soccer game in town and survey the first 100 people that will talk to you.

9. Amanda wants to determine the favorite professional sport of students in her high school. Which of the following samples is most likely to give her a representative sample? Explain your answer.

a. A random sample of the students in the art honor society

b. A random sample of students on the basketball team

c. A random sample of students on the official school enrollment roster

d. A random sample of students in the library during lunch

10. Mrs. Wheeler, the school librarian, wants to determine how many students use the library on a regular basis. What type of sampling method (stratified, simple random, convenience sample, interval sample) would she use if she chose to:

a. Choose every 3rd student who enters the library on Tuesday.

a. Use a random number generator to randomly select 50 students from the school's attendance roster.

b. Randomly select 5 students from every student organization.

c. Stand outside the school door and interview the first 50 students who arrive at school on Wednesday.

11. Each of the following surveys has some form of bias. Explain why the type of sampling that was chosen for the survey might lead to biased results.

a. Dr. Aleman wants to survey her patients to determine what kind of foods they like so that she may better understand their dietary habits. She decides to ask the next 50 patients that she sees about what kind of foods they like to eat.

b. Mrs. Benson decided to survey her students about the amount of crime in their neighborhoods. She numbered her students consecutively and then used a random number generator to randomly select 15 students to speak with a uniformed police officer about the crimes that they witness in their neighborhoods.

c. Mr. Cosenza decided to ask the parents of each of his students how they felt about the homework he was assigning. He decided to mail a survey home to each of his students' parents. Many of the surveys came back in the mail as "undeliverable."

12. Data can be gathered from a sample, an experiment, a simulation, or a census. Recall that sampling involves a selection from a population while a census involves gathering data from every member of the population. Which of those four techniques could have been used to gather data in the following studies?

a. From a list of 30,000 patients at a Seattle hospital, 500 patients were interviewed to determine how they felt about the quality of care they received.

b. The number of touchdowns from every college football championship game played is researched to determine the mean number of touchdowns of college football championship games.

c. The effects of wind shear on the wings and tails of airplanes during take-off and landing are studied using complex computer programs.

d. A new cancer drug is tested on cancer patients. Half of the patients in the study receive the drug and half receive conventional treatment. The results of the two patient groups are compared.

Glossary

KEY CONCEPTS

Bias: A condition in a survey that causes the results for the sample to differ (either higher or lower) from the results for the population.

Bimodal: A histogram or frequency distribution graph in which there are two distinctly separated classes with the largest frequencies.

Blinding: A procedure used in experimental design studies to keep the participants in the study from knowing if they are receiving the treatment or not.

Box-and-whiskers plot: A box-and-whiskers plot is a graphical representation depicting five values from a data set: minimum, first quartile, median, third quartile, and maximum. A rectangle is used to represent the spread of data among the first quartile, the median, and the third quartile of a set of data and "whiskers" are used to represent the spread of data between the minimum and first quartile and the spread of data between the third quartile and maximum.

Census: Measurements or observations from the entire population.

Class: An interval of data used in a frequency table or in a histogram.

Class boundaries: The halfway points of the intervals between the upper limit of one class and the lower limit of the next class.

Class width: The difference between the lower class limit and the upper class limit.

Control group: The group in an experimental design study that does not receive the treatment, continuing with business as usual.

Convenience sample: A method of non-probability sampling in which the researcher selects people that are easy to contact.

Dot plot: A diagram showing frequency of data on a number line.

Double-blind: A procedure used in experimental design studies where neither the participants nor the people administering the treatment know who is receiving the treatment.

Experimental design: A study in which a treatment is deliberately imposed on individuals in a treatment group but withheld from individuals in a control group. The researcher then studies the two groups in order to observe a possible change in the response or variable being measured.

Experimental error: The difference between the theoretical value and the measured value is called the experimental error of the measurement. Experimental error is usually expressed as a percent of the theoretical value.

$$\text{Experimental Error} = \frac{(\text{Actual Value} - \text{Theoretical Value})}{\text{Theoretical Value}} \times 100$$

First quartile: The median of the lower half of a data set.

Five number summary: The summary of five statistical measures displayed in a box-and-whiskers plot: minimum, first quartile, median, third quartile, and maximum.

Frequency: The number of times that a data point falls within a certain class.

Frequency table: A table that shows the distribution of data into classes or intervals.

Histogram: A bar graph in which the labels for the bars are numerical intervals. The width of a bar represents a quantitative value such as age rather than a category, and the height of each bar indicates the frequency of occurrence of the elements in the data set within the numerical interval.

Interquartile range: The difference between the first quartile and the third quartile.

Interval sample: Another term for systematic random sampling that is used because choosing every nth person creates a data set from an interval of n people.

Leading questions bias: A form of survey bias resulting when the questions that the surveyor asks can make a person responding to a survey more likely to respond in a way that may not reflect his or her true beliefs.

Left skewed: A histogram or frequency distribution graph in which the left tail is stretched out further than the right tail. The bars on the right of the middle will be taller than the bars on the left of the middle because the mean is less than the median.

Lower class limit: The lowest data value that can fit in a class.

Lurking variables: Variables other than the independent and dependent variables that influence the outcome of an experiment.

Maximum: The largest value in the data set.

Mean: The average value of a data set. Mean is computed by finding the sum of the data and dividing by the number of data values in the set.

Median: The value in the middle of an ordered data set. If there is an odd number of data values, find the value in the middle of the data set. If there is an even number of data values, find the average of the two middle values of the data set.

Minimum: The smallest value in the data set.

Mode: The value in the data set with the greatest frequency, or the value that occurs most often.

Non-probability methods of sampling: Methods of sampling in which each member of the population does not have an equal chance of being selected for the sample.

Nonresponse bias: A form of survey bias resulting when a significant number of people,

usually from one group within the population, that are selected for a sample do not respond to the survey

Normal curve: The graph of a normal distribution, also called a bell curve because of its bell-like shape.

Normal distribution: A frequency distribution in which the mean, median, and mode are all equal and the rest of the frequencies are symmetric about this middle point.

Outlier: A number in a set of data that is much larger or smaller than most of the other numbers in the set. A number is considered to be an outlier if it is less than 1.5 times the interquartile range below the first quartile or if it is more than 1.5 times the interquartile range above the third quartile. For example, for a data set with a first quartile of 9.5 and a third quartile of 11, the interquartile range is $11 - 9.5$ or 1.5. Multiply 1.5 by 1.5 to get 2.25. Subtract the calculated value from the first quartile, $9.5 - 2.25 = 7.25$. Add the calculated value to the third quartile, $11 + 2.25 = 13.25$. An outlier in this data set would have a value greater than 13.25 or less than 7.25.

Percentile: A value, P, such that P% of the data fall below it.

Placebo: A substitute for the treatment that has no effect on the variables being studied.

Placebo effect: A result from experimental design studies when participants think they are experiencing the benefits of the treatment even when they are not receiving the treatment.

Population: An entire group of people, objects, or events that fit a particular description or category.

Probability methods of sampling: Methods of sampling in which each member of the population has an equal chance of being selected for the sample.

Qualitative data: Data that are categorical, such as favorite color, occupation, or marital status, that cannot be represented using numbers.

Quantitative data: Data that can be represented using measurements or numbers.

Randomization: A procedure used in experimental design studies, in which members of the treatment and control groups are randomly chosen, helping to distribute the participants more evenly between the two groups so that the effects of any lurking variables are more evenly distributed between the two groups.

Range: The spread of the data found by subtracting the minimum value from the maximum value.

Response bias: A form of survey bias resulting from how the survey is conducted.

Right skewed: A histogram or frequency distribution graph in which the right tail is stretched out further than the left tail. The bars on the left of the middle will be taller than the bars on the right of the middle because the mean is greater than the median.

Sample: A number of people, objects, or events chosen from a given population to represent the entire group. A sample is a subset of a population.

Sample survey: Measurements or observations from a representative part of the population that are used to describe the entire population.

Selection bias: A form of survey bias resulting from results from how the sample was selected from the population.

Simple random sample: A method of probability sampling in which each member of the population has an equal chance of being selected for the sample. Also, each sample from the population has an equal chance of being drawn from the population. In this method, each member of the population is usually assigned a number, and numbers are randomly drawn until a sample is created.

Social desirability bias: A form of survey bias resulting from participants' tendency not to respond honestly because they want to appear in a better light than they otherwise might.

Standard deviation: A measure of spread about the mean that describes a typical deviation of data points in a set from the mean value of the data set. Standard deviation is the square root of the variance.

Statistics: A mathematical science related to the collection, analysis, interpretation, and representation of data.

Stratified sample: A method of non-probability sampling in which the population is broken into categories called strata. Within each category, sample participants are chosen randomly.

Systematic random sample: A method of probability sampling in which the members of the population are listed in no particular order, a starting point is randomly chosen, and then every nth person is selected for the sample.

Tail: In a histogram or frequency distribution graph, the left and right ends of the graph.

Third quartile: The median of the upper half of a data set.

Treatment: Different levels of the independent variable that are experienced by half of the participants in an experimental design study.

Treatment group: The group in an experimental design study that actually does receive the treatment.

Undercoverage: A form of survey bias resulting when some groups within the population are not represented in the sample.

Upper class limit: The highest data value that can fit in a class.

Variance: An average of the squares of the differences between each data point and the mean of the data set.

INDEX

Symbols and Numerics

Δ (delta), 25
16% model, 107

A

acceleration, 282, 333
  due to gravity, 282, 330
accuracy of predictions, checking, 102–105, 128
addition method. *See* linear combination method
addition of matrices, 155–156, 192
additive inverse property, 151, 192
additive property of probability, 445
  defined, 509
Age of Enlightenment, 4
air volume and pressure. *See* Boyle's Law
altitude of triangles, 227–228
apparent height, 227
approximating data with trend lines, 75–77
Archimedes, 3, 6
Archimedes' Principle, 3
area of triangles, 228
areas of regions, 367–370
arrow diagrams, 295
art transformations, 197–198, 202–204, 254, 341
  algebraic representation of, 207–211
Astrodome, 166
asymmetric data sets, 563–565
atrial fibrillation, 500
average, 76–77, 128, 519
average, types of, 519
axes, 12, 67

B

Barber, Jackson, 195
base (exponents), 347, 396, 413
  changing, formula for, 402, 407
bell curves, 549–554, 557
  graphing with calculator, 552–554
  selecting range within, 558–559
  68-95-99.7 rule, 558
best fit, line of, 103–104
bias in surveys, 580–581, 582
  defined, 603

bimodal data sets, 565
  defined, 603
binomial perfect square, completing, 298
binomials, defined, 341
blinding, 589, 590
  defined, 603
body height, estimating, 74
  femur length and, 89–90, 92
  forearm length and, 93
  tibia length and, 91–92
bone length. *See* body height, estimating
box-and-whiskers plots, 520–525
  defined, 603
  using graphing calculator for, 523–525
Boyle, Robert, 4, 54
Boyle's Law, 4, 54–56, 67
Brown, Dan, 148
Brown, Warren, 131
Burns, Karen, 71

C

Caesar, Julius, 147
Cake Love, 131
Cardano, Gerolamo, 417
cardiovascular disease, 498
census, defined, 572, 603
central tendency, measures of, 76–77, 128, 519
chamber of commerce, 513, 514
change, rate of, 11, 25, 31, 37, 68, 78
change of base formula, 402, 407
class boundaries (histograms), 535
  defined, 603
class width, defined, 603
classes (histograms), 533, 535
  defined, 603
climate, 495, 570
climatology, 570
clockwise rotations, 205, 210
codes and coded messages
  breaking with known frequencies, 150
  Internet information, 149
  matrices for, 150–151
  shift transformations, 147–148
coefficient matrix, 161, 192
coefficients, defined, 341
columns in a matrix, 150
combinations, 470
  defined, 509
  formula for calculating, 471

  using graphing calculator for, 471–472
common logarithms, 396
common multiplier (common ratio), 355–356, 413
complementary events, 439
  defined, 509
completing the square, 296–300, 341
components of a matrix, 154
conditional probability, 450–451
  defined, 509
congruent polygons, 226
constant matrix, 162, 192
constant of proportionality, 11, 21, 26, 67
continuous graphs, 12, 67
control groups, 588, 590
  defined, 603
convenience samples, 578, 581
  defined, 603
convergence and vanishing points, 232–237, 253–254
coordinate plane, 12, 67
coordinates, 12, 67
  symmetries and isometries, 207–211
corner stones, 236–238
correlation between variables, 11–13, 43, 67–68
  inversely proportional relationships, 50, 67
  linear. *See* linear relationships
  positive and negative, 13, 43, 67–68, 98–99, 128
  proportional relationships, 26, 68, 83
  strong and weak relationships, 97, 128
corresponding angles, defined, 253
corresponding elements, defined, 192
counterclockwise rotations, 205, 210
counting principle, 462–463
  defined, 509
cross-multiplication, 34
cryptanalysis, 148
cryptography, 148
curved graphs. *See* quadratic functions
cycles, frequency of, 150, 192

triangles
    altitude of, 227–228
    area of, 228
    similar, 225–226, 254
Trotter, Mildred, 89
two-headed coins, 436
two-point perspective, 232–237, 254
"typical," defining, 513, 538, 542

U

undercoverage bias, 580, 582
    defined, 605
units of measurement, 10, 68
upper class (histograms), 535
    defined, 605

V

Vallejo, Cerapio, 197
vanishing point, 233–237, 254
variable matrix, 161, 193
variable relationships, 11–13, 43, 67–68
    inversely proportional relationships, 50, 67
    linear. *See* linear relationships
    positive and negative, 13, 43, 67–68, 98–99, 128
    proportional relationships, 26, 68, 83
    strong and weak relationships, 97, 128
variables, 10, 68

dependent and independent, 10, 12, 48, 67
input and output variables, 138
proportional, 13
rate of change, 11, 25, 31, 37, 68, 78
variables, lurking, 587
variance, 513, 545
    defined, 605
Venn diagrams, 451
    defined, 510
"versus," in graphs, 24, 128
vertex form of quadratic functions, 295–298, 303, 310, 341
vertex of a parabola, 264, 341
vertical compression/stretch of exponential functions, 356, 363
vertical shift of lines. *See* y-intercepts
volume, defined, 68
volume of sphere, 15
volume–pressure relationship. *See* Boyle's Law

W

wages. *See* earnings
water displacement, 6, 8–10
weak relationships, 97, 128
weather forecasts, 495, 570
width of histogram classes, defined, 603
"with replacement", 449

X

x-axis, reflection across, 209, 211
x-intercepts, 288, 341

Y

y-axis, reflection across, 208
y-intercepts, 32, 37, 68, 84
    exponential functions, 356, 363
$y = a(x - h)^2 + k$ family, 295–298, 303, 310, 341
$y = a(x - r_1)(x - r_2)$ family, 288, 303, 310, 341
$y = ax^2 + bx + c$ family, 264, 288, 303, 310, 341. *See also* quadratic functions
$y = b^x$ parent function, 355. *See also* exponential functions
$y = mx$ family. *See* direct variation function
$y = mx + b$ family (slope-intercept form), 32, 38, 68, 84, 90, 128, 261, 263. *See also* y-intercepts
$y = x$ parent function, 263, 322
    reflections across. *See* inverses
$y = x^2$ parent function, 264

Z

z-scores, 561–562
Zero-Product Property, 289, 303, 342
zeros of quadratic functions, 288, 342

ACKNOWLEDGMENTS

Project Leadership

Jo Ann Wheeler
Region 4 ESC, Houston, TX

David Eschberger
Region 4 ESC, Houston, TX

Solomon Garfunkel
COMAP Inc., Lexington, MA

Lead Authors

Gary Cosenza
Region 4 ESC, Houston, TX

Paul Gray
Region 4 ESC, Houston, TX

Julie Horn
Region 4 ESC, Houston, TX

Authors

Sharon Benson
Region 4 ESC, Houston, TX

David Eschberger
Region 4 ESC, Houston, TX

Jo Ann Wheeler
Region 4 ESC, Houston, TX

Publisher

Craig Bleyer

Executive Marketing Manager

Cyndi Weiss

Director of High School Sales and Marketing

Mike Saltzman

Supplements and New Media Editor

Roland Cheyney

COMAP Staff

Laurie Aragón, Rafael Aragón, Gary Feldman, Gary Froelich, Solomon Garfunkel, Daiva Chauhan, Anne Sterling, John Tomicek, George Ward

Index Editor

Seth Maislin
Focus Publishing Services, Arlington, MA

Illustrations

Lianne Dunn, George Ward

Photo Research

COMAP Production

PHOTO/ILLUSTRATION CREDITS

David Barber: 112, 120, 147, 411

Jackson Barber: 195

Bridgeman Art Library International LTD: 216, 217, 239, 244

Vin Catania Studios: 45, 220, 221, 234, 237

Corbis Images: 62, 70, 82, 94, 96, 100, 114, 117, 119, 125, 127, 130, 337

Dover Publications Inc.: 76, 147, 352

Lianne Dunn: 41, 71, 74, 88, 93, 112, 122, 123

EyeWire: 109

Mark Finkensteadt: 131

Gary Froelich: 200, 201

Hewlett-Packard: 258

Image Bank: 233, 243

Daiva Chauhan: 123, 124

NASA: 282

National Anthropological Archives: 89

Novica.com: 197

Purdue University: 71

Shutterstock: 2, 6, 8, 14, 16, 18, 20, 22, 23, 30, 35, 42, 47, 57, 59, 79, 98, 132, 137, 142, 143, 145, 149, 154, 163, 164, 165, 166, 171, 172, 176, 177, 182, 184, 186, 187, 190, 191, 194, 206, 248, 256, 257, 261, 266, 280, 285, 294, 295, 302, 314, 323, 332, 340, 344, 345, 347, 351, 356, 359, 361, 362, 376, 381, 395, 400, 405, 406, 414, 415, 417, 419, 425, 430, 432, 434, 436, 452, 456, 457, 460, 465, 467, 468, 472, 473, 475, 477, 478, 480, 489, 505, 512, 513, 520, 530, 536, 537, 540, 542, 545, 548, 555, 556, 566, 568, 570, 572, 574, 575, 578, 587, 589, 596

Syi Tong: 215

Susan Van Etten: 106, 107, 266

George Ward: 215

PLACE : WILLIAM & MARY COLLEGE, VIRGINIA.
DATE : 08·03·'09 (MONDAY)